PROPERTIES OF THE FUNDAMENTAL INTERACTIONS

VOLUME 9
PART C

EDITOR
A. ZICHICHI

CONTRIBUTORS

PART A

Opening Lecture
    G. F. CHEW

Theoretical Lectures
    G. F. CHEW
    V. DE ALFARO
    M. GOURDIN
    M. JACOB
    A. MARTIN
    J. J. SAKURAI
    G. PREPARATA
    S. COLEMAN

PART B

Review Lectures
    S. B. TREIMAN
    G. MORPURGO
    G. GOLDHABER
    K. W. J. BARNHAM
    and G. GOLDHABER
    A. BARBARO-GALTIERI
    S. COLEMAN
    S. GASIOROWICZ
    A. M. WETHERELL

PART C

Seminars on Specialized Topics
    K. H. ALTHOFF
    F. BUCCELLA
    N. CABIBBO
    S. L. GLASHOW
    P. KESSLER
    A. PEVSNER
    A. H. ROSENFELD
    I. T. TODOROV

The Glorious Days of Physics
    V. F. WEISSKOPF

Closing Remarks
    G. F. CHEW

The 1971 International Physics Prize
« Ettore Majorana »

The 1971 International Physics Prize has been awarded to Professor Giancarlo Wick with the following motivation:

« *Professor Giancarlo Wick is one of the truly outstanding theoretical physicists. His contributions to quantum field theory and scattering theory are both basic and extensive, they have become foundations of these two vast and fruitful areas of research. The Wick theorem and the Wick product are common vocabulary in today's literature, not only in high-energy physics but in solid-state physics and many-body problems as well. His very recent work on a finite theory of quantum electrodynamics is again of fundamental importance* ».

The prize was presented to Professor G. C. Wick by the Mayor of Erice, Geom. Gaspare Oddo. During the official ceremony held in Erice on the 14th July, 1971, a concert was given by the Sicilian Philharmonic Orchestra, conducted by Ottavio Ziino, in honour of Professor G. C. Wick.

PROPERTIES OF THE FUNDAMENTAL INTERACTIONS

*1971 International School of Subnuclear Physics
a NATO-MPI-MRST Advanced Study Institute
Sponsored by the Regional Sicilian Government
and the Weizmann Institute of Science
Erice, Trapani - Sicily: 8-26 July 1971*

EDITOR

A. ZICHICHI

**1973
EDITRICE COMPOSITORI BOLOGNA**

Copyright © 1973, by Editrice Compositori - Bologna

ALL RIGHTS RESERVED

NO PART OF THIS BOOK MAY BE REPRODUCED IN ANY FORM,
BY PHOTOSTAT, MICROFILM, OR ANY OTHER MEANS,
WITHOUT WRITTEN PERMISSION FROM THE PUBLISHERS.

subnuclear series — 9.

Foreword

During three weeks in July 1971, one hundred and forty five physicists from ninety laboratories met in Erice to attend the ninth Course of the International School of Subnuclear Physics.

The countries represented at the School were: Argentina, Australia, Austria, Belgium, Brazil, Bulgaria, Burma, Canada, Czechoslovakia, Denmark, the Federal Republic of Germany, Finland, France, Ghana, Greece, Hungary, India, Iran, Israel, Italy, Japan, Mexico, the Netherlands, Norway, Pakistan, Poland, Portugal, Rumania, Spain, Sweden, Switzerland, Taiwan, the United Kingdom and the United States.

The School was sponsored by the Italian Ministry of Public Education (MPI), the Italian Ministry of Scientific and Technological Research (MRST), the North Atlantic Treaty Organization (NATO), the Regional Sicilian Government (ERS) and the Weizmann Institute of Science.

The program of the School was mainly devoted to the elucidation and discussion of the progress achieved in the theoretical and experimental understanding of particle physics during the last year.

I hope the reader will enjoy the book as much as the students enjoyed attending the lectures and the discussion sessions, which are one of the most attractive features of the School. Thanks to the work of Scientific Secretaries the discussions have been reproduced as faithfully as possible.

At various stages of my work I have enjoyed the collaboration of many friends whose contributions have been extremely important for the School and are highly appreciated. I would like to thank most warmly: Miss D. Giaj-Via for help in the checking of the lecture-notes, Mrs. M. Denzler, Mr. A. Gabriele, Mrs. I. Poli and Miss M. Zaini for the general administrative work, Dr. G. Ecker for his work as Scientific Secretary, and Prof. G. Preparata.

A final word of acknowledgement to all those who, in Erice, Bologna and Geneva, helped me on so many occasions and to whom I feel very much indebted.

A. ZICHICHI

Bologna, December 1971

Contents

PART A

CONTRIBUTORS V
FOREWORD XI

OPENING LECTURE

G. F. Chew: **Quark or Bootstrap: Triumph or Frustration for Hadron Physics?** . . . 3
   1. Introduction 3
   2. Electromagnetism as the bridge between real and quantum worlds 5
   3. The hadron S-matrix bootstrap 8
   4. Supplementary S-matrix principles 10
   5. Experimental implications; models 12
   6. Conclusion 14
   References (for all lectures) 14
   Discussion 17

THEORETICAL LECTURES

G. F. Chew: **Generalization of Regge Asymptotic Behaviour** 25
   Lecture no. 1 25
   Lecture no. 2 34
      A. The Mueller formula relating inclusive cross-sections to discontinuities . 34
      B. Regge poles. Factorization 37
      C. One Regge-pole model of single-particle inclusive cross-sections 38
   Lecture no. 3 44
      A. The triple Regge limit in single-particle inclusive distributions 44
      B. Hints about Regge spectrum from multiperipheral models 47
   Discussion 1 52
   Discussion 2 55
   Discussion 3 59

Contents

V. de Alfaro: Old and New Ideas about Currents and Their Commutators 63
   1. Introduction 63
   2. Algebra of currents 63
   3. Representation of an ordered product 68
   4. Old-fashioned perturbation theory: $p \to \infty$ limit and partons 69
   5. p and q infinite: asymptotic sum rules 74
   6. Commutators of currents on the light cone 79
   7. Scaling and light cone commutators. Light cone version of the asymptotic sum rules 82
   8. Connection between the light cone and $p \to \infty$ limit of equal time commutator matrix element 85
   9. Light cone commutators and sum rules 87
   Appendix 88
   References 90
   Discussion 1 91
   Discussion 2 93
   Discussion 3 97

M. Gourdin: The Quark Parton Model for Deep Inelastic Lepton Scattering . . . 103
   1. Introduction 103
   2. Kinematics 104
      2˙1. Structure functions 104
      2˙2. Variables 105
      2˙3. Elastic scattering 106
      2˙4. Scaling 106
      2˙5. High-energy differential cross-sections 106
      2˙6. High-energy total cross-sections 107
   3. The parton model 107
      3˙1. Adler sum rule 110
   4. The quark parton model 111
   5. Sum rules 113
   6. Positivity constraints 115
   7. Symmetries 122
   Concluding remarks 127
   References 129
   Discussion 1 130
   Discussion 2 131

M. Jacob: **Strong Interaction Dynamics** **139**

   Foreword 139

  I. A short review of topical questions in hadron phenomenology 141
     1. Introduction 141
     2. Regge exchange 143
     3. Duality and exchange degeneracy 149
     4. Many-particle phenomena 151
     References 155

  II. Inclusive reactions and Regge behaviour 156
     1. Introduction 156
        1˙1. Foreword 156
        1˙2. Exclusive and inclusive descriptions 162

     2. From Jacobians to dynamics 164
        2˙1. The fragmentation region 165
        2˙2. The rapidity distribution 167
        2˙3. The missing mass distribution 170
        2˙4. The scaling property 172

     3. General dynamical problems 177
        3˙1. The multiperipheral model 177
        3˙2. Multiplicity of secondaries 179
        3˙3. Diffraction and multiperipheralism 180
        3˙4. Factorization 184

     4. Regge approach to inclusive cross-sections 184
        4˙1. Mueller analysis 184
        4˙2. Approaching the limiting distribution 190
        4˙3. Triple Reggeon couplings 193

     5. Is there a deep inelastic hadron-hadron scattering? 197
        5˙1. Feynman scaling and Bjorken scaling 202

     6. Pomeranchon exchange 205
        6˙1. Single and multi-Pomeranchon exchange 205
        6˙2. The longitudinal phase space method 207

     7. Conclusions and outlook 211

     References 212
     Discussion 1 215
     Discussion 2 218

Contents

A. Martin: High-Energy Behaviour of Total and Elastic Cross-Sections **221**
    1. Introduction and experimental background 221
    2. The problem of equality of total cross-sections (Pomeranchuk theorem) . . 222
    3. Equality of differential cross-sections, fixed t dispersion relations and the phase problem 224
    4. Controlling the phase by positivity 228
    5. The small t behaviour 232
    6. Putting everything together 234
    References 235
    Discussion 1 236
    Discussion 2 238

J. J. Sakurai: Dynamical Models Based on Vector-Meson Dominance and Universality   **243**
    1. Historical review of the basic ideas 243
    2. Vector-meson universality in purely hadronic processes 251
    3. ρ-photon analogy; hadronic behaviour of the photon 255
    4. Charged-pion photo- and electroproduction and $\pi^- + p \to \rho^0 + n$ 266
    5. Inelastic electron-proton scattering 287
    Acknowledgement 292
    References 292
    Discussion 1 296
    Discussion 2 300
    Discussion 3 301

G. Preparata: The Physics of the Light Cone **309**
    1. Introduction 309
    2. The kinematical relevance of the light cone 310
    3. Products of operators near the light cone 312
    4. How to work with the light cone expansions 315
    5. Measuring light cone singularities. The SLAC experiments 317
    6. The BNL-Columbia massive μ-pairs production experiment 321
    7. Towards a theory of canonical dimensions 328
    8. Large mass behaviour as described by the light cone 332
    9. Theory of mass dispersion relations 335
   10. Some applications of light cone controlled mass dispersion relations . . . 338
    Conclusion 349
    References 349
    Discussion 1 352
    Discussion 2 354

S. Coleman: **Dilatations** **359**

   1. Introduction 359

   2. The formal theory of broken scale invariance 360
      2˙1. Symmetries, currents, and Ward identities. 360
      2˙2. Scale transformations and scale dimensions 362

   3. More about the scale current and a quick look at the conformal group . 364

   4. Hidden scale invariance 369

   5. The death of scale invariance 373
      5˙1. Some definitions and technical details 373
      5˙2. A disaster in the deep Euclidean region 375
      5˙3. Anomalous dimensions and other anomalies 377
      5˙4. The last anomalies: the Callan-Symanzik equations 379

   6. The resurrection of scale invariance 383
      6˙1. The renormalization group equations and their solution 383
      6˙2. The return of scaling in the deep Euclidean region 385
      6˙3. Scaling and the operator product expansion 389

   7. Conclusions and questions 392

   Footnotes and references 393

   Discussion 396

PART B

REVIEW LECTURES

S. B. Treiman: **Current Topics in Weak Interaction Physics** **403**

   1. Introduction 403
   2. $K_L \to \mu^+ + \mu^-$ decay. 406
   3. Second class currents 411
   4. Deep inelastic lepton-hadron scattering 415
   References 419
   Discussion 1 421
   Discussion 2 427

XVIII   Contents

G. Morpurgo: **The Present Status of the Radiative Decays of Mesons** **433**

   A. Phenomenological description 433

      1. Introduction 433
      2. The experimental material 434
      3. SU_3 parametrization of the $V \to P\gamma$ amplitudes 436
      4. Mixing problems 437
      5. Parametrization of the $P \to \gamma\gamma$ decays 441
      6. Connection between $P \to \gamma\gamma$ and $V \to P\gamma$ decays: *a*) The π^0 case . . . 442
      7. Further discussion of the connection between $P \to \gamma\gamma$ and $V \to P\gamma$ decays:
         b) The η, X^0 case 445
      8. Lagrangian models and current field identity 448
      9. Summary 452
      References 453

   B. Attempts to relativistic calculations of vertices in the quark model 455

      1. Introduction 455
      2. The $\omega \to \pi\gamma$ calculation in the N.R. quark model 456
      3. The Bethe-Salpeter equation for the vertex function 457
      4. Calculation of the triangular vertex with particularly simple Bethe-Salpeter
         wave functions 461
      5. Normalization of the wave function 463
      6. The decays $V \to P\gamma$ 465
      7. The $\pi \to \mu\nu$ and $K \to \mu\nu$ decays 467
      8. The $V\gamma$ couplings 469
      9. An example of different prescription for the wave functions. Concluding
         remarks 470
      References 471
      Discussion 1 472
      Discussion 2 476

G. Goldhaber: **Selected Topics on Boson Resonances** **479**

   I. The ω-ρ interference effect revisited 479
      1. Review 479
         1`1. The ω-ρ interference pattern 479

2. New experimental results. 481
　　　　2˙1. Photoproduction data from the DESY-MIT group: $-\gamma+A \to \pi^+\pi^-A$　482
　　　　2˙2. Photoproduction data from the Rochester-Cornell-NAL group: $-\gamma A \to \pi^+\pi^- A$ 485
　　　　2˙3. New results from Orsay on $e^+e^- \to \pi^+\pi^-$ 488
　　　　2˙4. A mystery still with us: The Daresbury $\gamma+C \to e^+e^-C$ data compared to the DESY-MIT $\gamma+Be \to e^+e^-Be$ data on ω-ρ interference　491
　　　　2˙5. Combined analysis of the vector meson photoproduction and $e^+e^- \to \pi^+\pi^-$ experiments. 494
　　3. Interfering boson resonances as a tool in strong interactions 496
　　　　3˙1. Charge symmetric reactions for ρ^0 and ω production; breakdown of charge symmetry. 497
　　　　3˙2. Search for C violation in electromagnetic or semi-strong interactions via ω-ρ interference 499
　References 508

II. The A_2 puzzle becomes a mystery 509
　References 512
　Discussion 1 513
　Discussion 2 514

K. W. J. Barnham and G. Goldhaber: **Interfering Resonances and the A_2 Mass Spectrum**　521
　Acknowledgements. 530
　References 530

A. Barbaro-Galtieri: **Selected Topics on Baryon Resonances** 533
　1. Introduction: General remarks. 533
　2. Resonance formulae: Parameters for $\Delta(1236)$ 536
　3. Decay of $\Lambda(1520)$ and $\Lambda(1690)$ into $\Sigma(1385)+\pi$. 549
　4. SU_3 fits 562
　　　4˙1. General considerations 563
　　　4˙2. Problems with the $J^P = 3/2^-$ states 569
　　　4˙3. The $J^P = 3/2^+$ decuplet 576
　5. Study of $\Lambda(1405)$: CDD pole *vs.* bound state. 581
　　　5˙1. Formalism for low-energy $\overline{K}\mathcal{N}$ scattering 582
　　　5˙2. Formalism for the $S0_1$ partial wave. 585
　　　5˙3. Data used in the fits. 587
　　　5˙4. Results of analysis. 588
　6. Conclusions 592
　Footnotes and references. 593
　Discussion 1 596
　Discussion 2 600

S. Coleman: **Renormalization and Symmetry: a Review for Non-specialists** 605

    1. Introduction 605
    2. Bogoliubov's method and Hepp's theorem 606
    3. Renormalizable and non-renormalizable interactions 611
    4. Symmetry and symmetry-breaking: Symanzik's rule 613
    5. Symmetry and symmetry-breaking: Currents 615
    Footnotes and references 619
    Discussion 621

S. Gasiorowicz: **Inelastic Processes** 625

    1. Introduction 625
    2. Kinematics 625
    3. The multiperipheral point of view 628
    4. Limiting distributions and diffractive processes 635
    5. The extension of Reggeism to inclusive reactions 642
    References 652
    Discussion 654

A. H. Wetherell: **High-Energy Hadronic Collisions** 659

    1. Introduction 659
    2. Total cross-sections 659
    3. Two-body processes 669
        A. Elastic scattering 671
        B. Charge exchange processes 687
        C. Quasi two-body processes 691
    4. Inclusive experiments 697
    5. Particle multiplicity 716
    References 722
    Discussion 725

PART C

SEMINARS ON SPECIALIZED TOPICS

K. H. Althoff: **Physics with the Bonn Electron Synchrotrons** 735

    1. Introduction 735
    2. Beams available at the two accelerators 736
    3. Photon and electron as primary particles 738
    4. Real and virtual photons 739

5. Photoproduction of pseudoscalar mesons	740
6. Helicity and multipole amplitudes	742
7. Experiments at the 500 MeV machine	744
8. Differential cross-section for the reactions $\gamma+p \to \pi^0+p$ and $\gamma+p \to \pi^++n$	745
9. Measurement of the recoil nucleon polarization	749
10. Analysis of the π^+- and π^0-data below a photon energy of $E_\gamma = -500$ MeV.	751
11. Other experiments at the 500 MeV machine.	754
12. The experimental program at the 2.5 GeV synchrotron.	755
13. Photoproduction of pseudoscalar mesons at intermediate energies	758
References	768
Discussion	771

F. Buccella: An Algebraic Approach to the Saturation of Chiral $SU_3 \otimes SU_3$ **773**
    References ... 778
    Discussion ... 779

N. Cabibbo: Magnitude of the σ-Term, Chiral Symmetry and Scale Invariance .. **783**
    1. Chiral $SU_3 \otimes SU_3$, its breaking and the σ-commutator ... 783
    2. Pion-nucleon scattering, PCAC, and the σ-term ... 789
    3. The smoothness hypothesis and the value of the σ-term ... 793
    4. A brief discussion ... 798
    Acknowledgement ... 799
    References ... 799
    Discussion ... 801

S. L. Glashow: Positivity and Internal Symmetry **805**
    Discussion ... 815

P. Kessler: Photon-Photon Collisions in Electron-Positron Storage Rings **821**
    1. Historical point ... 821
    2. Background suppression and total cross-sections ... 823
    3. Energy dependence and angular distributions ... 827
    4. Effects of realistic experimental cut-offs ... 830
    5. Conclusion ... 851
    References ... 852
    Discussion ... 854

A. Pevsner: **Coherent Interactions** 857
1. Introduction 857
2. Kinematics. 859
3. Coherence 861
4. Experimental detection of coherent reactions 866
5. Discussion on some experimental results 867
6. Coherent pion production from complex nuclei 875
References 879
Discussion 880

A. H. Rosenfeld: **Photoproduction of Vector Mesons-Experimental** 883
1. Introduction 883
2. Polarized photon beams. 884
3. Polarization properties of the reaction $\gamma p \to \rho^0 p$ 888
   A. Helicity conservation 891
   B. Exchange of natural $vs.$ un-natural J^P. 895
   C. Does natural exchange imply helicity conservation? 899
   D. Rho mass shape and the interference model. 900
4. Polarization properties of the reaction $\gamma p \to \omega p$ 904
5. Polarization properties of the reaction $\gamma p \to \varphi p$ 907
6. Cross-sections of the reactions $\gamma p \to V^0 p$ 908
   A. Difficulties and uncertainties 908
   B. Results. 911
7. Test of the vector dominance model 918
8. Vector meson photoproduction on the deuteron 920
9. The reaction $\gamma A \to V^0 A$ on complex nuclei 927
10. The phase of the ρ, ω and φ forward elastic scattering 933
11. Photoproduction of heavy (vector) mesons; the $\rho'(1500)$ 936
Acknowledgement 941
References 941
Discussion 946

I. T. Todorov: **Quasipotential Approach to the Two-Body Problem in Quantum Field Theory** 953
1. Introduction: three-dimensional $vs.$ four-dimensional two-particle equations 953
2. Relativistic Lippmann-Schwinger equation for scalar particles 955

   A. Off-shell kinematics. General form of the equation 955
   B. On-shell and off-shell requirements. Explicit form of the Green function 956
   C. The homogeneous (Schrödinger) equation. 959

3. Scalar Yukawa interaction and relativistic eikonal formula 959
   A. Relativistic reduced mass 959
   B. The eikonal approximation 961
   C. Three-dimensional counterpart of the Wick-Cutkosky model 962

4. Quasipotential equation for electromagnetic interaction 962
   A. Determination of an effective four-potential for the interaction of scalar charged particles 962
   B. Relativistic Balmer formula with fine structure splitting 964
   C. Electromagnetic interaction of spin-$\frac{1}{2}$ particles 966

5. Concluding remarks 970

Acknowledgements 970

Appendix I. Breit equation and perturbative calculations for spin-0 and spin-$\frac{1}{2}$ particles 971

Appendix II. Derivation of the quasipotential equation for two Dirac particles 973

References 975

Discussion 978

THE GLORIOUS DAYS OF PHYSICS

V. F. Weisskopf: **My Life as a Physicist** 983

CLOSING REMARKS

G. F. Chew: **Platitudes on the State of Our Art** 1001

CLOSING CEREMONY 1007

LIST OF PARTICIPANTS 1009

SEMINARS ON SPECIALIZED TOPICS

Physics with the Bonn Electron Synchrotrons

K. H. ALTHOFF

1. Introduction 735
2. Beams available at the two accelerators 736
3. Photon and electron as primary particles 738
4. Real and virtual photons. 739
5. Photoproduction of pseudoscalar mesons 740
6. Helicity and multipole amplitudes 742
7. Experiments at the 500 MeV machine 744
8. Differential cross-section for the reactions $\gamma+p \to \pi^0+p$ and $\gamma+p \to \pi^++n$. 745
9. Measurement of the recoil nucleon polarization 749
10. Analysis of the π^+- and π^0-data below a photon energy of $E_\gamma = -$ 500 MeV 751
11. Other experiments at the 500 MeV machine 754
12. The experimental program at the 2.5 GeV synchrotron . 755
13. Photoproduction of pseudoscalar mesons at intermediate energies. 758
References 768
Discussion 771

Physics with the Bonn Electron Synchrotrons

K. H. Althoff

Physikalisches Institut der Universität
Bonn, Germany

1. Introduction.

In this seminar I will talk about the activities around the two electron accelerators at the Physics Department of the Bonn University.

Let me start with a few remarks about the two accelerators. The «old» machine has a maximum energy of 500 MeV. It was the first accelerator in Europe using the strong focusing system with alternating gradient magnets. It came into operation in 1958 and has now more than 50,000 h of running time. The design and the construction of this machine is somewhat unusual. For instance the word «strong focusing» had been taken seriously at that time: the gradient of the magnetic field went up to 1000 G/cm, which is much more than at any other machine built afterwards. Today it seems to be a miracle to everybody who was involved in the construction that this handwoven machine is still running, very reliable and stable, with a relatively high circulating current of 30 mA corresponding to $5 \cdot 10^{11}$ electrons/s ([1]). There are still many open questions in the energy range of this machine and we hope it will run for another couple of years.

To keep up with the development of high energy physics and the education of the students in this field, we decided to build another accelerator with higher energy and intensity. This was 1963. There existed several machines around 1 GeV and two electron synchrotrons at DESY and CEA with 6 GeV. NINA was under construction. So we filled the gap with a 2.5 GeV electron synchrotron ([2]).

This machine was also built as a University machine where the students participated in the design and the construction. The short construction time of only 2.5 years was partly due to a somewhat delicate decision: No magnet models have been made. The pole profile and the cross-section of the magnets were calculated on a computer including all saturation effects up to the maximum field of 11 kG at the closed orbit. It turned out that even the originally planed correction coils were not needed.

The internal current is about 30 mA (the highest was 60 mA). Due to the larger circumference this corresponds to about $2.5 \cdot 10^{12}$ electrons/s. The parameters of the machine were designed to give a good slow ejected electron beam. The efficiency is about 60%. The beam is very stable and has a cross-section of 2×2 mm² at the external target.

Some parameters of the two machines are listed in Table 1.

TABLE I. – *Parameter list of the two synchrotrons.*

	500 MeV machine	2.5 GeV machine
Max. energy	0.5 GeV	2.5 GeV
Focusing type	AG	AG
Repetition frequency	50 Hz	50 Hz
Mean radius	2.75 m	11 m
Field gradient (max.)	10,000 G/cm	300 G/cm
Injection	van der Graaf 3 MeV	Linac 25 MeV
RF (Acceleration)	160 MHz	500 MHz
Vacuum chamber	ceramic	ceramic
Internal elektr. beam	$5 \cdot 10^{11}$ el/sec	$2.5 \cdot 10^{12}$ el/sec
External beam	photons	photons + electrons
Duty cycle	5%	5%
First operation	1958	1967

Before discussing the physical problems around the machine I would like to say a few words about the Bonn laboratory itself. Both machines are pure University machines. That means, most of the actually working people are students. The aim of our laboratory is not only to do research in elementary particle physics but also to give the students a good experimental education of how to deal with the complicated equipment around modern accelerators. It might take more time to do an experiment but it turns out that this experimental style can be very healthy for the accuracy of the data.

2. Beams available at the two accelerators.

At the 500 MeV machine two photon beams are available. Rotating targets cross the electron beam at the maximum energy and produce a bremsstrahlung beam of 1 ms duration. The next pulse comes 20 ms later, so we get a duty cycle of about 5%.

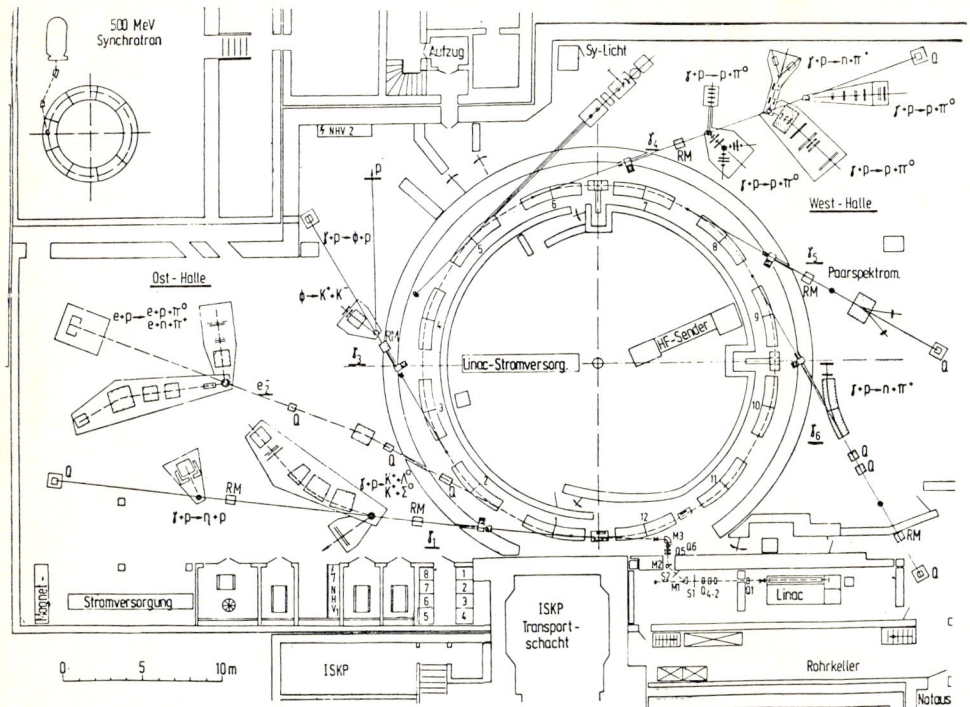

Fig. 1. – Floor plan of the 2.5 GeV synchrotron.

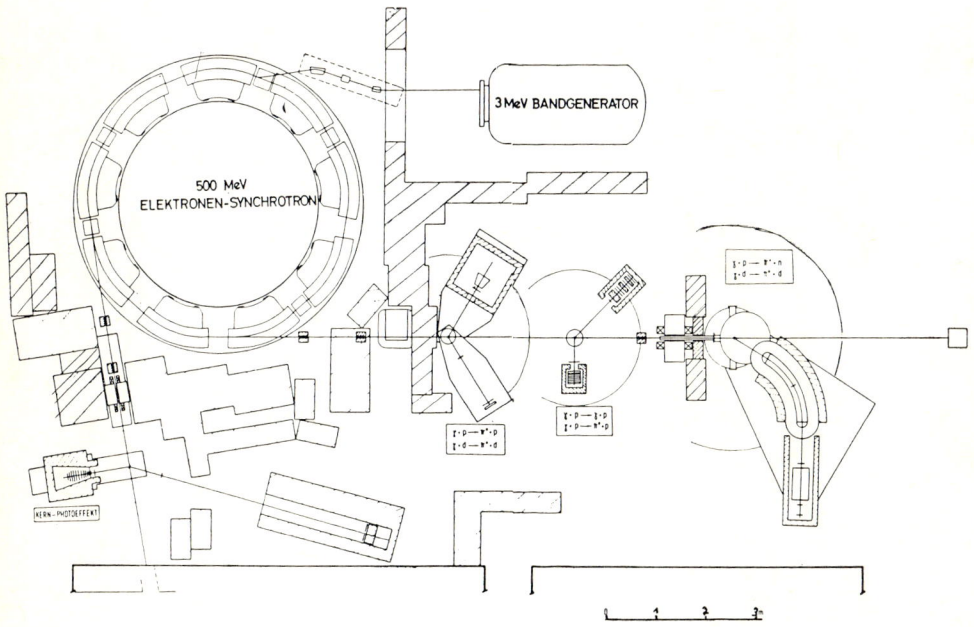

Fig. 2. – Floor plan of the 500 MeV synchrotron.

At the 2.5 GeV machine we have 5 photon beams generated either by a similar rotating target technique or by a closed orbit bump technique on a fixed target. The time structure is the same as at the 500 MeV machine. Figure 1 and Fig. 2 show the present floor plans of the two accelerators. Beside these high energy beams we can use the synchrotron radiation as an intensive light source with a continuous spectrum between 1 Å and 5000 Å.

3. Photon and electron as primary particles.

What can we study, if we use high-energy photon and electron beams?

1) We can look at interactions where only photons and leptons are involved. These processes are perfectly described by quantum electrodynamics up to the highest available energies and momentum transfers.

2) Photons and electrons are a very good tool to study the electromagnetic structure of the strong interacting particles. They have the nice property to react very « weakly » with the hadrons due to the small coupling constant α and the large mass of the hadrons.

3) We believe that charge and parity is conserved in strong interactions. But whether time reversal or charge conjugation holds for the hadronic current is not yet confirmed experimentally.

And how about the isotopic spin structure of the electromagnetic current of the hadrons? We have the well established Gell-Mann–Nishijima relation which connects the charge Q, the hypercharge Y and the third component of the isospin I_3:

$$Q = Y/2 + I_3.$$

This equation can be fullfilled if the electromagnetic current of the hadron would consist of an isoscalar and an isovector part. (An isospin operator would change the I_3 component but not the hypercharge Y.) But there might exist a third term which would not violate this relation, for instance a $I=2$-term corresponding to an isotensor part of the current. Recently Sanda and Shaw [3] reported evidence for the existance of such a term, but due to the latest experimental data it is dubious. So we have another interesting problem which can only be solved by new accurate experiments.

4. Real and virtual photons.

If we use, for instance, the photons in the external bremsstrahlung beam of an electron synchrotron, we have on shell photons with transverse polarization. The helicities λ, the component of the spin in the direction of motion, are $\lambda = \pm 1$. For the four momentum q we get $q^2 = m^2 = 0$.

For electrons as primary particles the coupling to the hadronic current is accomplished by virtual, off-shell photons with $q^2 = m^2 < 0$. They are space-like and have transversally and longitudinally polarized components.

The photons are time-like $q^2 = m^2 > 0$, if for instance electrons and positrons in a storage ring annihilate, producing particle and antiparticle pairs like $\pi^+\pi^-$ or $p\bar{p}$.

In Table II we find a summary of these examples together with some typical graphs.

TABLE II. – *Examples of pion production under different experimental conditions.*

Particle Beam	Photon	Mass	Polarization	Helicities	Name of reaction	Typical graph
external bremsstrahlung beam	real	$q^2 = m^2 = 0$	transverse	$\lambda = 1$	photoproduct.	
external electron beam	virtual space like	$q^2 = m^2 < 0$	transverse + longitudinal	$\lambda = \pm 1$ $\lambda = 0$	electroproduct.	
colliding electron and positron beams	virtual time-like	$q^2 = m^2 > 0$	transverse + longitudinal	$\lambda = \pm 1$ $\lambda = 0$	pair-annihilation	

5. Photoproduction of pseudoscalar mesons.

Let us start with the simplest photoproduction reactions $\gamma + \mathcal{N} \to \mathcal{N}' + \pi$, the photoproduction of single pions:

$$\gamma + p \to \pi^+ + n$$
$$\gamma + p \to \pi^0 + p$$
$$\gamma + n \to \pi^- + p$$
$$\gamma + n \to \pi^0 + n .$$

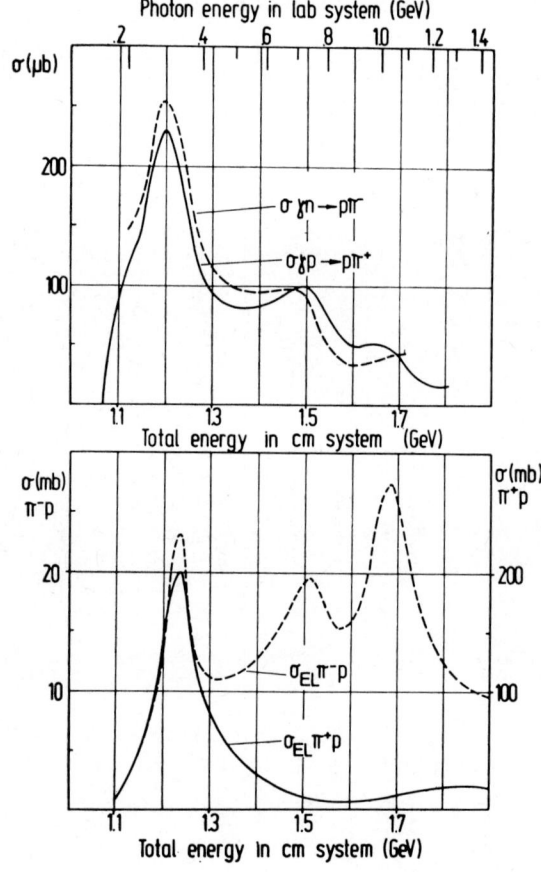

Fig. 3. – Total cross-sections for $\gamma + n \to p + \pi^-$, $\gamma + p \to n + \pi^+$; $\pi^- + p \to \pi^- + p$, $\pi^+ + p \to \pi^+ + p$ below a total energy of 2 GeV. Figure is taken from P. Brinckmann (invited talk at the *Electron and Photon Conference*, Hamburg, 1971).

The same final states can be produced in pion-nucleon scattering reactions $\pi + N \to N' + \pi'$.

In Fig. 3 the total cross-sections for the π^+- and π^--production are plotted for total energies below 2 GeV. Beside the difference in absolute values of about a factor of 200 we notice a similar structure. The well known excited levels of the nucleons, the first resonance and higher resonances N^* show up also in the photoproduction of pions. Unfortunately there is also a big background which causes considerable trouble as we will see later.

How can we describe the photoproduction amplitude?

The following graphs should contribute to the amplitude:

These are the « Born-graphs ». They can be calculated since all coupling constants are known. This is not the case for the following graphs:

Resonances can be exchanged in the s- and u-channel or vector mesons in the t-channel. The theorists are not able to calculate these graphs exactly, mainly because the strong interaction mechanism is not understood. What kind of experiments have to be done to determine the amplitudes phenomenologically?

6. Helicity and multipole amplitudes.

The best way to answer this question is to take the helicity formalism introduced by Jacob and Wick ([4]) and Walker ([5]).

CM-system:

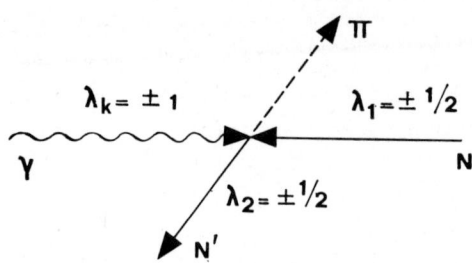

The authors describe the reaction $\gamma + \mathcal{N} \to \pi^+ + \mathcal{N}'$ in the c.m. system. The spins are quantized along the direction of the photon and nucleon momenta. The real photon has helicities $\lambda_k = \pm 1$, the target nucleon $\lambda_1 = \pm \frac{1}{2}$ and the recoil nucleon $\lambda_2 = \pm \frac{1}{2}$: (The helicity for the pion $\lambda_q = 0$.)

So we get for the *initial state* four possible values $\lambda = \lambda_k - \lambda_1 = \pm \frac{1}{2}$; $\pm \frac{3}{2}$. And for the *final state* two values $\mu = \lambda_q - \lambda_2 = \pm \frac{1}{2}$. We can define 8 amplitudes $A_{\mu\lambda}$ which we call the helicity amplitudes $H_1 \ldots H_8$. Since parity is conserved in these reactions the number of independent amplitudes reduces to 4 complex helicity amplitudes:

$$H_1;\ H_2;\ H_3;\ H_4;$$

corresponding to 8 real functions. All physical observables are bilinear in the amplitudes. So we can choose one phase arbitrarily and are left with 7 real functions. That means we have to make 7 independent experiments for each energy and angle to determine the 4 helicity amplitudes.

Up to now 4 different physical quantities have been measured:

1) *Differential cross-section*
   with unpolarized photons and target

2) *Recoil nucleon polarization*
   with unpolarized photons and target

3) *Asymmetry ratio* with *polarized photons* and unpolarized target

and since recently:

4) *Asymmetry ratio* with *polarized targets* and unpolarized photons

The definitions of these expressions and the combination of the helicity amplitudes are summarized in Table III.

TABLE III. – *Combinations of the helicity amplitudes for different measured quantities. (k and q are the momentum of the photon and pion).*

Measured quantity	Definition	Helicity combinations	Photon beam	Target
Differential cross-section	$d\sigma/d\Omega = \sigma$	$\dfrac{q}{k}(H_1^2 + H_2^2 + H_3^2 + H_4^2)$	not polarized	not polarized
Polarization of recoil nucleons	$P = \dfrac{N\uparrow - N\downarrow}{N\uparrow + N\downarrow}$ spin $\perp$ to production plane	$\dfrac{q}{k \cdot \sigma} \operatorname{Im}(H_1 H_3^* + H_2 H_4^*)$	not polarized	not polarized
Asymmetry ratio	$\Sigma = \dfrac{\sigma_\perp - \sigma_\parallel}{\sigma_\perp + \sigma_\parallel}$	$\dfrac{q}{k \cdot \sigma} \operatorname{Re}(H_1 H_1^* - H_2 H_3^*)$	polarized $\perp$ and $\parallel$ to production plane	not polarized
Asymmetry ratio	$T = \dfrac{\sigma\uparrow - \sigma\downarrow}{\sigma\uparrow + \sigma\downarrow}$	$\dfrac{q}{k \cdot \sigma} \operatorname{Im}(H_1 H_2^* + H_3 H_4^*)$	not polarized	polarized $\perp$ to production plane

Looking at the helicity combinations for the different measured quantities, we notice that the differential cross-section is composed of the squares of the helicity amplitudes. If *one* amplitude is dominant, it is hard to get information about the smaller amplitudes.

This is different for the polarization and asymmetry measurements. *Only* interference between different helicity amplitudes leads to polarization and asymmetry. So these methods are very sensitive for contributions of small amplitudes and are important to test different models and calculations. Unfortunately these experiments are very difficult and need many hours of machine time.

Another way to describe the photoproduction amplitude is the well known *multipole formalism*.

The photon is coupled to the charge and the magnetic moment of the nucleon via the electric and magnetic field. The nucleon can be excited under conservation of angular momentum and parity. When the photon is absorbed the excited state can have a fixed orbital angular momentum l and a fixed total angular momentum J, depending upon the coupling of the nucleon spin:

$$J = l \pm \tfrac{1}{2}.$$

The amplitudes leading to these states are the electric and magnetic multipole amplitudes

$$E_{l\pm} \quad \text{and} \quad M_{l\pm}$$

for instance:

E_{0+} corresponds to an electric dipole transition leading to a $N\pi$-system with $l = 0$ and $J = \tfrac{1}{2} \to S_{\tfrac{1}{2}}$;

M_{1+} corresponds to a magnetic dipole transition leading to a $N\pi$-system with $l = 1$, $J = 1 + \tfrac{1}{2} = \tfrac{3}{2} \to P_{\tfrac{3}{2}}$;

etc.

7. Experiments at the 500 MeV machine.

The energy of our 500 MeV machine covers the area of the first nucleon resonance $\Delta(1236)$, which is excited by a magnetic dipole transition, described by the M_{1+} multipole amplitude. This has been well established experimentally for a long time. In the theory the pioneering work has been done by Chew, Low, Goldberger and Nambu ([6]) using dispersion relations. They were able to predict the M_{1+} and the E_{0+} amplitudes quite well but not the other small amplitudes. In spite of a great effort at different institutes this situation could not be very much improved.

For a phenomenological analysis it is necessary to have reliable and extended experimental data. This was our intention at the 500 MeV machine. It will be the next topic of this seminar.

8. Differential cross-section for the reactions $\gamma+p \to \pi^0+p$ and $\gamma+p \to \pi^++n$.

In order to reduce the systematic error of the differential cross-section for $\gamma+p \to \pi^0+p$ down to $\pm 5\%$, *four* different and independent experimental arrangements have been used at the 500 MeV machine. Three groups measured the recoil proton, one detected the two photons from the π^0-decay. The experiments had some overlapping regions for comparison (Table IV).

TABLE IV. – *Experimental information for 4 independent experiments for* $\gamma+p \to \pi^0+p$

Exp. No.	Exp. Technique	Detect. Particl.	Photon range	Angle range	Number of data points	Target	Remarks
1 Ref ([7])	Magnetic spectrometer	p	(200÷410) MeV	(60÷160)°	300	hydrogen (liquid)	$E_p > 35$ MeV
2 Ref ([7])	Range telescope	p	(200÷440) MeV	(50÷140)°	230	hydrogen (liquid)	$E_p > 25$ MeV
3 Ref ([8])	time of flight telescope	p	(220÷400) MeV	(40÷60)°	17	hydrogen (gas)	$E_p > 13$ MeV
4 Ref ([9])	Leadglass Cerenkov Counter	2γ	(340÷420) MeV	(10÷70)°	30	hydrogen (liquid)	two Cerenkov counters in coincidence for the π^0-decay photons

The magnetic spectrometer and the range telescope (Experiment nos. 1 and 2) covered about the same angle and energy region. More than 500 data points have been taken. For those kinematic regions where the recoil proton does not come out of the target anymore (forward angles for the pions) two lead class Cerenkov counters have been used for the detection of the $2\pi^0$-decay photons (Experiment no. 4). The disadvantage of this experiment is the low counting rate. The fourth experiment (no. 3) is especially designed for low photon energies and small pion angles. The recoil proton comes out of a gas target and protons with energies greater than 13 MeV can be detected.

In Fig. 4 some angular distributions from experiment no. 1 and no. 2 are shown. The agreement between these completely independent experiments is good. Both agree quite well with the Orsay data ([10]).

Experiment no. 4 is designed for small pion c.m. angles. We can see some of these data together with the other Bonn data and data from Orsay (Fig. 5).

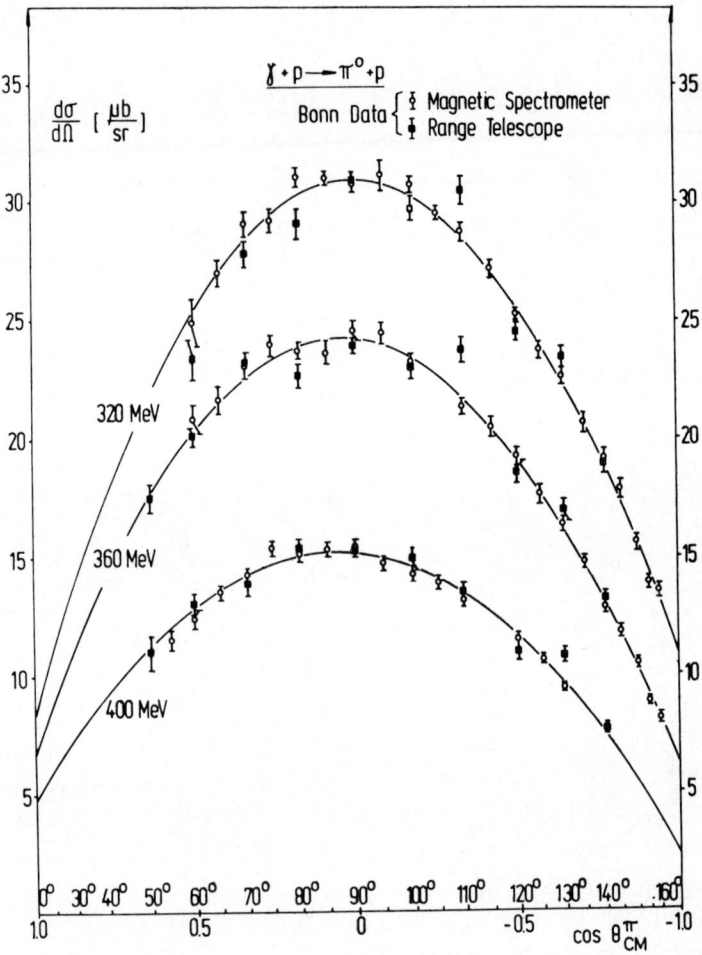

Fig. 4. – Angular distributions of π^0 photoproduction differential cross-section for various energies. Combined data of the magnetic spectrometer and the telescope group ref. (⁷). Full line: polynomial fit to the spectrometer data.

The solid line is a fit curve from Noelle et al. (¹¹). (We come back to this later.) In the overlapping region there are some systematic deviations which are, however, inside the total systematic errors.

Some data points from experiment no. 3 are shown in Fig. 6, together with data from other experiments. The solid curve is again taken from ref. ([11]).

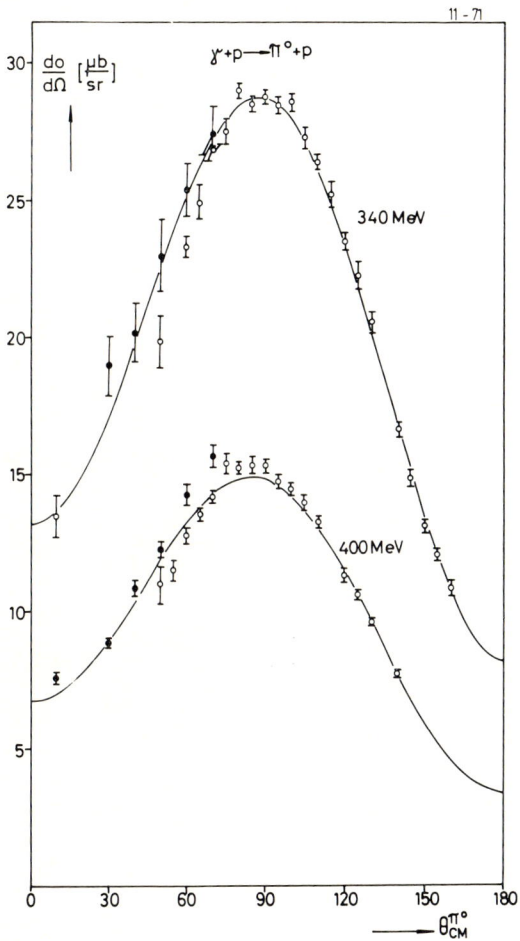

Fig. 5. – Comparison of the differential cross-section at two energies on π^0 photoproduction of different experiments. Full points: Data from ref. ([9]); open points: ref. ([7]); full line: multipole analysis by Noelle et al., ref. ([11]).

For the reaction $\gamma+p \rightarrow \pi^+ +n$ a new set of data with the magnetic spectrometer has been obtained ([12]). More than 400 differential cross-sections have been measured for c.m. angles between 15° and 180° and photon lab. energies between 220 MeV and 425 MeV. The systematical errors are also

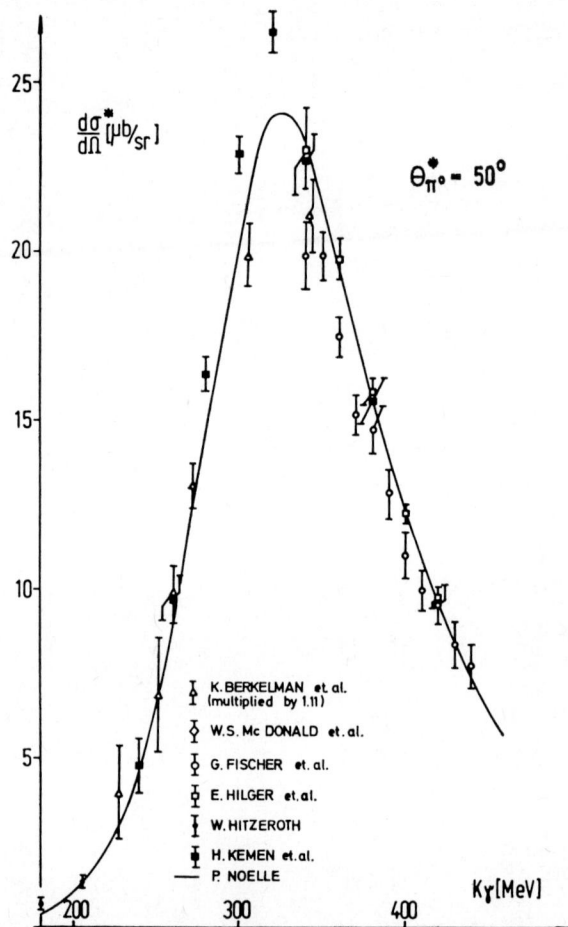

Fig. 6. – Excitation curve for π^0 photoproduction at θ_π(c.m.) = 50°. The full points are the data from Kemen et al., ref. ([8]). They are compared with the theoretical curve from ref. ([11]) and data from various other experiments. The figure is from H. Kemen: *Thesis*, Bonn, 1971.

less than $\pm 5\%$. In Fig. 7 some angular distributions are shown as an example. A more detailed discussion on these experimental results is given in ref. ([13]).

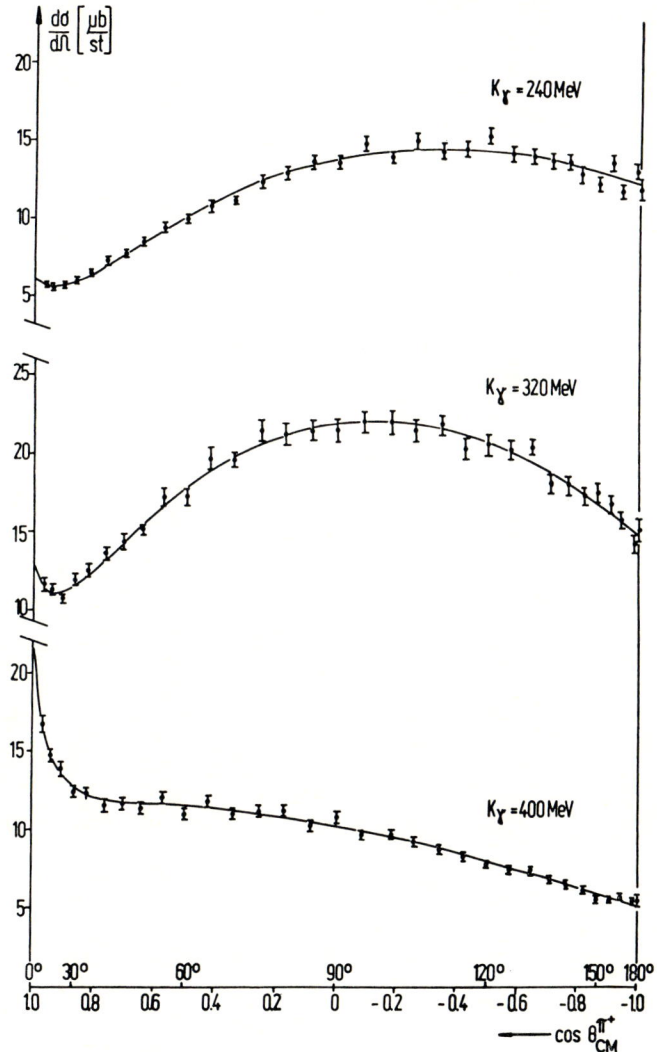

Fig. 7. – Angular distributions at three energies for $\gamma + p \to \pi^+ + n$ from ref. (^{12}). Full line: least square fit to the data.

9. Measurement of the recoil nucleon polarization.

We already mentioned the significance of the polarization measurements for the determination of the small amplitudes. A simple example may illustrate this.

In the region of the first resonance the M_{1+} amplitude is dominating. Considering only multipoles with $l=0$ and $l=1$, we can express (neglecting the small terms) the polarization through the multipoles M_{1+}, E_{0+} and M_{1-}

$$p \sim \sin\theta(a + b\cos\theta)$$

$$a = \mathrm{Im}(E_{0+} \cdot M_{1+}^*)$$

$$b = 3 \cdot \mathrm{Im}(M_{1+} \cdot M_{1-}^*).$$

For a c.m. angle $\theta = 90°$ the b-coefficient vanishes and the interference between the M_{1+} and the small E_{0+}-amplitude gives the main contribution to the polarization.

To estimate the electric dipole amplitude E_{0+} in the two reactions

$$\gamma + p \to \pi^0 + p \quad \text{and} \quad \gamma + p \to \pi^+ + n,$$

we can make a very simple model which might tell us something about the static electric dipole moment of the two final states $n\pi^+$ and $p\pi^0$.

The dipole moment is classically defined as the charge times the distance from the center of mass. This simple minded picture would predict a much greater electric dipole moment for the $n\pi^+$-system than for the $p\pi^0$-system. So we expect for a c.m. angle of 90°, where only the a-coefficient contributes:

small polarization for $\gamma + p \to \pi^0 + p$

large polarization for $\gamma + p \to \pi^+ + n$.

In Fig. 8 some angular distributions of the recoil proton polarization are shown together with fit curves from ref. ([11]). We find indeed a very small polarization at 90° and a distribution of the polarization compatible with a $\sin\theta \cdot \cos\theta$ distribution. From this we get information about the small M_{1-} amplitude.

The first measurement of the polarization of a recoil neutron has been made at the small synchrotron at $E_\gamma = 390$ MeV ([14]). As we expected, the E_{0+} amplitude and consequently the polarization is much larger at a c.m. angle of 90°, it turned out to be 80%.

The polarization of protons have been measured by looking at the asymmetry of the scattered protons from helium or carbon ([15]). The analyser for the recoiling neutrons was a liquid hydrogen target (40 cm⌀).

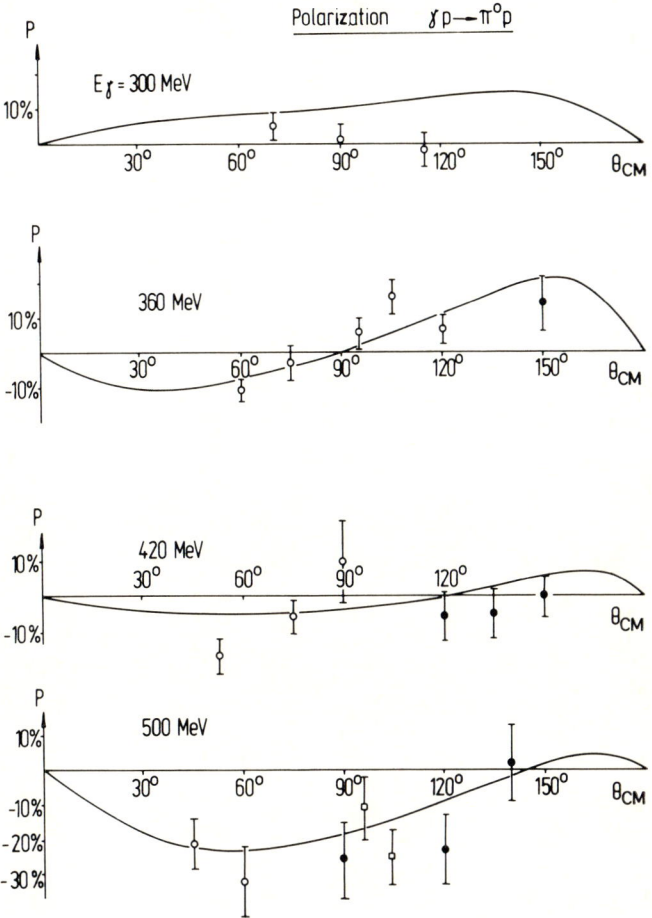

Fig. 8. – Recoil proton polarization $\gamma + p \to \pi^0 + p$. Angular distributions for four different energies. Data from ref. ([15]). Full line: Analysis by Noelle et al., ref. ([11]).

10. Analysis of the π^+- and π^0-data below a photon energy of $E_\gamma = -500$ MeV.

Looking at the total cross-section for the pion nucleon scattering and the photoproduction of single pions, the similar structure gives already a hint that there might be a connection between the theoretical description of the two reactions. The pion nucleon phase shifts and the phase of a multipole amplitude in photoproduction are connected by the Watson theorem, which is valid for energies below the two-pion production threshold and is based on T-invariance and unitarity of the S-matrix. One possible approach is the *fixed t dispersion relation* mentioned before. Independent of different refinements, only the dominant M_{1+}-amplitude and the nonresonant E_{0+}-amplitude can be calculated fairly well, but the predictions of other smaller multipoles are still very uncertain. A discussion of these attempts can be found in ref. ([16]).

Another approach uses only measured quantities from pion nucleon scattering and photoproduction, together with general theoretical assumptions, but *no* dynamical model. Values for the multipoles are obtained for each energy from fits to the experimental data. Such energy independen *phenomenological* calculations have been carried out recently ([11]) and ([17]).t

A remarkable consistency for the analysis for π^0 and π^+ production has been obtained. This is mainly due to the new carefully made differential cross-section measurements at Orsay, Moscow and Bonn and the polarization measurements at Bonn.

One nice feature of the analysis of ref. ([11]) will conclude this section. We already know that the M_{1+}-amplitude is responsible for the excitation of the first resonance $\Delta(1236)$, and we can ask how good this resonance is. What are the conditions for a « good resonance »?

Let us go back to classical mechanics. We calculate the amplitude x_0 of an oscillating spring periodically excited by $K = K_0 \exp[-i\omega t]$.

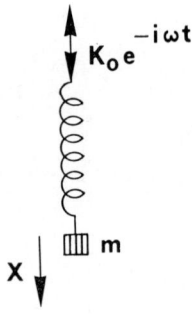

$m\ddot{x} + \gamma\dot{x} + Dx = K_0 \cdot \exp[-i\omega t]$ with $\gamma/m = \Gamma$ and $D/m = \omega_0^2$ we get for the amplitude:

$$x_0 = \frac{K_0}{m}\left(\frac{1}{\omega_0^2 - \omega^2 - i\Gamma\omega}\right).$$

In the vicinity of the resonance we can write: $\omega_0 + \omega \approx 2\omega$ and $\omega/\omega_0 \approx 1$. We get:

$$x_0 = \frac{K_0}{2m\omega_0}\left(\frac{1}{\omega_0 - \omega - i\Gamma/2}\right) \quad \text{or}$$

$$x_0 = \frac{K_0}{\omega_0 \gamma}\left(\frac{\Gamma/2}{\omega_0 - \omega - i\Gamma/2}\right).$$

We can plot this amplitude in two different ways:

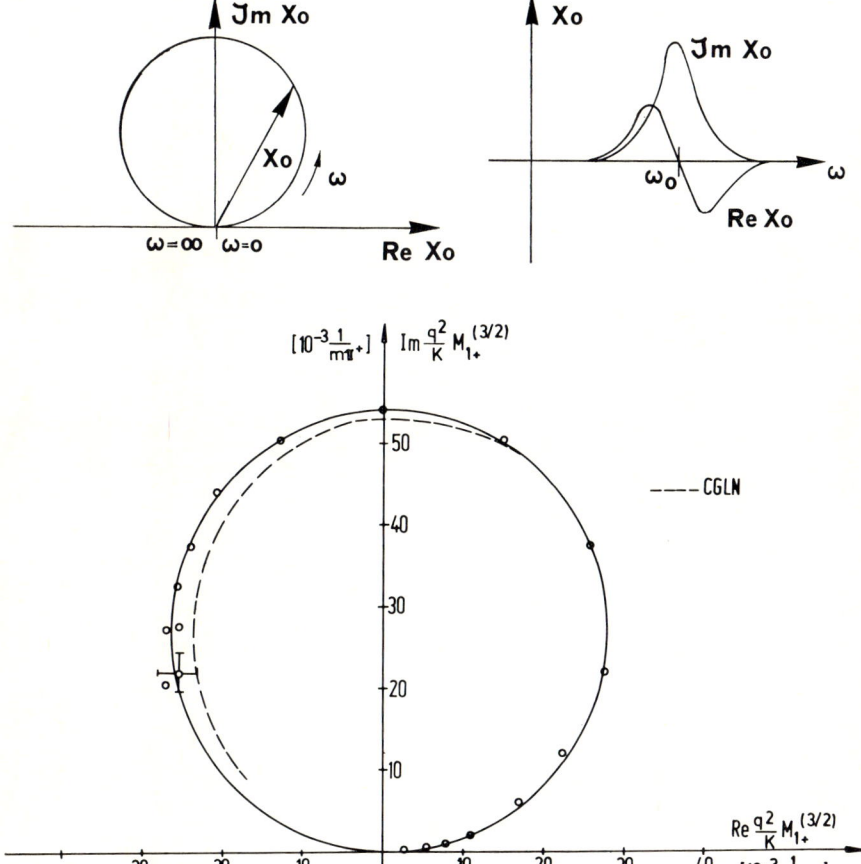

Fig. 9. – Argand diagram for the $M_{1+}^{(3/2)}$ multipole. Analysis from ref. ([11]). The broken line is the « old » CGLN-prediction, ref. ([6]).

If we replace ω by the total energy $E/\hbar$, we have the well known non-relativistic Breit-Wigner–formula for the amplitude.

In Fig. 9 the $M_{1+}^{(3/2)}$ multipole is plotted. It shows a beautiful circle demonstrating that the magnetic dipole multipole $M_{1+}^{(3/2)}$ is an almost clean resonant amplitude. Only a small contribution of a non-resonant part is responsible for the slight shift of the middle point of the circle. The dashed curve is the « old » prediction by CGLN ([6]) which is quite reasonable.

11. Other experiments at the 500 MeV machine.

Measurements of the differential cross-section for the reaction

$$\gamma + n \to \pi^- + p$$

for photon energies between 240 MeV and 400 MeV and angles between 10° and 180° are in progress ([18]). Liquid deuterium is used as a target. The magnet spectrometer is the same used for the π^0- and π^+-production.

Of growing interest during the last time has been the *proton Compton effect*.

$$\gamma + p \to p' + \gamma'.$$

At the small machine three angular distributions for photon energies of 320 MeV, 380 MeV and 420 MeV have been measured ([19]). The recoil protons are detected by a range telescope and the photons in a *Pb*-scintillator sandwich counter. The evaluation is not yet completed.

Two experiments have just been finished measuring the coherent π^0 production from deuterium:

$$\gamma + d \to \pi^0 + d.$$

One group used the magnetic spectrometer for the detection of the deuteron. Data are obtained for photon energies between 260 MeV and 400 MeV and for c.m. angles between 70° and 160° ([20]). The second group detected the decay photons of the π^0 in two lead glass Cerenkov counters and measured two excitation curves for 6° and 80° ([21]). At 80° protons and deuterons have been detected in coincidence with the photon branch to distinguish between the coherent and incoherent process

$$\gamma + d \to \pi^0 + p + n.$$

Finally, I would like to mention the first experiment done at the 500 MeV machine belonging to the field of nuclear physics. Short range nucleon correlations in O^{16} have been investigated:

$$\gamma + O^{16} \rightarrow N^{14} + p + n.$$

Protons and neutrons are detected in coincidence. Measurements have been done in the photon energy range from 130 MeV to 380 MeV ([22]).

There are plans to continue these measurements with a tagged photon beam.

12. The experimental program at the 2.5 GeV synchrotron.

The photoproduction of single pions in the reaction $\gamma + p \rightarrow \pi^0 + p$, $\gamma + p \rightarrow \pi^+ + n$ and $\gamma + n \rightarrow \pi^- + p$ around the first resonance is in a good shape as far as the experimental situation is concerned. A considerable number of new data is available, the agreement at different laboratories is remarkable.

This situation becomes much worse at higher energies. In Fig. 10 a summary of the pion nucleon resonances known from pion nucleon scattering is shown together with the threshold energies for different photoproduction channels. This picture is taken from a recently published review article by H. Fischer ([23]). In this paper we can also find a compilation of the experimental data and a discussion of different attempts for the analysis of the data. A more detailed theoretical description is given in ref. ([16]) and ([24]).

In Fig. 10 we can form three groups of resonances:

1) A single resonance at 1236 GeV;
2) A group of four resonances around 1670 GeV;
3) A fairly wide range of resonances between 1780 and 2040 GeV.

This « resonance region » can be covered with our 2.5 GeV synchrotron. At the moment we are far away from the situation at lower energies.

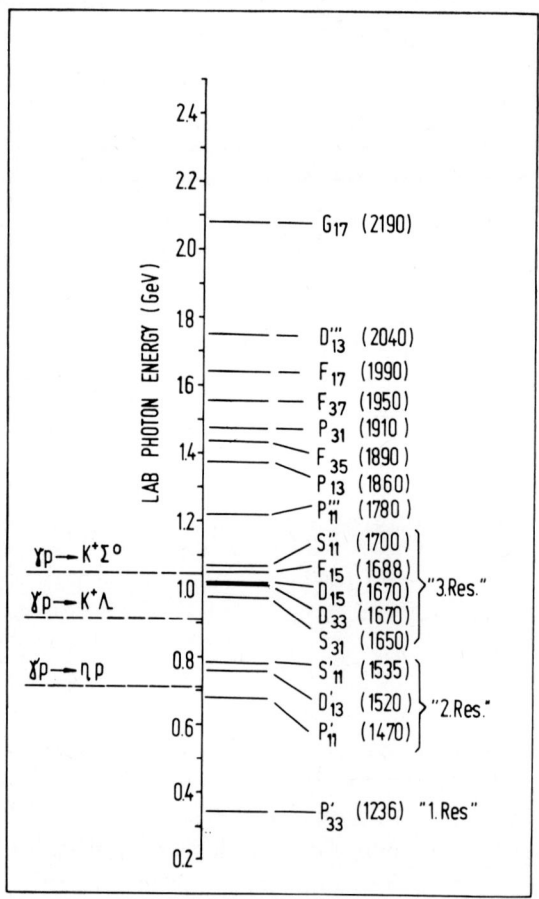

Fig. 10. – Summary of the known pion nucleon resonances in the energy range of our machines. Figure from ref. ([23]).

At present there is no chance to make a successful energy independent analysis. There are not enough data and the Watson theorem, which connected the pion nucleon scattering data with the photoproduction, can not be used anymore.

So one part of the experimental program at the 2.5 GeV machine was obviously to continue the investigation of pseudoscalar meson photoproduction to higher energies. Above $E_\gamma = 700$ MeV the η-meson production,

TABLE IV. – *List of experiments at the 2.5 GeV synchrotron.*

Reaction	Measured quantities and remarks
$\gamma + p \to \pi^0 + p$ Ref. ([25])	$d\sigma/d\Omega$; proton detected with magnetic spectrometer; backward pion angles
$\gamma + p \to \pi^0 + p$ Ref. ([26]) a) b) c)	recoil proton polarization analyzer: helium; time of flight telescope analyzer: carbon; time of flight telescope analyzer: hydrogen; magnetic spectrometer
$\gamma + p \to \pi^0 + p$ Ref. ([27])	$d\sigma/d\Omega$; π^0-decay photons with two Cerenkov counters
$\gamma + p \to \pi^+ + n$ Ref. ([28])	$d\sigma/d\Omega$; π^+ detected with magnetic spectrometer 180° backwards pion production
$\gamma + p \to \pi^+ + n$ Ref. ([29])	asymmetry $(\sigma\uparrow - \sigma\downarrow)/(\sigma\uparrow + \sigma\downarrow)$ with polarized proton target
$\gamma + p \to \pi^+ + n$ Ref. ([30])	recoil neutron polarization hydrogen as analyzer; π^+-n coincidence
$\gamma + p \to \eta^0 + p$ Ref. ([31])	$d\sigma/d\Omega$; two Cerenkov counters
$\gamma + p \to K^+ + \Lambda^0 \to$ $\to K^+ + \Sigma^0$ Ref. ([32])	$d\sigma/d\Omega$; K^+ detected with magnetic spectrometer photon-difference method for Λ-Σ separation
$\gamma + p \to K^+ + \Lambda^0$ Ref. ([33])	Λ^0-polarization; detection of π^--p-mode hodoscopes + sparkchambers; K^+ from magnetic spectrometer as trigger
$\gamma + p \to \varphi + p$ Ref. ([34])	K^+K^- detected in magnetic spectrometer; p in coincidence; angular distribution at $E_\gamma = 2$ GeV
$e^- + p \to e^- + p + \pi^0 \to$ $\to e^- + n + \pi^+$ Ref. ([35])	scattered e^- detected in magnetic spectrometer; σ_T and σ_L in the region of the $\Delta(1236)$ resonance. p and π^+ detected in magnetic spectrometer; coincidence with e^-
synchrotron radiation Ref. ([36])	a) investigation of the electron beam structure inside the synchrotron ring b) optical investigations in atomic physics and solid state physics with photons of 10 Å to 1000 Å

above $E_\gamma = 900$ MeV the $K^+\Lambda^0$ and above $E_\gamma = 1050$ MeV the $K^+\Sigma^0$ production can be studied.

Another part of the effort is devoted to the scattering of electrons on nucleons and the investigation of the electroproduction of pions.

One experiment deals with the vector meson production on protons. And finally the synchrotron radiation is used as a light source.

In Table IV the present experiments around the 2.5 GeV synchrotron are listed.

13. Photoproduction of pseudoscalar mesons at intermediate energies.

Let us start with the reaction $\gamma + p \to \pi^0 + p$. The number of *differential cross-section* data have been increased considerably during the last years, but there are still large « white areas » in the map for the diff. cross-section, the recoil proton polarization p and the asymmetry ratio Σ. This is clearly demonstrated in Fig. 11 taken from ref. [23].

At the 2.5 GeV machine the diff. cross-section is measured at *backward pion angles* by detecting the proton in a magnetic spectrometer in the forward direction [25].

In Fig. 12 a preliminary excitation curve for a pion c.m. angle of 40° is shown. The agreement with data from Caltech and Nina is very good in the overlapping region. A distinct bump appears around $E_\gamma = 1400$ MeV.

For the measurement of the *forward pion angles* a set up with two lead glass Cerenkov counters is used [27]. The experiment is in progress.

The polarization of the recoil proton has been investigated with three different arrangements [26].

The polarization is obtained from the left-right-asymmetry of the scattered protons from a second target. The analyzing power of this second target is a very important factor for these experiments. Only few materials are « good » analyzers. The analyzing power should be high, its energy and angle dependence for the scattered protons should be fairly weak, a necessary condition for an apparatus with a large solid angle. Unfortunately there is not such a good analyzer for the whole energy range of the protons covered by these experiments.

For different energies of the recoil protons different analyzers have to be used:

$$\begin{array}{lll} \text{helium} & \text{for} & 20 < E_p < 50 \text{ MeV} \\ \text{carbon} & \text{for} & 100 < E_p < 300 \text{ MeV} \\ \text{hydrogen} & \text{for} & E_p > 300 \text{ MeV} \,. \end{array}$$

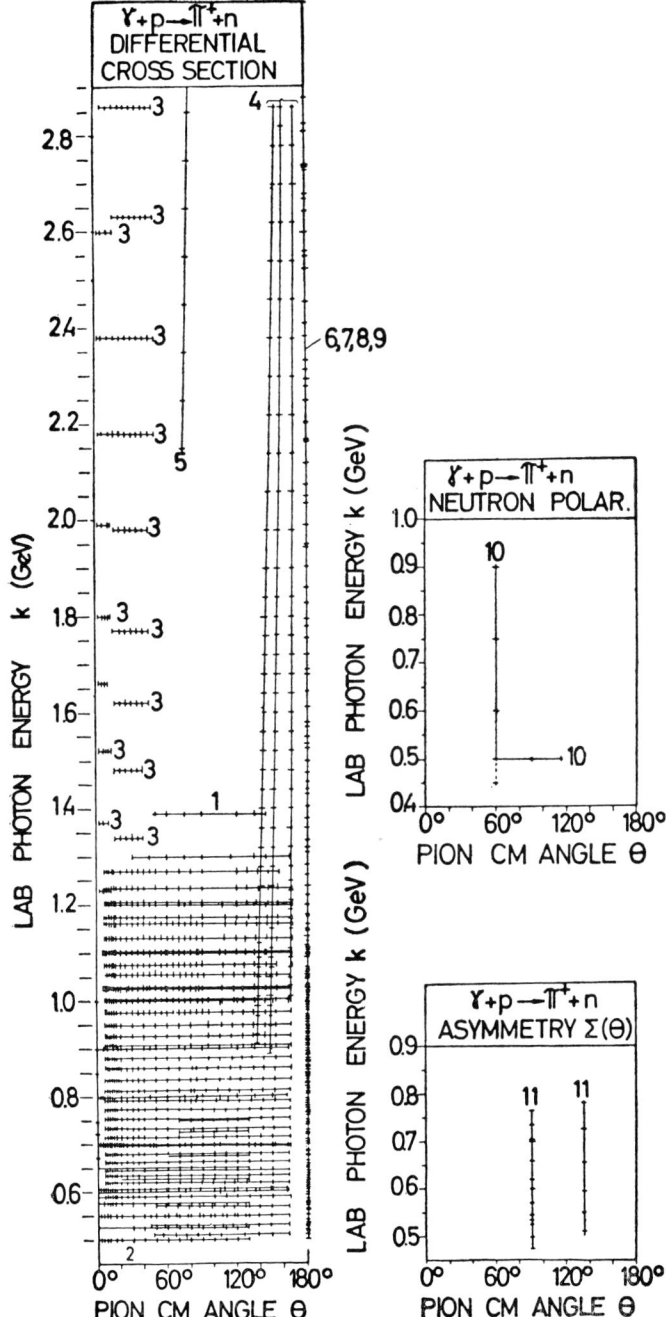

Fig. 11. – Fischer map for the experimental data $\gamma + p \to \pi^+ + p$ on differential cross-section, recoil proton polarization and asymmetry. Angular distributions are shown by horizontal lines, excitation curves by vertical lines. Only the most recent cross-section data are included. Figure is from ref. ([23]).

More details about the experiment and a discussion of the analyzers can be found in a recent article by P. Brinckmann ([37]).

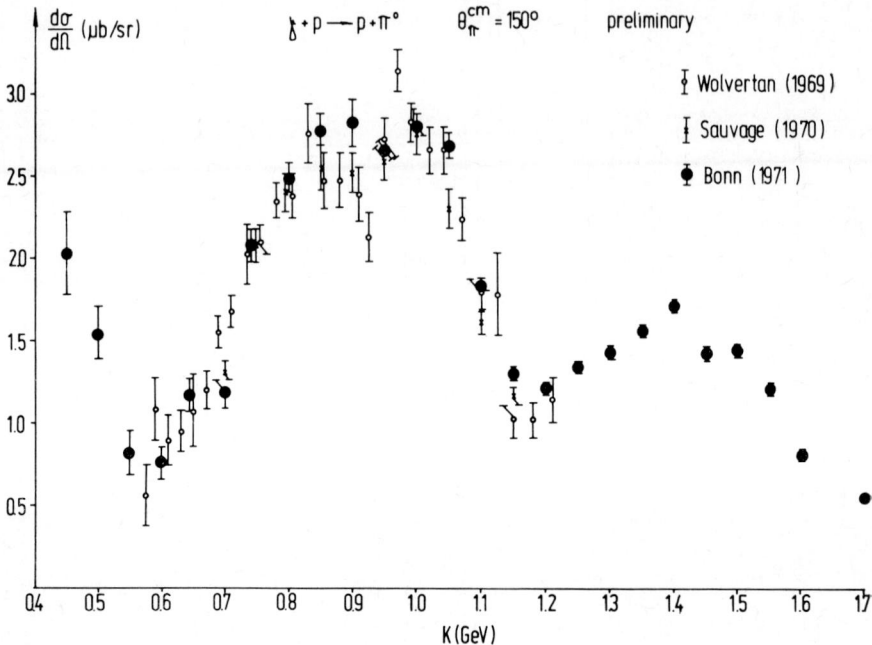

Fig. 12. – Preliminary data from ref. ([25]) on $\gamma+p \to \pi^0+p$ for θ_π(c.m.) = 150°, together with data from Caltec and Orsay.

Let us now turn to the reaction $\gamma+p \to \pi^++p$. In Fig. 13 Fischer's map shows us a summary of the π^+-data in the energy range of our machine. Up to 1.3 GeV there are many diff. cross-section data, but at higher energies only few measurements have been done.

Of special interest is the photoproduction of *pions at an angle of* 180°. In this case no additional angular momentum can be given to the pion nucleon system and only amplitudes with helicities $\frac{1}{2}$ can contribute to the cross-section.

Several laboratories measured this reaction independently. In our laboratory the detection of the π^+ mesons is done with the help of a magnetic spectrometer (composed of the synchrotron spare magnet (!) and 2 quadrupole magnets) ([28]). A preliminary set of data together with data from other institutes is plotted in Fig. 14. There are still considerable deviations in the absolute values of the cross-section, but the overall behaviour is the same.

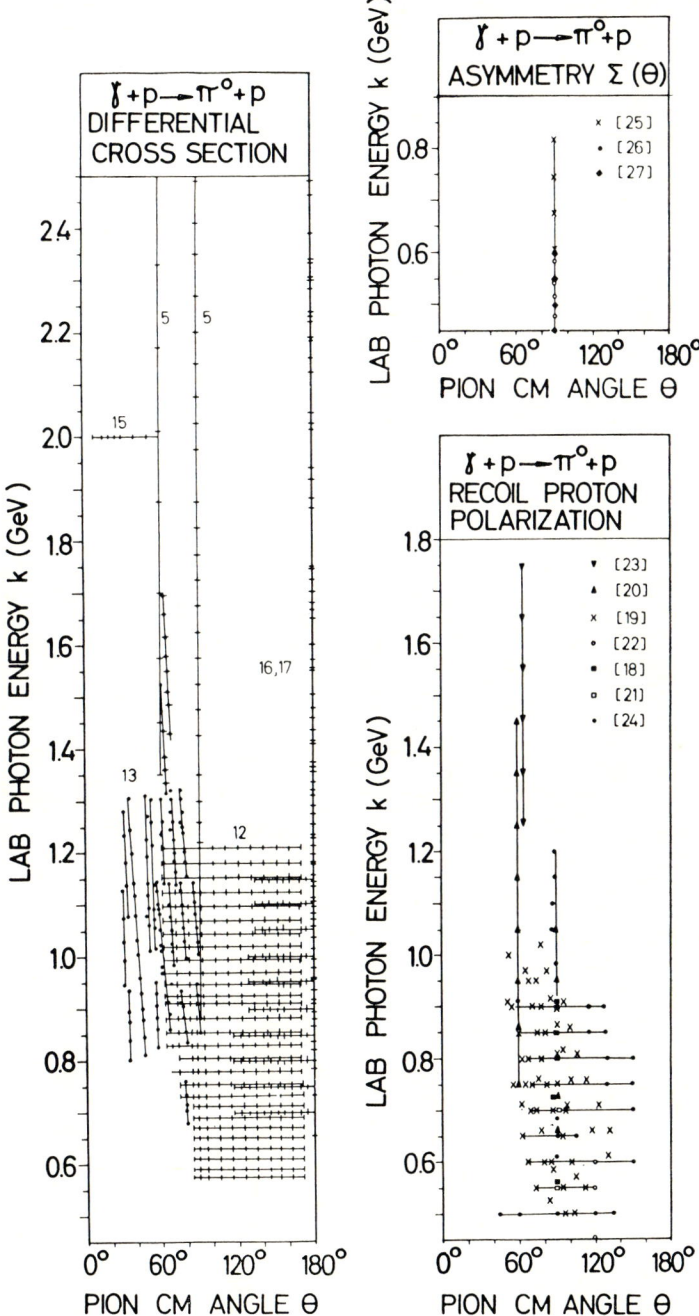

Fig. 13. – Fischer map for the $\gamma+p \to \pi^0+n$ data. Ref.([23]).

The bump structure is not yet fully understood and the experiments are continuing.

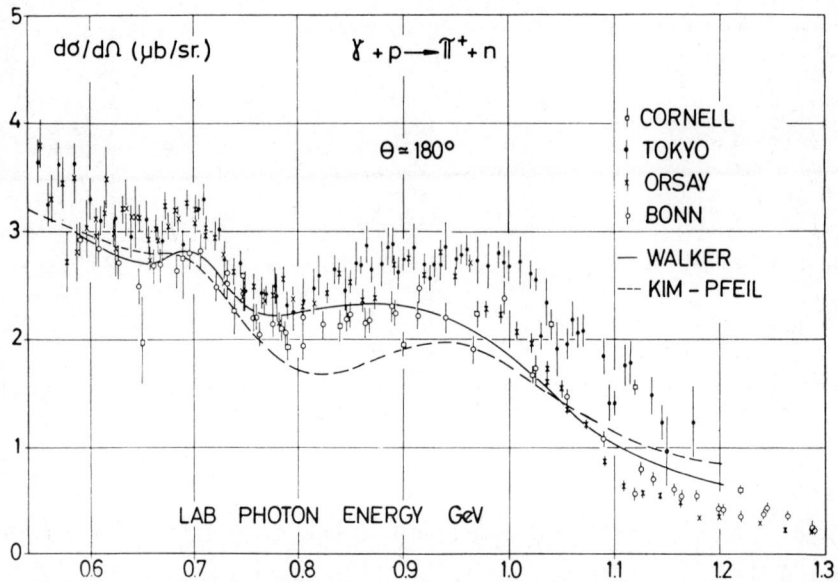

Fig. 14. – 180° cross-section data for $\gamma+p \to \pi^+ +n$ from Cornell, Tokyo, Orsay and Bonn, ref. ([23]). Curves from ref. ([5]) and ([38]).

Another interesting problem is the measurement of the *recoil neutron polarization*. Unfortunately the data can not be compared with results of other laboratories because only one group is investigating this question ([30]). The pions are detected with a magnetic spectrometer and the neutrons are scattered from a large liquid hydrogen target into two big plastic scintillators. In Fig. 15 two excitation curves for a c.m. angle of 60° and 90° are shown. The curves are fits obtained by Walker ([5]) and Pfeil ([38]). Both authors did not include these measurements in their analysis. There are considerable discrepancies.

It would be very interesting to compare the predictions of these calculations with a measurement of the asymmetry T on a *polarized proton target*.

Polarized proton targets have been used widely around proton machines. Since the discovery of butanol as a good material for the polarization, combining a high degree of orientation with a good resistance against radiation damage, it became possible to use such a target in intensive electron or photon beams.

A polarized target has been built in our laboratory, which is a slightly modified CERN-version ([39]). It is operating at 1° K and 25 kG. About 35% of the free protons in the butanol could be polarized.

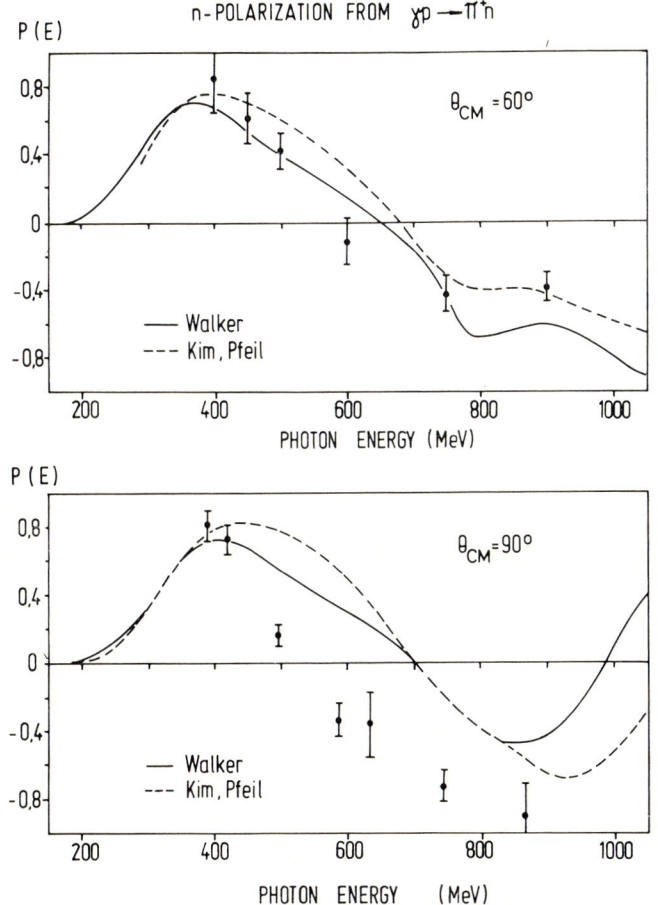

Fig. 15. – Recoil neutron polarization data from ref. ([30]). Full line: Analysis by Walker ref. ([5]); broken line: Analysis by Kim and Pfeil, ref. ([38]).

In a first run the asymmetry ratio T has been measured for a pion c.m. angle of 40° and photon energies between 400 MeV and 1.4 GeV ([29]). Figure 16 shows the data together with the prediction of Walker ([5]). Here we can notice a similar deviation from the data as for the recoil neutron polarization points.

The diff. cross-section of the reaction $\gamma + p \to \eta^0 + p$ is measured with the same experimental set up which is used for the π^0 production under forward angles ([31]). First data have been taken, but the evaluation is not yet completed.

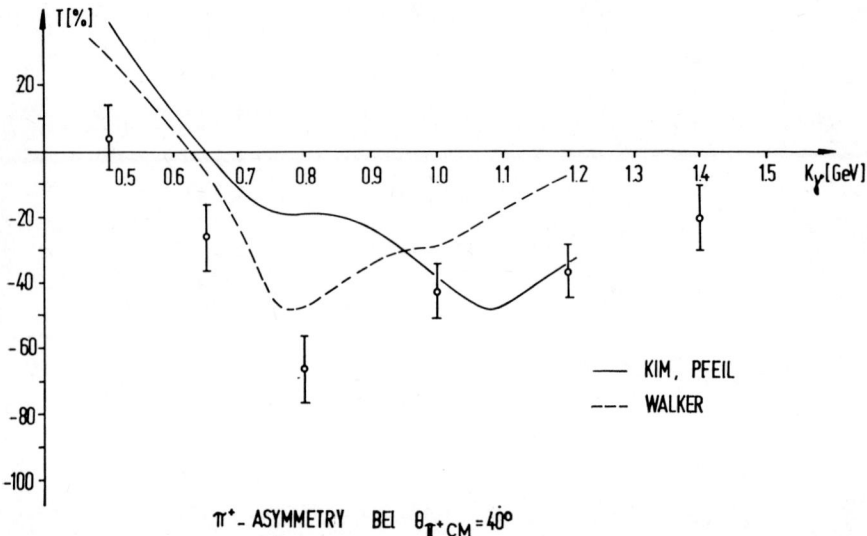

Fig. 16. – Measurement of the polarized target asymmetry T for $\gamma+p \to \pi^++n$, ref. ([29]). Curves from ref. ([5]) and ([38]).

Extensive diff. cross-section measurements have been carried out for the reaction $\gamma+p \to K^++\Lambda^0$ and $\gamma+p \to K^++\Sigma^+$. The experimental problem is the detection of the K^+ in a large background of pions. An especially designed magnetic spectrometer and different types of Cerenkov counters have been used.

Both reactions have been measured for a fixed momentum transfer and photon energies between 1 GeV and 2.2 GeV. Also, angular distributions for $E_\gamma = 1.3$ GeV and $E_\gamma = 1.4$ GeV have been taken. For the separation of the two reactions, which cannot be distinguished by the decay particles, the photon difference method has been used.

In Fig. 17 the latest results for the $K^+\Lambda^0$ production are shown. The curve is a calculation made by Meyer zu Hörste and Pfeil ([40]) using a Regge cut model. They cannot explain the steep increase above threshold. There may be some connection with the bumps measured at backward direction ([41]) at the same total energy of about 1.7 GeV. At this total energy a bump has also been seen in the $\pi^-p \to K^0\Lambda^0$ scattering ([43]). A lot of experimental and theoretical investigation has to be done before the $K^+\Lambda^0$ and $K^+\Sigma$ reactions are fairly understood.

One further information can be obtained, if the *polarization of the Λ^0* is carefully measured. This will be tried at Bonn too. First test runs looked promising ([33]).

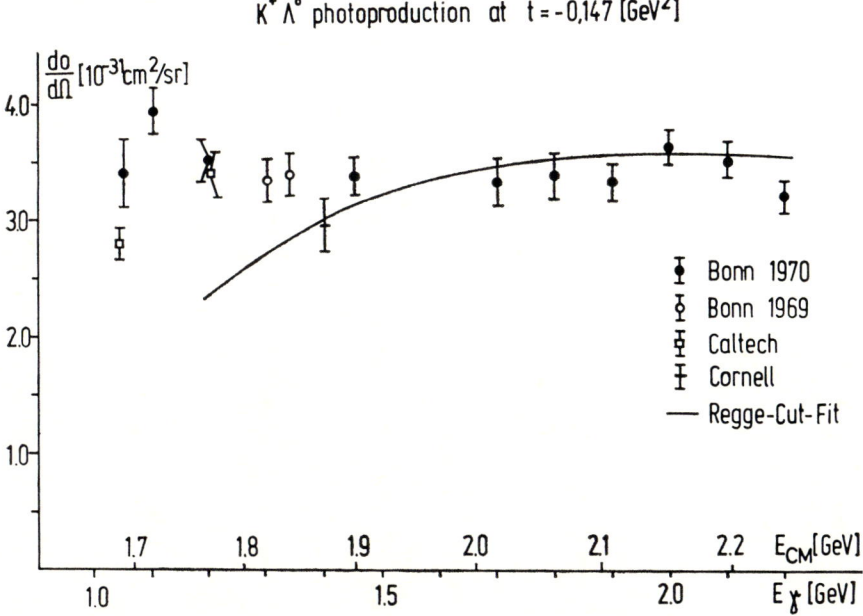

Fig. 17. – $K^+\Lambda^0$ photoproduction at $t = -0.147$ (GeV)^2 from ref. ([32]). Full curve from ref. ([40]).

One of the most difficult experiments around our machine seems to be the measurement of the diff. cross-section for the reaction $\gamma + p \to \varphi^0 + p$. The K^+ and K^- from the φ-decay are detected in a magnetic spectrometer in coincidence with the proton. A hodoscope spark-chamber combination is used ([34]). It is planned to measure an angular distribution for $E_\gamma = 2$ GeV and $\varphi_{c.m.}$ angle between $20°$ and $80°$. The group is taking data.

Inelastic electron-nucleon scattering is one of the most interesting fields in elementary particle physics right now. The question whether the nuclear matter consists of smaller building blocks (like quarks or partons) is not yet answered.

If we want to look deep into the nucleon, we can use virtual photons far away from the mass shell and look for deep inelastic processes. This can be done with high energy electrons (SLAC).

This region is outside the range of our 2.5 GeV machine, but there is a connection between the deep inelastic region and the resonance region via the finite energy sum rules. The information obtained at lower energies can be used to predict the behaviour of the amplitude at high energies. There we have another field which can be investigated in our laboratory.

Let us look again at the graph:

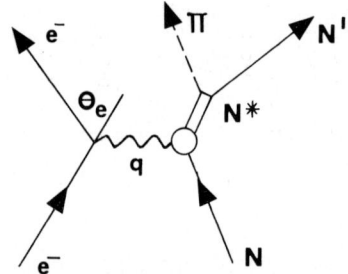

The photon is off-shell. The momentum transfer q to the nucleon depends on the energy E' and the angle θ_e of the scattered electron:

$$q^2 = 4EE' \sin^2 \frac{\theta_e}{2}.$$

The « equivalent energy » K of the photon is:

$$K = v - \frac{q^2}{2M_p}; \qquad v = E - E^-.$$

These photons are different from the real photons used in photoproduction in two ways:

1) They are monochromatic.
   The energy can be varied experimentally.
2) They have « mass » and are composed out of transverse and longitudinal parts. $\lambda = \pm 1; 0$.

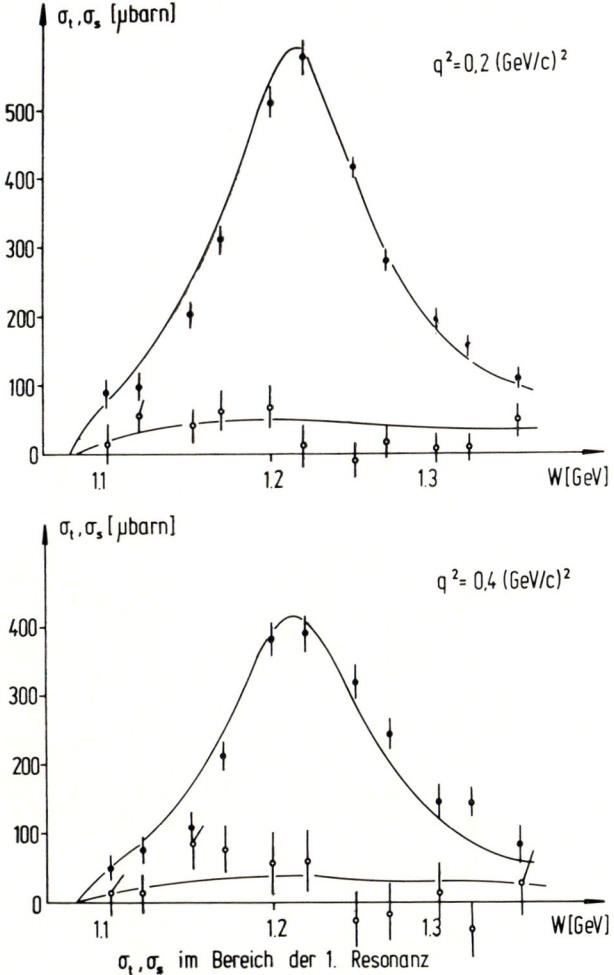

Fig. 18. – σ_T and σ_L for inelastic electron scattering on protons in the area of the first resonance, ref. ([35]). Full lines from ref. ([42]).

So we can write the differential cross-section in the following way:

$$\frac{d^2\sigma}{d\Omega \cdot dE'} = \Gamma(\sigma_T + \varepsilon\sigma_L)$$

σ_T, σ_L are the transverse and longitudinal cross-sections. Γ is a kinematical factor and ε, the polarization parameter, depends upon the variables v and θ_e:

$$\varepsilon = \frac{1}{1 + 2(1 + v^2/q^2)\,\mathrm{tg}^2\,\theta_e/2}.$$

It can also be varied by changing the experimental set up. This offers the possibility to measure the σ_T and σ_L separately.

This has been done in an experiment at the external electron beam ([35]).

The measurement covered the region of the $\Delta(1236)$ resonance. The scattered electron has been detected in a sloped-window magnetic spectrometer (single arm experiment). The momentum transfer q^2 has been choosen between 0.1 and 0.7 (GeV/c)^2.

The results are shown in Fig. 18. σ_T has the well known resonance behaviour, σ_L is very small. The solid curves are calculations of von Gehlen ([42]). The agreement is very good.

A two arm experiment, where the electron and the exchanged particle (p or π^+) from the reactions $e^- + p \to \pi^+ + n + e^-$ and $e^- + p \to \pi^0 + p + e^-$ are measured in coincidence, is in progress.

REFERENCES

1) H. Ehrenberg and W. Paul: *Atomwirtschaft*, **7/8**, 300 (1959).
2) K. H. Althoff, K. Bätzner, J. Drees, A. Febel, O. Gildemeister, G. von Holtey, G. Knop, P. Lütter, H. Netter, W. Paul, F. J. Schittko, A. Schultz von Dratzig, H. E. Stier and E. Weisse: *Nucl. Instr. and Meth.*, **61**, 1 (1968).
3) A. Sanda and G. Shaw: *Phys. Rev. Lett.*, **24**, 1310 (1970).
4) M. Jakob and G. C. Wick: *Ann. of Phys.*, **7**, 404 (1960).
5) R. L. Walker: *Phys. Rev.*, **182**, 1729 (1969).
6) G. F. Chew, M. L. Goldberger, F. E. Low, Y. Nambu: *Phys. Rev.*, **106**, 1345 (1957).
7) G. Fischer, H. Fischer, G. von Holtey, H. Kämpgen, G. Knop, P. Schulz, W. Wessels, W. Braunschweig, H. Genzel and R. Wedemeyer: BONN UNIV PI 1-44 (1968); *Nucl. Phys.*, B **16**, 93 (1970).
8) H. Kemen, R. Wedemeyer and H. J. Weyer: private communication.
9) E. Hilger, H. J. Roegler, L. M. Simons and M. Tonutti: BONN UNIV PI 1-103 (1970).
10) R. Morand, E. F. Erickson, J. P. Pahin and M. G. Groissaux: *Phys. Rev.*, **180**, 1299 (1969).
11) P. Noelle, W. Pfeil and D. Schwela: BONN UNIV PI 2-92 (1971); *Nucl. Phys.*, B **26**, 461 (1971).
12) G. Fischer, H. Fischer, M. Heuel, G. von Holtey, G. Knop and J. Stümpfig: *Nucl. Phys.*, B **16**, 119 (1970); BONN UNIV PI 1-101.
13) G. von Holtey: *Springer Tracts*, **59**, 3 (1971).

14) K. H. ALTHOFF, H. PIEL, W. WALLRAFF and G. WESSELS: *Phys. Lett.*, **26** B, 640 (1968).
15) K. H. ALTHOFF, D. FINKEN, N. MINATTI, H. PIEL, D. TRINES and M. UNGER: *Phys. Lett.*, **26** B, 677 (1968); P. FELLER, W. NIEHAUS, N. MINATTI, H. PIEL and M. UNGER: *Int. Conf. on Electron and Photon Interaction* (Liverpool, 1969), *XV Int. Conf. on High Energy Physics* (Kiew, 1970); D. E. LUNQUIST: *Phys. Lett.*, **188**, 1527 (1968).
16) G. VON GEHLEN and H. ROLLNIK: BONN UNIV PI 2-101 (1971).
17) F. A. BEHRENDS and D. L. WEAVER: *Nucl. Phys.*, B **30**, 575 (1971).
18) G. VON HOLTEY, H. STEIN, J. STÜMPFIG and H. WAHLEN: *International Symposium on Electron and Photon Interactions at High Energies* (Ithaca, 1971).
19) H. GENZEL, M. JUNG, K R. RAUSCH, R. WEDEMEYER and H. J. WEYER: BONN UNIV PI 1-138 (1971); *International Symposium on Electron and Photon Interactions at High Energies* (Ithaca, 1971).
20) L. HIEBER, G. VON HOLTEY, G. KNOP, H. STEIN, J. STÜMPFIG and H. WAHLEN: BONN UNIV PI 1-136 (1971); *International Symposium on Electron and Photon Interactions at High Energies* (Ithaca, 1971).
21) E. HILGER, H. J. ROEGLER and M. TONUTTI: Thesis Tonutti Bonn (1971); *International Symposium on Electron and Photon Interactions at High Energies* (Ithaca, 1971).
22) H. HARTMANN, H. HOFFMANN, B. MECKING and G. NÖLDEKE: private communication.
23) H. FISCHER: *Springer Tracts*, **59**, 188 (1971).
24) A. DONNACHIE, Rapporteur talk: *International Symposium on Electron and Photon Interactions at High Energies* (Ithaca, 1971).
25) P. FELLER, D. MENZE and W. J. SCHWILLE: private communication.
26) P. BLÜM, P. BRINCKMANN, R. BROCKMANN, P. LÜTTER, W. MOHR. P. FELLER, N. MINATTI, H. PIEL, W. NIEHAUS and D. TRINES: BONN UNIV PI 1-105 (1970) and private communication.
27) A. CHRIST, D. HUSMANN, B. LÖHR, G. NÖLDEKE, T. REICHELT and H. SCHILLING: private communication.
28) G. FISCHER, H. FISCHER, M. LENEKE and H. WESSELS: BONN UNIV PI 1-100 (1970); Thesis Wessels (Bonn, 1971).
29) K. H. ALTHOFF, P. FELLER, H. HERR, W. HOFFMANN, V. KADANSKY, D. MENZE, U. OPARA, F. J. SCHITTKO, W. SCHULZ and W. J. SCHWILLE: BONN UNIV PI 1-139 (1971); *International Symposium on Electron and Photon Interactions at High Energies* (Ithaca, 1971).
30) U. HAHN, H. HEINRICHS and W. WALLRAFF: BONN UNIV PI 1-143 (1971); *International Symposium on Electron and Photon Interactions at High Energies* (Ithaca, 1971).
31) A. CHRIST, D. HUSMANN, B. LOEHR, G. NÖLDEKE, T. REICHELT and H. SCHILLING *International Symposium on Electron and Photon Interactions at High Energies* (Ithaca, 1971); private communication.
32) P. FELLER, D. MENZE, U. OPARA, W. SCHULZ and W. J. SCHWILLE: BONN UNIV PI 1-137 (1971); *International Symposium on Electron and Photon Interactions at High Energies* (Ithaca, 1971).
33) R. HAAS, U. OPARA and W. J. SCHWILLE: private communication.
34) H. J. BESCH, G. HARTMANN, R. KOSE, F. KRAUTSCHNEIDER, K. LOSCHINSKI, W. PAUL and U. TRINKS: private communication.
35) K. BÄTZNER, U. BECK, K. H. BECKS, J. DREES, G. KNOP, M. LEENEN, K. MOSER, CH. NIETZEL and E. SCHLÖSSER: *International Symposium on Electron and Photon Interactions at High Energies* (Ithaca, 1971); private communication.

36) K. Thimm: *Thesis* (Bonn, 1970); B. Drerup and K. Thimm: private communication.
37) P. Brinckmann: BONN UNIV PI 1-135 (1971); *Springer Tracts*, to be published.
38) W. Pfeil and Kim Yong Taik: BONN UNIV PI 2-46 (1968).
39) S. Mango, Ö. Runolfson and M. Borghini: *Nucl. Instr. and Meth.*, **72**, 45 (1969).
40) V. Meyer zu Hoerste and W. Pfeil: BONN UNIV PI 2-85 (1970).
41) D. Decamp, B. Dudelzak, P. Eschrut and Th. Fourneron: Orsay Report L.A.L., 1236 (1970).
42) G. von Gehlen: *Nucl. Phys.*, B **9**, 17 (1969).
43) F. Wagner and C. Lovelace: *Nucl. Phys.*, B **25**, 411 (1971).

DISCUSSION

Chairman: Prof. K. H. ALTHOFF
Scientific Secretary: J. B. CARROTTE

DISCUSSION

— PICARD:
How do you plan to measure the isotensor part of the γ structure?

— ALTHOFF:
One should measure the π^+ and the π^- ratio on deuterium. Maybe the theorists can answer this question more precisely.

— MORPURGO:
I personally have no feeling that these are very good parameters for measuring the background. If you have just the 3-3 wave the ratio should be 1. If you have other waves the ratio may be different from 1, and it may also be different from 1 if you have just a 3-3 wave and an isotensor component. I believe the first attempt should be at fitting the data with no isotensor component.

— ALTHOFF:
I think one should do the experiment in the area of the first resonance where one knows the amplitude better than at high energies. That is the only chance you have, and in fact, this experiment is in progress on the small machine.

— KLEINERT:
Have you looked at photoproduction on neutrons?

— ALTHOFF:
We measured the photodisintegration on deuterium with the neutron and proton in coincidence, and right now we are measuring the π^- using a deuterium target.

— KLEINERT:
There is a theoretical estimate that the isovector coupling of the nucleon to the Roper resonance is large. Since one does not produce any Roper resonance on protons this means that the Roper resonance couples strongly to the neutron. There is some indication for this in the Frascati data reported recently at Trieste. Do you know whether they see any Roper resonance?

— ALTHOFF:
This P_{11} is always coming up and disappearing again. In the 180° pictures I showed there was a small bump at the energy of the P_{11} resonance, but I do not know if this is a statistical fluctuation.

— MARTIN:
How about the inequalities on cross-sections for $\gamma + n \to n + \pi$ which you certainly have?

— GLASHOW:
Most of the inequalities were particularly interesting for inclusive processes, whereas the things we have heard about today are much more simply due to Clebsch-Gordan coefficients.

An Algebraic Approach to the Saturation of Chiral $SU_3 \otimes SU_3$

F. Buccella

An algebraic approach to the saturation of chiral $SU_3 \otimes SU_3$ 773

References 778

Discussion 779

An Algebraic Approach to the Saturation of Chiral $SU_3 \otimes SU_3$

F. BUCCELLA

CERN - Geneva, Switzerland

The work we are going to describe amounts to the study of the algebraic equations [1]

$$[Q^\alpha, Q^\beta] = if^{\alpha\beta\gamma}Q^\gamma$$

$$[Q^\alpha, Q_5^\beta] = if^{\alpha\beta\gamma}Q_5^\gamma$$

$$[Q_5^\alpha, Q_5^\beta] = if^{\alpha\beta\gamma}Q^\gamma \qquad (1)$$

$$[m^2, Q^\alpha] = 0$$

$$[Q_5^+, [Q_5^+, m^2]] = 0$$

We try to saturate them within the set of one-particle states in the $P_z = \infty$ frame [2]. Equations (1) require the set of hadronic states to build up a representation (in general reducible) of the $SU_3 \otimes SU_3$ chiral algebra and the (mass)^2 to transform under the same algebra as the $(1, 1) + (3, \bar{3})_1 + (\bar{3}, 3)_1$ representation where there is no SU_3 exotic.

Lorentz invariance requires m^2 to be independent of helicity and Q_5^α to have negative normality $(P \exp[i\pi J_y])$ (*); one has to define the angular momentum J and P on the $SU_3 \otimes SU_3$ states so that both Q_5^α and m^2 have the proper behaviour.

A set of operators able to obey eq. (1) and the associated angular conditions may be found between the generators of the group $SU_6 \otimes O_3$, where the quantum numbers of the lower hadron states fit rather well [3].

(*) J and P are the angular momentum and parity defined in the $P_z = \infty$ frame.

In fact, with the identification

$$Q^x = A(\lambda^x)$$

$$Q_5^x = A(\to \sigma_z \lambda^x)$$

$$\vec{J} = \vec{L} + \frac{\vec{\sigma}}{2}$$

$$m^2 = A_L + B_L \vec{L} \cdot \frac{\vec{\sigma}}{2}. \tag{2}$$

Equations (1) are true and the right angular conditions hold, since Q^x and m^2 are 0^+ and Q_5^x is 1^+ [the particles of a $SU_6 \otimes O_3$ supermultiplet have the same parity].

The expressions given in eq. (2) for Q_5^x and m^2 reproduce some gross features of the experimental situation, indeed the largest matrix elements of the axial charge connect states belonging to the same multiplet (N and Δ; π, ω and ρ) and are smaller than the values given by eq. (2), but of the same order of magnitude. The particle spectrum consists roughly of clusters which fill the various $SU_6 \otimes O_3$ representations. There is evidence for the mesons of the 35 $L=1$, of a spin-orbit term responsible for the nice equispacing

$$m_{A_2}^2 - m_B^2 = m_B^2 - m_{A_1}^2 = m_{A_1}^2 - m_2^S.$$

These facts make plausible that the axial charges are given by the expansion

$$Q_5^x = U(\theta Z) A(\lambda^x \sigma_z) U^+(\theta Z) \tag{3}$$

with

$$U(\theta Z) U^+(\theta Z) = U(0) = 1$$

when the real number θ vanishes, eq. (2) is recovered.

A hint on the structure of the Z operator may be given from the empirical observation that the couplings of the states with $L = 0$ to the others seem to decrease with their orbital angular momentum L: this is true both for the baryons of the 56 and for the mesons of the 35. This makes it reasonable to assume that Z should connect supermultiplets with contiguous values of L.

An algebraic approach to the saturation of chiral $SU_3 \otimes SU_3$ 775

The assumption has been made that Z is built with operators with the simplest transformation properties under $SU_6 \otimes O_3$ consistent with having matrix elements both between the 56 $L=0$ and the 70 $L=1$ and the 35 $L=0$ and the 35 $L=1$.

One is left with the form [4]

$$Z = (\vec{W} \wedge \vec{M})_z \qquad (4)$$

where $\vec{W}$ is the spin 1 SU_3 singlet of a 35 representation and commutes with $\vec{L}$, while $\vec{M}$ is a vector under O_3 and a scalar in SU_6.

The axial charge defined in (3) and the vector charge $A(\lambda^\alpha)$ satisfy the $SU_3 \otimes SU_3$ commutation rules because Z is a singlet under SU_3. Under $J^P Z$ behaves as 1^-, which guarantees the angular condition for states of different mass and gives the nice threshold properties in the parameter θ (only P waves at zero order, s and d at first order and so on).

Up to now we have given the transformation properties of $\vec{W}$ and $\vec{M}$ under $SU_6 \otimes O_3$ so that we can express in terms of one parameter the matrix elements of Z between each pair of contiguous supermultiplets. We have neither stated the explicit expression for the mixing operator nor even the set of supermultiplets considered.

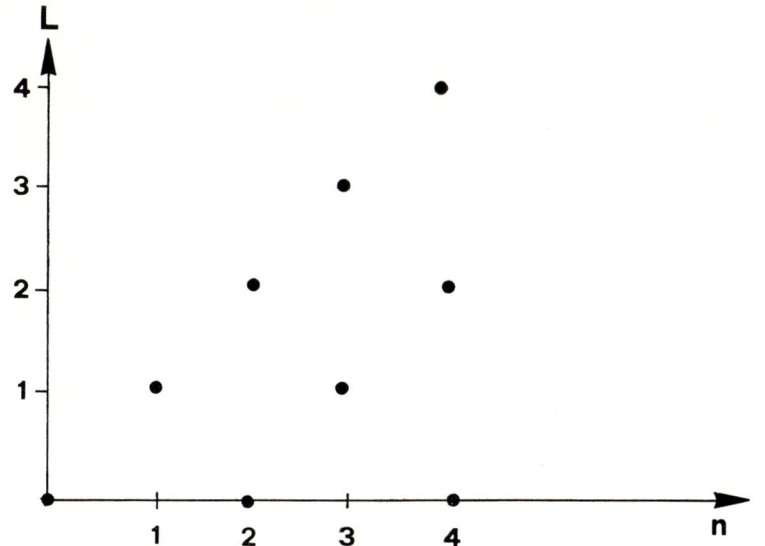

The absence of exotic states restricts the SU_6 representations available to 56, 70 and 20 for baryons, 35 and 1 for mesons; the vector $\vec{M}$ builds up the O_3 excitation, which is shown in the Figure, where in abscissa we report n, the number of steps needed to reach a state starting from the ground state, and in ordinate the values of L [$n-L$ even as long as $P\cdot(-1)^L = +1$ for baryons, -1 for mesons].

One has now to look for an m^2 able to obey the proper commutation rules (1) with the vector and axial vector charges:

$$\left[A\left(\frac{\tau^a}{2}\right), m^2\right] = 0$$

$$\left[A\left(\frac{\sigma_z\tau^+}{2}\right), \left[A\left(\frac{\sigma_z\tau^+}{2}\right), U^+(\theta Z)m^2 U(\theta Z)\right]\right] = 0. \tag{5}$$

We consider the smaller $SU_2 \otimes SU_2$ algebra since we study the nonstrange mesons ([5]).

With the intent to find the proper (mass)^2 operator we use the following method: first, we make the expansion

$$m^2 = m_0^2 + \theta^2 m_2^2 + \theta^4 m_4^2 + \ldots$$

where all the m_i^2 are scalar, isoscalar and diagonal in L and n, the additional quantum number introduced in the Figure. Then we impose eq. (5) at each order in θ [no $(1, 1)_{I=0}$ under $A[1 \pm \sigma_z)\tau]/4$ in $U^+(\theta Z)m^2(\theta)U(\theta Z)$ for any value of θ].

At 0th order one finds of course:

$$m_0^2 = A_{n,L} + \tfrac{1}{2} B_{n,L}(\vec{L}\cdot\vec{\sigma} + 1).$$

There is no constraint on $A_{n,L}$ at first order since Z behaves under $A[1 \pm \sigma_z)\tau]/4$ as a $(\tfrac{1}{2}, \tfrac{1}{2})_{I=0}$, while one gets

$$B_{n,L} = B_{1,1}(-1)^{L+1}.$$

The second order brings to a consistent determination of $A_{n,L}$, $\vec{W}$ and $\vec{M}$.

$$A_{n,L} = A_{0,0} + \Delta n$$

$\vec{W}$ acts the same way on $I = 0$ and $I = 1$ states. A simple form of $\vec{M}$ is

TABLE I.

$m_0^2(J)$	Spin J	C	Normality
$A_0 - B_1/2 + \Delta J + 2\Delta K$	all	+	−
$A_0 + B_1/2 + \Delta J + 2\Delta K$	all except 0	−	−
$A_0 - B_1/2 + (\Delta + B_1)J + 2\Delta K$	all even except 0	+	+
$A_0 - 3B_1/2 + \Delta + (\Delta - B_1)J + 2\Delta K$	all even	+	+
$A_0 + B_1/2 - \Delta + (\Delta - B_1)J + 2\Delta K$	all odd	−	+
$A_0 + 3B_1/2 + \Delta + (\Delta + B_1)J + 2\Delta K$	all odd	−	+
$A_0 = A_{0,0};\ B_1 = B_{1,1}.$			

achieved on the basis

$$|n^+ n_0 n_-\rangle$$

where n_+, n_0 and n_- denote respectively the number of angular momentum excitations in the up, collinear and down direction

$$n = n_+ + n_0 + n_-$$

$$L_z = n_+ - n_-.$$

One has

$$M_\pm = a_\pm + a_\mp^+$$

where $a_\pm$ is the creation operator acting on $n_\pm$. There is also a condition on m_2^2, which is predicted to give a constant splitting between the isovector states with spin 0 and 1. The sign is such to make the pion lighter than the ρ meson.

The term

$$\tfrac{1}{2} B_{1,1}(-1)^{L+1}(\vec{L}\cdot\vec{\sigma} + 1)$$

obeys eq. (5) at all orders in θ. Therefore, the alternating sign of the spin orbit splitting is a peculiar feature of this approach to be compared with experiment. In fact, the lowest particle of the $L = 2$ cluster seems to have

$J^P = 3^-$. The spectrum described by

$$m_0^2 = A_{0,0} + \Delta n + \tfrac{1}{2} B_{1,1}(-1)^{L+1}(\vec{L}\cdot\vec{\sigma} + 1)$$

consists of six families of equispaced linear trajectories, where K is a positive integer giving the order of the daughter. The term Δn is the energy of the three-dimensional harmonic oscillator; the operator $\vec{M}$ is the coordinate of the same quantum system.

REFERENCES

1) S. WEINBERG: *Phys. Rev.*, **177**, 2604 (1969).
2) R. DASHEN and M. GELL-MANN: *Coral Gables, Conference on Symmetry Principles at High Energy*, Vol. 3 (1966).
3) F. GÜRSEY and L. A. RADICATI: *Phys. Rev. Lett.*, **13**, 173 (1964); E. BORCHI and R. GATTO: *Phys. Lett.*, **14**, 352 (1965); R. H. DALITZ: *Proceedings, Oxford Conference on Elementary Particles* (1965).
4) F. BUCCELLA, E. CELEGHINI, H. KLEINERT, C. A. SAVOY and E. SORACE: *Nuovo Cimento*, **63 A**, 133 (1970).
5) F. BUCCELLA, E. CELEGHINI and C. A. SAVOY: *Nuovo Cimento* **72A**, 281 (1972).

DISCUSSION

Chairman: Prof. F. Buccella
Scientific Secretary: A. Conti

DISCUSSION

— Kleinert:

In a paper by Feynman, Kisslinger and Ravendal the axial charges appear also to be some unitarily transformed $SU_6 \otimes U_{3,1}$ charges. In addition, the mixing operator contains also the operator $M = a^+ + a$ of the harmonic oscillator. What is the relation to your mixing?

— Buccella:

The paper by Feynman *et al.* is not based on chiral algebra, but it describes a harmonic quark model on a heuristic basis.

— Morpurgo:

The paper by Feynman *et al.* has very little to do with Buccella's seminar. In it there is just a set of prescriptions for a harmonic oscillator, as Buccella said.

— Buccella

I would say about this that all these quark models end up for the decay of the $70, L=1$ and of the $35, L=1$ to the prescription of the $70, L=1$ which decays in a 56 (or 35) + 35 plus a spurion of the 35. What characterizes this model from the others is that here a particular coupling is chosen of the two possible ones, at first order in θ; this gives rise to the transversal decay of the Buddha meson. I would also mention that at every order in the mixing one finds $D/F = \frac{3}{2}$ for all the positive parity octet states, and this ratio is $-\frac{1}{3}$ for the $\frac{5^-}{2}$ and its Regge recurrence as one finds with exchange degeneracy.

— Kleinert:

I have another question. You said that last year you showed that the value of your mixing operator Z was confirmed at first order in θ. Now, which arguments do you have to suppose that a unitarization of this mixing operator Z is correct taking an exponential rather than, *e.g.*, $1 + i\theta Z/1 - i\theta Z$?

— Buccella:

I wrote an exponential, but the form of the function is not important since all I said still holds for every unitary function of Z.

— Gensini:

The mass formula which you derived does not seem in any way connected to the classification you adopted, say to the place where you put the various resonances in the representation $SU_6 \otimes O_3$. Does your mass formula simply come from the algebra you adopt or does it come also from the mass spectrum you classify?

— Buccella:

The mesons are classified in the 35 with an orbital excitation which is determined by the equations involving the double commutator of the (mass)^2. This gives rise both to the linear form of the (mass)^2 and to the alternating sign of the spin orbit splitting.

— Gensini:

Are you satisfied with that? In a model where $SU_3 \otimes SU_3$ is broken in such a way as to give good $SU_2 \otimes SU_2$, you are led to expect parity doublets. From a rough analysis of known baryons it is apparent that the splitting between partners of parity doublets does have the structure $(-1)^L$ times a function which is linear in L.

— Buccella:

In our approach the assumption we have done for the 0th order axial charge is to be 1^+. If one should believe in parity doublets one could as well have taken 0^-. But the experiment pushes to choose 1^+, which is also consistent. So, if this approach has something right in it, we should exclude the presence of parity doublets.

— Gensini:

Fine, if parity doublets are also consistent with 1^+.

— Buccella:

Starting from a general point of view one can say that the axial charge has transitions of the form 0^- as well as 1^+. But the approach followed is based on the SU_6 classification, which suggests to start from 1^+. In fact, the largest contributions are 1^+.

— Gensini:

But does the 1^+, or does it not, contradict parity doublets?

— Buccella:

Parity doublets should ask for 0^-. The fact that one starts from 1^+ points out that they could be there, but completely by chance, without any *a priori* reason.

— Gensini:

We have no *a priori* reasons for anything. We have just to look at experiments, and experiments till now seem to say that the picture of Gell-Mann, Oakes and Renner is not the next, but perhaps the farthest away from reality. So, if experiments tell us that parity doublets have to be there in the symmetry limit, why should they not be there with an 1^+ character for chirality?

— Buccella:

Which is the parity doublet partner of the nucleon and of the $\Delta(1236)$ resonance?

— GENSINI:

$N^*(1535)$ and $\Delta^*(1670)$. The contribution to the mass of the nucleon which comes out from the U_0 part of the symmetry breaking seems to be very large, and so it is possible that these states which are far away from each other can also be partners in a very strongly broken parity doublet. No one knows exactly how much the $SU_3 \otimes SU_3$ symmetry is broken, but some people claim it is broken very largely.

— BUCCELLA:

I would say that the work I described is not based on $SU_3 \otimes SU_3$ symmetry, but simply on the commutation relations of the chiral algebra.

— GENSINI:

Perhaps I have been brought away from the very point I wanted to stress, namely that if parity doublets are there, as it is evident from your analysis, the splitting has to be a linear function of the internal angular momentum. So, if one likes parity doublets, they must have a splitting which is a linear function of L, changing sign from odd to even values of L.

Magnitude of the σ-Term, Chiral Symmetry and Scale Invariance

N. Cabibbo

1. Chiral $SU_3 \otimes SU_3$, its breaking and the σ-commutator . . 783
2. Pion-nucleon scattering, PCAC, and the σ-term 789
3. The smoothness hypothesis and the value of the σ-term . 793
4. A brief discussion 798
Acknowledgement 799
References 799
Discussion 801

Magnitude of the σ-Term, Chiral Symmetry and Scale Invariance

N. CABIBBO

Istituto di Fisica dell'Università di Roma - Italy
Institute for Advanced Study - Princeton, N. J., USA

1. Chiral $SU(3) \otimes SU(3)$, its breaking and the σ-commutator.

In this lecture I will present and discuss some recent work on the σ-term in pion-nucleon scattering I did with G. Altarelli and L. Maiani ([1,2]).

The actual computations will be described in the third Section of the lecture. In the present Section I will outline some of the present ideas on the breaking of chiral $SU(3) \otimes SU(3)$, and the role of the σ-commutator in testing specific models of the breaking.

The second Section will contain an outline of the relations between the σ-term and π-N scattering. The interest of the σ-term is in the light it can throw on the structure of the breaking of chiral $SU(3) \otimes SU(3)$. The local algebra of axial and vector currents, specified by the equal time commutators

$$\left.\begin{array}{l} [V_0^a(x), V_0^b(y)] = if_{abc} V_0^c(x) \delta^3(x-y) \\ [V_0^a(x), A_0^b(y)] = if_{abc} A_0^c(x) \delta^3(x-y) \\ [A_0^a(x), A_0^b(y)] = if_{abc} V_0^c(x) \delta^3(x-y) \end{array}\right\} \quad (1.1)$$

has the local structure associated with an $SU(3) \otimes SU(3)$ group. The two $SU(3)$ groups would be generated by:

$$Q^{a(\pm)} = \tfrac{1}{2}[Q^a \pm Q_5^a]$$

where Q^a and Q_5^a are the space integral of axial and vector densities

$$\left.\begin{array}{l} Q^a = \int V_0^a(x)\,\mathrm{d}^3x \\ Q_5^a = \int A_0^a(x)\,\mathrm{d}^3x\,. \end{array}\right\} \tag{1.2}$$

The possibility arises that this algebra is associated with an approximate symmetry of strong interactions and it becomes interesting to study the possible structure of its breaking.

There are two different ways in which a symmetry can be exact, and correspondingly two ways in which it can be approximate. One is the normal way, where the vacuum is invariant and non degenerate, and states of higher mass appear in multiplets. This is the realization which is approximated by such symmetries as $SU(3)$ or isotopic spin.

Chiral $SU(3) \otimes SU(3)$, should it be an approximate symmetry, would be near the other situation, where the vacuum is not invariant, and current conservation—the mark of an exact symmetry—is achieved through zero mass bosons. A symmetry realized this way is called a dynamical symmetry. Synonymous with this are «dynamically broken» or «spontaneously broken» symmetry. The massless bosons associated with an exact dynamical symmetry are also given the name of Goldstone bosons. A spontaneous breaking of $SU(3) \otimes SU(3)$ to $SU(3)$ requires an octet of pseudoscalar massless «Goldstone» bosons. The fact that the lightest hadrons are indeed the members of the pseudoscalar octet (π, K, η) gives then some support to the idea that hadrons can be described by a lagrangian density of the form:

$$\mathscr{L} = \mathscr{L}^0 + \mathscr{L}^1 \tag{1.3}$$

where $\mathscr{L}^0$ is symmetric under $SU(3) \otimes SU(3)$ and $\mathscr{L}^1$ is a breaking term. This can be in general of the form

$$\mathscr{L}^1 = -(\varepsilon_0 u_0 + \varepsilon_8 u_8) \tag{1.4}$$

i.e., a combination of two scalar densities, an $SU(3)$ singlet, u_0, and the 8th component of an $SU(3)$ octet, u_8. $\mathscr{L}^1$ could also contain a mixture of higher $SU(3)$ representations. These should be fairly small, as suggested by the validity of the Gell-Mann–Okubo mass formulae. In our study of the weak interaction angle ([3]), L. Maiani and myself found that $\mathscr{L}^1$ should also contain a term $\varepsilon_3 u_3$ which breaks isotopic spin in competition with electromagnetic interactions.

This further term should in fact be accepted on its own merits, as it gives a solution to some puzzles on the $\eta \to 3\pi$ decay and the e.m. mass differences within the pseudoscalar octet. In the present discussion it can be safely neglected. Its effect on low energy pion-nucleon scattering has been computed and found to be very small ([3]).

We can then consider $\mathscr{L}^1(x)$ to be given by eq. (1.4), and inquire on the possible transformation properties of u_0 and u_8. For simplicity we can consider the case where u_0 and u_8 (and therefore $\mathscr{L}^1$) belong to one single representation of $SU(3) \otimes SU(3) \otimes P$ [P being the parity operation]. These are obtained by combining a given representation of $SU(3) \otimes SU(3)$, (a, b), with its adjoint $(\bar{b}, \bar{a})$. Representations which contain both a scalar singlet and octet, and can accommodate u_0 and u_8 are those of the form $(a, \bar{a}) + (\bar{a}, a)$, or (b, b) if b is a self-conjugate $SU(3)$ representation. The simplest such representation is the $(3, \bar{3}) \oplus (\bar{3}, 3)$ which would accommodate a scalar nonet (scalar plus octet) and a pseudoscalar nonet.

This possibility has been considered in detail, the first studies being those of Gell-Mann, Oakes and Renner ([4]), and of Glashow and Weinberg ([5]). If $\mathscr{L}^1$ belongs to $(3, \bar{3}) \oplus (\bar{3}, 3)$ and $\varepsilon_8 = -\sqrt{2}\varepsilon_0$, an $SU(2) \otimes SU(2)$ subgroup of $SU(3) \otimes SU(3)$ would be exact. This is the group of chiral isospin, generated by Q^a and Q_5^a with $a = 1, 2, 3$. In this case the pion would be massless.

This circumstance has an important role in the above-mentioned analyses, where the particular smallness of the pion mass is associated with a near exact $SU(2) \otimes SU(2)$.

Gell-Mann, Oakes and Renner, e.g. give

$$\varepsilon_8/\varepsilon_0 = c \approx -1.25 \,. \tag{1.5}$$

In the $(3, \bar{3})$ case it is convenient to define:

$$H_2 = \tfrac{1}{3}(\sqrt{2}\varepsilon_0 + \varepsilon_8)(\sqrt{2}u_0 + u_8) \qquad H_3 = \varepsilon_8 u_8 \,. \tag{1.6}$$

H_2 is that part of $H^1 = -\mathscr{L}^1$ which breaks $SU(2) \otimes SU(2)$, while H_3 is responsible for $SU(3)$ breaking.

Other possible assignments of $\mathscr{L}^1$ involve $(8, 8)$ or higher-dimensional representations. The breakdown of $(8, 8)$ into $SU(3) \otimes P$ representation is:

$$(8, 8) \begin{cases} \to 1 + 8 + 27 \text{ scalar} \\ \to 8 + 10 + \overline{10} \text{ pseudoscalar.} \end{cases}$$

Contrary to the $(3, \bar{3}) \oplus (\bar{3}, 3)$ case, u_0 and u_8 are not any longer the only scalar-isoscalar operators in the representation, and we have a third one belonging to the 27.

The situation is worse in two respects.

i) The octet breaking of $SU(3)$ requires an extra assumption, absence of u_{27}, which is not needed in the $(3, \bar{3}) \oplus (\bar{3}, 3)$ case.

ii) The octet breaking is now incompatible with an exact $SU(2) \otimes SU(2)$. If we insist on octet breaking, $SU(2) \otimes SU(2)$ will be as badly broken as $SU(3)$. The pion mass can be *fitted* to be small, but the interesting link with a nearly exact chiral isospin is lost.

The situation is similar for more complicated representations, such as $(6, \bar{6}) \oplus (\bar{6}, 6)$.

A possible way to discriminate among these possibilities is the study of the σ-operator defined as

$$\sigma^{ab}(x) = -i[Q_5^a, \partial^\mu A_\mu^b(x)]. \tag{1.7}$$

Since

$$\partial^\mu A_\mu^b(x) = -i[Q_5^b, H^1(x)]$$

we have

$$\sigma^{ab} = -[Q_5^a, [Q_5^b, H^1]].$$

Let us now consider σ^{ab} when a and b take the values 1, 2, 3. In the $(3, \bar{3}) \oplus (\bar{3}, 3)$ case we obtain:

$$\sigma^{ab}(x) = \delta^{ab} H_2(x) \qquad (a, b = 1, 2, 3) \tag{1.8}$$

$H_2(x)$ being defined in eq. (1.6). From this follows that:

$(3, \bar{3}) \oplus (\bar{3}, 3)$ $\begin{cases} a) \text{ the } \sigma\text{-operator is « small » compared with the } SU(3) \\ \quad \text{breaking operator } H_3. \\ b) \text{ the } \sigma\text{-operator is an isosinglet.} \end{cases}$

In the (8, 8) and more complicated cases these are substituted by

(8, 8) etc. $\begin{cases} a') & \sigma^{ab} \text{ is of same order as } \varepsilon_8 u_8 \\ b') & \sigma^{ab} \text{ has both } I=0 \text{ and } I=2 \text{ parts}. \end{cases}$

In a recent study of the σ-term in π-N scattering, Cheng and Dashen ([6]) found

$$\tfrac{1}{3}\langle p| \sum_{a=1}^{3}(\sigma^{aa})|p\rangle \equiv \sigma \approx 110 \text{ MeV}. \tag{1.9}$$

In the $(3, \bar{3}) \oplus (\bar{3}, 3)$ model this would mean

$$\langle p|H_2|p\rangle \approx 110 \text{ MeV}. \tag{1.10}$$

[Later in the third Section I will sketch a computation by Altarelli, Maiani and myself ([2]) which leads to $\sigma = (80 \pm 30)$ MeV]. We should compare this with

$$\langle p|H_3|p\rangle \approx 210 \text{ MeV} \tag{1.11}$$

obtained from an analysis of the mass differences within the $(\tfrac{1}{2})^+$ baryon octet. This seems to contrast statement a).

The situation can be looked at this way: if we use eqs. (1.5) and (1.6), a comparison of eqs. (1.10) and (1.11) yields

$$\langle p|u_0|p\rangle \simeq 8\langle p|u_8|p\rangle. \tag{1.12}$$

This means that operators which are equally normalized in the $(3, \bar{3}) \oplus (\bar{3}, 3)$ representation have very different matrix elements in a single proton state. I do not consider this as a bad crisis for the $(3,\bar{3}) \oplus (\bar{3}, 3)$ but rather as a crisis for the simple interpretation of the concept of « equally strong » operators. The comparison between two operators A B is in fact well founded if we have non-linear conditions of the kind:

$$[A, A^+] = [B, B^+].$$

[Relations of this kind are the basis of comparison between axial and vector charges in the algebra of currents.]

Another possibility for establishing a relation is when two operators are related by a unitary operator.

Neither of the cases is realized for u_0 and u_8. Although they are related by $SU(3) \otimes SU(3)$ symmetry, this symmetry has a strong spontaneous breaking so that, even in the limit $\varepsilon_8 = \varepsilon_0 = 0$, there would exist no unitary operator relating u_0 and u_8.

In spite of our intuition to the contrary, we have no formal way of arguing that matrix elements of u_0 should be comparable to those of u_8.

Should we think that eq. (1.12) requires an explanation, one can be obtained if we assume that hadrons have a further symmetry under the dilation group. This hypothesis leads to an enhancement of matrix elements of u_0. Details of this are given in ref. ([1]).

The $(3, \bar{3}) \oplus (\bar{3}, 3)$ hypothesis can be tested in a different context, through Weinberg's predictions on low energy pion-pion scattering ([7]). These predictions are:

$$2a_0 - 5a_2 = 6L \tag{1.13a}$$

$$a_0 = -(7/2)a_2 \tag{1.13b}$$

where a_0 and a_2 are $I = 0, 2$, S-wave π-π scattering length, and L is the Weinberg length:

$$L = \frac{\mu}{4\pi F_\pi^2} \approx \frac{g_{\pi N}^2 \mu}{8\pi m^2} \left(\frac{g_V}{g_A}\right)^2 = 0.11 \mu^{-1}$$

m and μ are the nucleon and pion mass, $g_{\pi N}$ the P.S. pion-nucleon coupling constant. The two relations together lead to:

$$a_0 = 0.20 \mu^{-1}, \quad a_2 = -0.06 \mu^{-1}. \tag{1.14}$$

Equations (1.13a) and (1.13b) both depend upon smoothness assumptions similar to those discussed in the next Section for π-N scattering. Equation (1.13a) further requires the current algebra commutators eq. (1.1), while eq. (1.13b) depends explicitly upon the absence of a $\Delta I = 2$ part in the σ-commutator. A verification of (1.13b) is therefore a test of the $(3, \bar{3}) \oplus (\bar{3}, 3)$

model, together with Weinberg's smoothness assumptions. We should finally mention that the model with nearly exact $SU(2) \otimes SU(2)$ was challenged by R. Brandt and G. Preparata in their « weak PCAC » papers, especially on the basis of an analysis of the $K_{\mu 3}$ decay ([8]).

2. Pion-nucleon scattering, PCAC, and the σ-term.

Let us consider the process:

$$\pi^a(q) + N^\alpha(p) \to \pi^b(k) + N^\beta(p') \tag{2.1}$$

where a, α, b, β are isospin indices, while q, p and k, p' are the momenta of the initial and final particles.

The amplitude for this process can be described in terms of two invariant amplitudes for each of the two possible isospin combinations, $I_t = 0$ and $I_t = 1$. [The choice of t-channel isospin is convenient for our problem.] The invariant amplitudes are defined by:

$$\mathcal{M}^{()}(q, p; k, p') = \bar{u}(p')[A^{()}(v, t) + \tfrac{1}{2}(q + k)B^{()}(v, t)]u(p) \tag{2.2}$$

where ( ) stands for a set of I-spin indices. The independent variables are defined as:

$$v = (q+k)(p+p')/4m \qquad t = (q-k)^2 \tag{2.3}$$

m being the nucleon mass.

If we know A and B in the physical region in the v-t plane we can continue them in a unique way to unphysical and complex values of v and t. We will, in fact, use a more ambitious continuation in which we allow the pions to leave their mass shell. A and B will then be functions of four variables: v, t, q^2 and k^2.

Such a continuation can be defined in terms of a local operator which has nonvanishing matrix elements between the vacuum and one pion state. Such an operator could be a pseudoscalar density $\varphi^a(x)$ which behaves as an isovector, a being an isospin index:

$$\langle \pi^b, q|\varphi^a(0)|0\rangle \delta_{ab} = \frac{1}{(2\pi)^{\frac{3}{2}}\sqrt{2\omega_q}} \tag{2.4}$$

Consider the causal correlation function:

$$F^{a\alpha,b\beta}(p,q;p',k)\delta^4(p+q-p'-k)(2\pi)^4$$
$$=\int dx^4 dy^4 \exp[-iqx]\exp[iky]\langle N^\beta, p'|T[\varphi^a(x),\varphi^b(y)]|N^\alpha, p\rangle \qquad (2.5)$$

F will have a double pole at

$$q^2 = \mu^2, \qquad k^2 = \mu^2$$

the residue of which is just the on-mass shell pion-nucleon scattering amplitude. We can then define an off-mass shell continuation of the π-N amplitude as ([9]):

$$\mathcal{M}^{a\alpha,b\beta}(p,q;p',k)$$
$$= -i(2\pi)^3 \sqrt{\frac{EE'}{m^2}} \frac{2}{F_\pi^2 \mu^4}(q^2-\mu^2)(k^2-\mu^2)F^{a\alpha,b\beta}(p,q;p',k). \qquad (2.6)$$

This continuation is not unique. Given the existence of one pion field $\varphi^a(x)$ we can define a family of others by $(\varphi'^a x) = f(\Box/\mu^2)\varphi^a(x)$ where f is a polynomial such that $f(-1) = 1$, and each of these gives a different off-mass shell continuation. There may be other « pion fields » not simply related to $\varphi^a(x)$. Furthermore, an off-shell continuation can be defined in terms of axial vector densities (we will shortly see an example of this) or higher tensors. In spite of these potential ambiguities, the existence of at least one pseudoscalar density satisfying eq. (2.4) is not a trivial fact. It is here that the V-A theory of weak interactions is of great help in allowing us to build such a quantity in terms of the weak axial current. The matrix element of the weak axial current between a π^- and the vacuum state is defined in terms of F_π, the π-$\mu\nu$ decay constant.

$$\langle 0|A_\lambda^W(0)|\pi^-, q\rangle = +iF_\pi \cos\theta\, q_\lambda [(2\pi)^3\sqrt{2\omega_q}]^{-1}$$

where $\cos\theta$ is the weak interaction angle,

$$A_\lambda^W = \cos\theta(A^1 + iA^2) + \sin\theta(A^4 + iA^5).$$

The $\pi \to \mu\nu$ decay rate is then given by $\Gamma_{\pi \to \mu\nu} \sim G^2 \cos^2\theta F_\pi^2 m_\mu^2 (\mu^2 - m_\mu^2)^2 / 8\pi\mu^3$ which leads to $F_\pi \sim 0.96\,\mu$.

In terms of cartesian I-spin coordinates we have

$$\langle 0|A_\lambda^b(0)|\pi^a q, \rangle = +i\frac{F_\pi}{\sqrt{2}} \delta_{ab} q_\lambda [(2\pi)^{\frac{3}{2}} \sqrt{2\omega_q}]^{-1}$$

We then see that

$$\varphi_\pi^a(x) = \frac{\sqrt{2}}{F_\pi \mu^2} \partial^\mu A_\mu^a(x) \qquad (2.7)$$

is a well normalized pion field, *i.e.* a local operator satisfying eq. (2.4). Equation (2.7) is the PCAC relation. The physical content of eq. (2.7) by itself is however small, and to turn it into a useful tool, we have to make a further assumption. The new assumption is that the PCAC choice of a pion field gives a particularly smooth off-mass shell extrapolation of amplitudes involving pions. With this further assumption eq. (2.7) leads to the Goldberger-Trieman relation, and to the Adler consistency condition on π-N scattering. In conjunction with current algebra, PCAC leads to other remarkable results, such as the Adler-Weisberger relations and the Weinberg predictions on scattering lengths. We substitute eq. (2.7) in eq. (2.5) and obtain:

$$F^{a\alpha,b\beta}(p,q;p',k) \delta^4(p+q-p'-k)(2\pi)^4$$

$$= \frac{2}{F_\pi^2 \mu^4} \int d^4x\, d^4y\, \exp[-iqx]\, \exp[iky] \langle N^\beta, p'|T\{\partial_x^\mu A_\mu^a(x) \partial_y^\nu A_\nu^b(y)\}|N^\alpha, p\rangle.$$

If we now integrate by parts in the usual way, we obtain:

$$F^{a\alpha,b\beta}(p,q;p',k) = q^\mu k^\nu F^{a\alpha,b\beta}_{\mu\nu}(p,q;p',k)$$

$$+ F^{a\alpha,b\beta}_{[\sigma]}(p,q;p',k) + F^{a\alpha,b\beta}_\nu(p,q;p',k) \qquad (2.8)$$

where

$$F_{\mu\nu}^{a\alpha,b\beta} = \frac{2}{F_\pi^2 \mu^4} \int d^4x \exp[-iqx]\langle N^\beta, p'|T\{A_\mu^a(x), A_\nu^b(0)\}|N^\alpha, p\rangle, \qquad (2.9)$$

$$F_{[\sigma]} = -\frac{2i}{F_\pi^2 \mu^4} \langle N^\beta, p'|\frac{\sigma^{ab}(0) + \sigma^{ba}(0)}{2}|N^\alpha, p\rangle, \qquad (2.10)$$

$$F_{[V]} = -\frac{2}{F_\pi^2 \mu^4} \frac{q^\mu + k^\mu}{2} \varepsilon_{abc}\langle N^\beta, p'|V_\mu^c(0)|N^\alpha, p\rangle. \qquad (2.11)$$

The second term contains the matrix element of the σ-commutator defined as in eq. (1.7):

$$[A_0^a(x), \partial^\nu A_\nu^b(y)]\delta(x_0 - y_0) = i\sigma^{ab}(x)\delta^4(x-y).$$

From eqs. (2.10) and (2.11) it is clear that the σ-term is even under $a \leftrightarrow b$, and will therefore contribute to the $I_t = 0$ amplitude, while the V term is odd, and will therefore contribute to the $I_t = 1$ amplitude.

In the following we will concentrate on the $I_t = 0$ amplitude, which, in terms of definite elastic scattering amplitudes, is given by: (From now on no superscript will be used to denote an $I_t = 0$ amplitude.)

$$\mathcal{M} = \tfrac{1}{2}[\mathcal{M}^{(\pi^+ p)} + \mathcal{M}^{(\pi^- p)}] \qquad (2.12)$$

and, in terms of s-channel isospin, by

$$\mathcal{M} = \tfrac{1}{3}[\mathcal{M}^{(I_s = \frac{1}{2})} + 2\mathcal{M}^{(I_s = \frac{3}{2})}]. \qquad (2.13)$$

From eqs. (2.6) and (2.8) we obtain

$$\mathcal{M}(p, q; p', k) = \mathcal{M}'(p, q; p', k) - \frac{2}{F_\pi^2} \frac{(q^2 - \mu^2)(k^2 - \mu^2)}{\mu^4} \sigma(t)[\bar{u}(p')u(p)] \qquad (2.14)$$

$\sigma(t)$ being defined as:

$$\langle N^\beta, p'|\tfrac{1}{3}\sum_a \sigma^{aa}(0)|N^\alpha, p\rangle = \sqrt{\frac{m^2}{EE'}} \frac{1}{(2\pi)^3} \sigma(t)(\bar{u})p')u(p)) \qquad (2.15)$$

and

$$\mathcal{M}'(p, q; p', k) = -i(2\pi)^3 \sqrt{\frac{EE'}{m^2}} \frac{2(q^2-\mu^2)(k^2-\mu^2)}{F_\pi^2 \mu^4} q^\mu k^\nu F_{\mu\nu}(p, q; p', k). \quad (2.16)$$

Consider the limit where q^μ and k^μ tend to zero. Since $\mathcal{M}'$ is proportional to $q^\mu k^\nu$, in this limit the only contribution in $\mathcal{M}'$ will be from nucleon pole terms in $q^\mu k^\nu F_{\mu\nu}$. If we then define a new amplitude $\widetilde{\mathcal{M}}$ equal to $\mathcal{M}$-[N-pole contribution to $\mathcal{M}'$] we find that in the limit $q^\mu, k^\mu = 0$ only the σ contribution in $\widetilde{\mathcal{M}}$ survives, and we have

$$\widetilde{\mathcal{M}}(0, p, 0, p) = -\frac{2}{F_\pi^2} \sigma [\bar{u}(p)u(p)] \quad (2.17)$$

where for brevity we have put $\sigma(0) = \sigma$. σ is the so-called σ-term.

Instead of working with $\widetilde{\mathcal{M}}$ it is convenient to use the following combination of invariant amplitudes:

$$\widetilde{F}(\nu, t, q^2, k^2) = A + \nu B - [A + \nu B]_{N\text{-pole}}. \quad (2.18)$$

Equation (2.17) reduces then to

$$\widetilde{F}(0, 0, 0, 0) = -\frac{2}{F_\pi^2} \sigma. \quad (2.19)$$

This combination is convenient because $A + \nu B$ gives, for $t = 0$ and pions on the mass shell, the forward scattering amplitude.

3. The smoothness hypothesis and the value of the σ-term.

In order to evaluate σ we need $\widetilde{F}$ at an off-mass shell point (eq. (2.18)). This point cannot be reached by analytic continuation from physical data, since we know that the off-mass shell extrapolation is not unique. We need some help to get us there. The only off-mass shell information we can use is the Adler condition ([10]):

$$\tilde{F}(0, \mu^2, \mu^2, 0) = 0. \tag{3.1}$$

This is just sufficient if we make the following smoothness assumption: «$\tilde{F}$ is a smooth function of its variables in the neighborhood of $v = t = q^2 = k^2 = 0$ except when required by nearby singularities.» We are interested in a neighbourhood where all components of q^μ and k^ν are of the order of μ. This includes the threshold region, where $v \approx \mu$, $t \approx 0$, $q^2 = k^2 = \mu^2$. Let us write ([11])

$$\tilde{F} = A\mu^2 + Bt + C(q^2 + k^2) + Dv^2 + R(v, t, q^2, k^2) \tag{3.2}$$

where we have separated explicitly the terms of 0th and 2nd order in the components of q^μ and k^ν. [$\tilde{F}$ is even under crossing, so that there are no first order terms.] The procedure now is:

i) Compute the contribution to R of the low resonant states. Other terms can be neglected on the basis of the smoothness hypothesis.

ii) Use low energy data and the Adler condition to determine A, B, C, D. Since only one coefficient, C, involves an off-the-mass shell extrapolation, the Adler condition is sufficient. The smoothness hypothesis is essential: if higher terms (such as q^2k^2) were important, we would not know how to determine them. We *have* thus to assume them to be negligible. It is a reasonable assumption, but an assumption it is.

The only resonance we have to consider in R is the $\mathcal{N}^*(1233)$. This gives a singularity at

$$v = \left[\frac{t}{2} + M^2 - m^2 - \mu^2\right]/2m$$

where M is the $\mathcal{N}^*$ mass. At $t = 0$ this gives $v \sim 2\mu$, close to our region. The $\mathcal{N}^*$ can only contribute to $\mathcal{M}'$ (see eq. (2.14)), so that this contribution is defined in terms of the $\mathcal{N} \to \mathcal{N}^*$ matrix element of the axial current

$$\langle \mathcal{N}|A^a_\mu|\mathcal{N}^*\rangle.$$

This is, however, equivalent to computing the $\mathcal{N}^*$ contribution to $\pi \mathcal{N}$ scattering in a pseudovector coupling. We use a narrow resonance approximation with the following effective interaction:

$$\mathscr{L}_{\pi NN^*} = \frac{g^*}{\mu} (\bar{\psi}_\mu \psi \partial^\mu \varphi + \text{h.c.}) \tag{3.3}$$

where ψ_μ is the Rarita-Schwinger field for the N^*. In order to compute R one first computes the N^* contribution to $\tilde{F}$ and subtracts out the 0th and first terms in an expansion in powers of ν, t, q^2, k^2. The result is:

$$R(\nu, t, q^2, k^2) = \frac{8}{9\mu^2} \frac{g^{*2}}{(\nu_B^{*2} - \nu^2)} \left\{ (m+M)\left(\nu_B + \frac{m}{2M^2}\nu^2\right) \left[\nu_B^* - \frac{2m}{M^2-m^2}(\nu_B^{*2}-\nu^2)\right] \right.$$

$$\left. + \nu^2 \left[\frac{m}{2M^2}\nu^2 + \frac{m+M}{8mM}\left(1+\frac{2m}{M}\right)(q^2+k^2) + 3\nu_B \frac{M-m}{2m}\left(1+\frac{2m}{3M}\right)\right] \right\} \tag{3.4}$$

where $\nu_B = (t - q^2 - k^2)/4m$, $\nu_B^* = \nu_B + (M^2 - m^2)/2m$.

There are ambiguities in this computation, related to the propagator for the N^* which is only defined up to contact terms. The ambiguity is not important, since contact terms give non-singular contributions which should give negligible contributions to R. (Their contributions to A, B, C, D may be important, but these parameters are determined directly.) Contributions to R of higher s-channel resonances are negligible, and there are no known low lying resonances in either the t, q^2 or k^2 channels. We can then proceed to step ii), assuming R to be a known function.

A, B, C, D, will now be computed on the basis of the following information:

I) The Adler condition, which is:

$$\mu^2(A + B + C) + R(0, \mu^2, \mu^2, 0) = 0. \tag{3.5}$$

II) Forward dispersion relations, which give:

$$\widetilde{F}(\mu, 0, \mu^2, \mu^2) - \widetilde{F}(0, 0, \mu^2, \mu^2) = \frac{\mu^2}{\pi} \int_\mu^\infty \frac{d\nu}{\nu\sqrt{\nu^2 - \mu^2}} [\sigma^{\pi^+ p}(\nu) + \sigma^{\pi^- p}(\nu)] \equiv A_0. \quad (3.6)$$

We have called the integral A_0. It is a well determined integral:

$$A_0 = (1.45 \pm 0.02)\, \mu^{-1}. \quad (3.7)$$

Using now eq. (3.2) we have:

$$D\mu^2 + R(\mu, 0, \mu^2, \mu^2) - R(0, 0, \mu^2, \mu^2) = A_0. \quad (3.8)$$

III) S-wave scattering lengths.

At threshold the amplitude $A(\nu, t) + \nu B(\nu, t)$ can be expressed in terms of scattering lengths. If we subtract the threshold contribution of the N-pole terms (see eq. (2.17)) we have the threshold value of $\widetilde{F}$:

$$\widetilde{F}(\mu, 0, \mu^2, \mu^2) = (A + 2C + D)\mu^2 + R(\mu, 0, \mu^2, \mu^2) =$$

$$A_1 + \frac{4\pi f^2}{m} \quad (3.9)$$

where

$$A_1 = 4\pi \left(1 + \frac{\mu}{m}\right) \frac{a_1 + 2a_3}{3}. \quad (3.10)$$

IV) P-wave scattering length. Just above threshold we can expand $A(\nu, t) + \nu B(\nu, t)$ in powers of $|q|^2$ and $\cos\theta$ where q and θ are the momentum and scattering angle in the c.m. frame. The coefficient of $|q|^2 \cos\theta$ is a certain combination of S- and P- wave scattering lengths. This gives a further relation:

$$\left(2B + \frac{\mu}{m}D\right)\mu^2 + 2\mu^2 \frac{\partial R}{\partial t}(\mu, 0, \mu^2, \mu^2) + \frac{\mu^3}{m}\frac{\partial R}{\partial v^2}(\mu, 0, \mu^2, \mu^2) =$$

$$A_2 - \frac{8\pi f^2}{m}\left(1 + \frac{\mu}{2m}\right) \quad (3.11)$$

where

$$A_2 = \frac{4\pi}{3}\mu^2\left[\frac{a_1 + 2a_3}{4m^2} + (a_{11} + 2a_{31}) + 2\left(1 + \frac{3\mu}{2m}\right)(a_{13} + 2a_{33})\right]. \quad (3.12)$$

We can now solve eqs. (3.5), (3.8), (3.9), (3.11) and obtain:

$$\sigma = -\frac{F_\pi^2 \mu^2 A}{2} = 4\pi\left[\left(1 + \frac{\mu}{2m}\right)^2\left(\frac{a_1 + 2a_3}{3}\right) + \mu^2 \frac{a_{11} + 2a_{31}}{3} + \right.$$

$$\left. 2\mu^2\left(1 + \frac{3\mu}{m}\right)\frac{a_{13} + 2a_{33}}{3}\right] - \left(1 + \frac{\mu}{m}\right)\left(A_0 + \frac{4\pi f^2}{m}\right) + \Delta_R \quad (3.13)$$

where

$$\Delta_R = \frac{\mu}{m} R(\mu, 0, \mu^2, \mu^2) - \left(1 + \frac{\mu}{m}\right) R(0, 0, \mu^2, \mu^2) + 2R(0, \mu^2, \mu^2, 0)$$

$$- 2\mu^2 \frac{\partial R}{\partial t}(\mu, 0, \mu^2, \mu^2) - \frac{\mu^3}{m}\frac{\partial R}{\partial v^2}(\mu, 0, \mu^2, \mu^2). \quad (3.14)$$

In the numerical evaluation of Δ_R we have used the following parameters:

$$\left.\begin{array}{l} g^* = 3.32 \\ \\ M = 1219 \text{ MeV}. \end{array}\right\} \quad (3.15)$$

This choice is suggested ([12,13,14]) as one which gives a good representation of the amplitude near threshold, so as to compensate for finite width effects. This choice gives

$$\Delta_R = -0.47 \pm 0.05 \,. \tag{3.16}$$

The 10 percent error reflects the errors attributed to g^* and M in ref. ([13]). If we take the « recommended values » for the scattering lengths as compiled in ref. ([14]) we find

$$-A\mu^3 = 1.24 \pm 0.5$$

$$\sigma = [80 \pm 30] \text{ MeV} \,.$$

The error arises for 40 percent from S-wave scattering lengths, 40 percent from P-waves, 20 percent from Δ_R. It is interesting to look at the table, where we list different sets of values for the scattering lengths. In the first row are the recommended values of ref. ([14]). In the next three rows are values (we list central values only) obtained by groups which have attempted a complete determination of S- and P-wave parameters. The last of this is from a paper of Höhler and collaborators ([13]) in a research which also led ([15]) to a low value for the σ-term, and obtained $\sigma = 40$ MeV. From this we see that:

a) Our procedure reproduces correctly this value directly in terms of S-and P-wave scattering lengths.

b) The low value is related to a value of S-wave scattering lengths which disagrees with previous results of the same and other groups.

4. A brief discussion.

There is little to add to the discussion contained in the first Section, except for a few remarks.

The real trouble in the argument is that the smoothness hypothesis cannot be *tested* in pion-nucleon scattering. This makes more interesting an accurate study of π-π scattering, where the sum rule of eq. (1.13a) is a consequence of smoothness as well as of the well established commutation relations of eq. (1.1).

Let us note that our treatment of smoothness is self consistent in that the coefficient C turns out smaller than A, B, D. The relatively large σ-term is thus related to relatively large variations on the energy shell and not to a non-smooth behaviour off the mass shell.

The large errors in the σ-term and the discrepancy between the results of Cheng and Dashen and Höhler et al. seem to reflect the relatively poor state of our knowledge of π-N low-energy scattering.

I have only discussed in detail our determination of the σ-term. This is strictly related to those of Cheng and Dashen ([6]), of Höhler, Jacob and Strauss ([15]), and that of Osypowski ([11]) which led to $\sigma \approx 60$ MeV, which are all based on a study of π-N scattering.

I should finally mention two other determinations of the σ-term. One of them uses data from both π-N and k-N scattering ([16]). The other, which appeared recently, uses data from π-nucleus scattering ([17]). They both give relatively small values for the σ-term.

Acknowledgement.

The author is grateful to Dr. Carl Kaysen for the hospitality extended to him at the Institute for Advanced Study.

TABLE I. – Values of σ-term, and of A, B, C, obtained from different determinations of scattering lengths. Δ_R is in all cases taken from eq. (3.16).

	$a_1 + 2a_3$	$a_{11} + 2a_{31}$	$a_{13} + 2a_3$	$-A\mu^3$	σ MeV	$B\mu^3$	$C\mu^3$
Compilation of ref. ([14]) «recommended values»	$0.000^{+0.045}_{-0.035}$	-0.164 ± 0.008	0.414 ± 0.021	$1.24^{+0.50}_{-0.46}$	80 ± 30	1.24 ± 0.11	0.00 ± 0.35
Höhler et al. ([14]) I	-0.021	-0.168	0.396	0.94	60	1.14	-0.20
Samaranayake et al. Collins et al., ref. ([14])	-0.026	-0.160	0.431	1.31	85	1.33	-0.02
Höhler et al. II, ref. ([13])	-0.075	-0.162	0.408	0.68	44	1.15	-0.47

REFERENCES

1) G. ALTARELLI, N. CABIBBO, L. MAIANI: *Phys. Lett.*, **35** B, 1445 (1971).
2) G. ALTARELLI, N. CABIBBO, L. MAIANI: *Nucl. Phys.* **34** B, 621 (1971).
3) N. CABIBBO, L. MAIANI: *Phys. Rev.*, D **1**, 707 (1970); N. CABIBBO, L. MAIANI, in *Evolution in Particle Physics*, ed. M. CONVERSI, Academic Press, (New York, 1970), p. 49.

4) M. GELL-MANN, R. J. OAKES, B. RENNER: *Phys. Rev.*, **175**, 2195 (1968).
5) S. L. GLASHOW and S. WEINBERG: *Phys. Rev. Lett.*, **20**, 224 (1968).
6) T. D. CHENG and R. DASHEN: *Phys. Rev. Lett.*, **26**, 594 (1971).
7) S. WEINBERG: *Phys. Rev. Lett.*, **20**, 475 (1968).
8) R. BRANDT, G. PREPARATA: *Phys. Rev. Lett.*, **26**, 1605 (1971) and references contained therein.
9) The definition of $\mathcal{M}$, as well as of the invariant functions A and B, is consistent with that of B. I. BJORKEN and S. D. DRELL: *Relativistic Quantum Fields* (New York, 1965). I also use here their convention as to metric, state normalization etc.
10) S. L. ADLER: *Phys. Rev.*, **139** B, 1638 (1965).
11) Our use of this expansion is close to that of E. T. OSYPOWSKI: *Nucl. Phys.*, B **21**, 615 (1970), and to that of ref. ([13]).
12) D. AMATI, S. FUBINI: *Am. Rev. Nucl. Sci.*, **12**, 359 (1962).
13) G. HÖHLER, H. P. JACOB, R. STRAUSS: *A Critical Test of Models for the Low Energy Pion Amplitude*, Karlsruhe preprint (March, 1971).
14) G. EBEL et al.: *Compilation of Coupling Constants and Low Energy Parameters*, Sept. 1970, edition; *Springer Tracts in Modern Physics*, edited by G. HÖHLER, Vol. **55**.
15) E. HÖHLER, H. P. JACOB, R. STRAUSS: *Phys. Lett.*, **35** B, 445 (1971).
16) F. VON HIPPEL and J. KIM: *Phys. Rev. D* **1**, 151 (1970).
17) M. ERICSON and M. RHO: CERN preprint TH1350, June 1971.

DISCUSSION

Chairman: Prof. N. CABIBBO
Scientific Secretary: R. KERNER

DISCUSSION

— GENSINI:

I would like to add another value to the list you showed for $\sigma_{\pi N}$: by use of nothing more exotic than fixed-t dispersion relations one is able to get $\sigma_{\pi N} = 93 \pm 20$ MeV. Then I have a remark to make: the value of $\varepsilon_8/\varepsilon_0 \approx -1.25$ comes out from the model of the $(3, \bar{3})$ chiral symmetry-breaking, assuming that the mass of the pion comes entirely from the symmetry-breaking part of the Langrangian, so that the fact that m_π^2 is of order $(\sqrt{2}\varepsilon_0 + \varepsilon_8)$ is a further assumption and not a consequence of the theory of Glashow and Weinberg, which practically allows any value for $\varepsilon_8/\varepsilon_0$ from 0 to -1.3.

— CABIBBO:

I realize $\varepsilon_8/\varepsilon_0$ is not well determined, but it enters only in the interpretation of the result in terms of $\langle u_0 \rangle / \langle u_8 \rangle$, not in the derivation of the numerical value for the σ-term.

— KLEINERT:

First, I have a remark: the property of the amplitude to be odd under reflection on the straight line connecting the Adler zeros can be tested also for the odd amplitude. P. Weisz and myself have calculated $g_A/g_V = 1.25$ this way without any off-mass shell correction.

— CABIBBO:

The Cheng-Dashen symmetry is expected to be true to order μ^2, while terms of order μ^2/M^2 are neglected. The neglected terms correspond indeed to the off-mass shell corrections. Your result on the odd amplitude confirm that these corrections are indeed small.

— KLEINERT:

Secondly, you are working with a theory that has a meaning only to lowest order in SU_3. You used this while estimating $\langle u_8 \rangle$ from the SU_3 mass splitting. We know from other models, e.g. those containing a σ-term in the t-channel, that u_0 can have quite a strong SU_3 dependence. Thus you are dealing with a theory which has intrinsically an inaccuracy of 200 MeV in all calculations involving baryons. So I think any theoretical estimate on the σ-term is ± 200 MeV in excellent agreement with all calculations of πN scattering.

— CABIBBO:

Perturbation theory in SU_3 breaking is only used in estimating $\varepsilon_8 \langle u_8 \rangle \approx 210$ MeV, and not in the computation of the σ-term. Having said this, one could recall that the use of first order perturbation theory is in this case supported by the validity of the Gell-Mann-Okubo relation between the baryon masses.

— KLEINERT:

My third comment: I think that as long as you invoke the PCAC approximation it is meaningless to try and answer questions on the off-shell π-N amplitude concerning the size of 100 MeV close to the nucleon pole. You choose to subtract the nucleon pole term out in the form $g_{\pi N}(q_1^2)g_{\pi N}(q_2^2)$ and require the remaining amplitude $\widetilde{F}$ to satisfy the Cheng-Dashen reflection principle, $\widetilde{F}(0, 0, 0, 0) = \widetilde{F}(0, 2, \mu^2, \mu^2, \mu^2)$. Within PCAC you could as well have taken out $g_{\pi N}(0)g_{\pi N}(0)$. This would have given a difference of 100% in the determination of the σ-term. Thus any statement on the σ-term obtained from such a procedure in an exact PCAC theory, as that of Gell-Mann, Oakes and Renner, carries a systematic error of this size.

— CABIBBO:

The Cheng-Dashen symmetry is obtained by using the following properties of $\widetilde{F}$:

1) The Adler zero: $\widetilde{F}(0, \mu^2, \mu^2, 0) = 0$.

2) The smoothness hypothesis.

The prescription we use is unique in the sense that we subtract the nucleon pole completely from $A^+ + \nu B^{(+)}$. In the one you propose a piece of the nucleon pole remains, so that one cannot consider the resulting amplitude smooth. This prescription may therefore lead to difficulties we do not encounter.

— DE WIT:

I would like to make a comment. There is a theoretical estimate by Okubo and Mathur for the ratio $\langle u_0 \rangle / \langle u_8 \rangle$ which is about 5. That is in good agreement with the numbers you presented.

— CABIBBO:

That is interesting. I will have to look into it.

— DE WIT:

In the second place there is a recent paper by Li and Pagels in which they gave arguments for the existence of terms like $m_\pi^2 \log m_\pi^2$ in the soft pion region. Did you assume the absence of these terms or can you give arguments for their absence?

— CABIBBO:

No, we did not consider this. I would not think such terms would modify our results significantly.

— MANNHEIM:

What scattering length would be required by a σ-term of, say, 20 MeV, to check how sensitive the calculation is to the scattering length?

— CABIBBO:

In order to change $\widetilde{F}(0, 2\ \mu^2, \mu^2, 0)$ by 0.5 you have to change $(a_1 + 2a_3)$ by about 0.1, which is a very large change, since accepted values are of order of 0.02. Of course you could change a little the p-wave scattering lengths.

— DE ALFARO:

I want to make a point which to my view is particularly important. You should not be guided by the error in the Goldberger-Treiman formula in these sort of calculations. The Goldberger-Treiman formula is obtained through the dispersion relations in the mass of a vertex. When you are doing this sort of evaluation or analytic continuations for the amplitudes, *e.g.* for α_1-α_3, what you are confronted with is the problem of the simultaneous continuation in two variables, the mass and the energy. And in general the problem is just different from the Goldberger-Treiman problem. It may be that you are less wrong than in the Goldberger-Treiman case, or more wrong—if I remember well, α_1-α_3 must be of order of 4%. What is important is that these are completely different problems.

Positivity and Internal Symmetry

S. L. Glashow

Positivity and internal symmetry 805
Discussion 815

Positivity and Internal Symmetry (*)

S. L. GLASHOW

Lyman Laboratory of Physics, Harvard University
Cambridge, Mass., U.S.A.

The work I shall present is largely due to my student Andrew Yao. We are concerned with the constraints on cross-sections that are imposed by invariance under an internal symmetry group, like isospin or $SU(3)$. These constraints are of two kinds: equalities, like

$$\sigma_T(\pi^+ P) = \sigma_T(\pi^- n) \tag{1}$$

and inequalities, like

$$3\sigma_T(\pi^- P) \geqslant \sigma_T(\pi^+ P) \geqslant 0 . \tag{2}$$

It is the inequalities, which are not adequately treated in the literature, to which we direct our attention.

To deduce (2), we may write the total cross-sections for pion-nucleon scattering in terms of the scattering matrix T,

$$\sigma_T(\pi_i P_a) \sim \langle \pi_i P_a | T^+ T | \pi_i P_a \rangle . \tag{3}$$

From this construction, it is clear that the total cross-sections are all non-negative. But, positivity of T^+T implies more than just the positivity of its diagonal entries. The entire six-by-six matrix

$$M_{ia,jb} = \langle \pi_i P_a | T^+ T | \pi_j P_b \rangle \tag{4}$$

(*) Work supported in part by the Air Force Office of Scientific Research under Contract No. F44620-70-C-0030 and the National Science Foundation under Grant No. GP-30819X.

must be positive semidefinite. Writing M in terms of direct channel isospin projection operators,

$$M = AP_{\frac{1}{2}} + BP_{\frac{3}{2}},\qquad(5)$$

(and thereby using isospin invariance), we find for the condition that it is positive semidefinite, the constraints

$$A \geqslant 0, \quad B \geqslant 0.\qquad(6)$$

These conditions insure that no cross-section described by M may be negative. This includes more than the physically measurable cross-sections, but also those cross-sections that are not measurable due to superselection rules. (Consider for example, the total cross-section for a linear combination of π^+ and π^0 off protons.) Thus, the constraint that (6) gives on measurable cross-sections is, of course, stronger than mere positivity: relation (2) is obtained.

In a precisely similar fashion, this analysis may be applied to the total cross-sections for isospins $\frac{1}{2} + \frac{1}{2}$ (e.g. kaon-nucleon scattering) or $1 + 1$ (e.g. pion-hyperon scattering). Some of the corresponding inequalities are

$$2\sigma_T(K^+n) \geqslant \sigma_T(K^+P) \geqslant 0,\qquad(7)$$

$$\sigma_T(\pi^-\Sigma^+) \geqslant \sigma_T(\pi^+\Sigma^+) \geqslant 0.\qquad(8)$$

The results (2), (7), (8) are, or should be, familiar consequences of isospin invariance. However, similar inequalities may be deduced for inclusive rather than total cross-sections. Let P denote a projection operator onto an isotopically invariant family of states. Then,

$$\sigma_P(K_i P_a) \sim \langle K_i P_a | T^+ P T | K_i P_a \rangle\qquad(9)$$

gives the inclusive cross-section for $K_i + P_a$ into the family of states specified by P. Since P is isotopically invariant, and since T^+PT is a positive semidefinite matrix, we conclude immediately that the results (2), (7) and (8) are true for σ_P as well as for σ_T.

The projection operator P may be chosen, to give some concrete examples, to yield

i) at least one produced anti-nucleon of unmeasured charge.

ii) an $I = 0$ particle (e.g., Λ, D, η) of measured momentum.
iii) a definite partial wave.

In each case, the inequalities described above must hold.

Our analysis can directly be applied to inclusive neutrino-proton scattering. With the neglect of strangeness changing events (or, equivalently, with the neglect of $\tan^2\theta \approx 0.04$) and under the hypothesis that the weak current and its adjoint behave like members of an isotopic triplet, we obtain, with the usual definitions of q^2 and ν,

$$3\frac{d^2\sigma(\bar{\nu}p)}{dq^2\,d\nu} \geqslant \left(\frac{1-\Delta}{1+\Delta}\right)\frac{d^2\sigma(\nu P)}{dq^2\,d\nu} \tag{10}$$

where

$$\Delta = \frac{E+E'}{2EE'}(\nu^2+q^2)^{\frac{1}{2}}\left[1+\frac{2\nu^2+q^2}{4EE'}\right]^{-1}. \tag{11}$$

In the kinematic region where $\nu^2 \gg q^2$ and $\nu \gg 2M_N$, this inequality becomes simply

$$3\frac{d^2\sigma(\bar{\nu}P)}{dq^2\,d\nu} \geqslant \left(\frac{E'}{E}\right)^2\frac{d^2\sigma(\nu P)}{dq^2\,d\nu}. \tag{12}$$

We next examine meson-baryon total cross-sections under the hypothesis of exact $SU(3)$ invariance. Let us not discuss whether this is a safe approximation for the real world. The matrix

$$M \sim \langle \pi_i B_a | T^+ T | \pi_j B_b \rangle, \tag{13}$$

with indices describing members of the baryon and pseudoscalar meson octets, must be $SU(3)$ invariant, and thus may be expressed in terms of direct channel $SU(3)$ projectors,

$$M \sim a_1 P_1 + a_{10} P_{10} + a_{\overline{10}} P_{\overline{10}} + a_{27} P_{27} + a_d P_d + a_f P_f + b Q_{df} + b' Q_{fd}. \tag{14}$$

The P_j are normalized projection operators onto the various irreducible representations in 8×8, where d and f signify the symmetric and antisymmetric octets. The matrices Q map one octet into the other and are normalized so that $Q_{df}Q_{fd} = P_d$ and $Q_{fd}Q_{df} = P_f$.

The requirement of time-reversal invariance is simply

$$b = b' \tag{15}$$

and the positivity of M is equivalent to the constraints

$$a_i \geqslant 0 \tag{16}$$

$$a_d a_f \geqslant bb' . \tag{17}$$

It is convenient to reexpress the last four terms in (14) by diagonalizing the 2×2 matrix referring to the octets. We obtain

$$M \sim a_1 P_1 + a_{10} P_{10} + a_{\overline{10}} P_{\overline{10}} + a_{27} P_{27} + a_\alpha P_\alpha + a_\beta P_\beta \tag{18}$$

where P_α projects onto an octet with $d/f = \alpha$ and P_β projects onto the orthogonal octet with $d/f = \beta = -\alpha^{-1}$. Positivity is just the requirement that all the coefficients in (18) are non-negative. In general, α will depend on energy.

There are six isotopically distinct measured total cross-sections: $\pi^\pm P$, K^+P, K^+n, K^-P, K^-n. We have computed the inequalities they must satisfy from the positivity conditions. They are:

$$2\sigma(\pi^+ P) \geqslant \sigma(K^+ P) \geqslant 0 \tag{19}$$

$$2\sigma(K^+ n) \geqslant \sigma(K^+ P) \tag{20}$$

and, with the definitions

$$A = 11/40 \, \sigma(K^+P) - 1/2[\sigma(K^+n) + \sigma(\pi^+ P)]$$
$$- \sigma(K^-P) + [\sigma(\pi P) + \sigma(K^- n)] \tag{21}$$

$$B = -7/72 \, \sigma(K^+P) - 1/18[\sigma(K^+n) + \sigma(\pi^+ P)]$$
$$+ \sigma(K^-P) - 1/3[\sigma(\pi^- P) + \sigma(K^- n)] \tag{22}$$

there are two cases

$$B \geqslant A \quad \text{and} \quad A + B \geqslant 2/3 |\sigma(\pi^- P) - \sigma(K^- n)| \tag{23}$$

or

$$A \geqslant B \geqslant 0 \quad \text{and} \quad AB \geqslant 1/9[\sigma(\pi^-P) - \sigma(K^-n)]^2. \quad (24)$$

Beyond energies of a few GeV, these inequalities are satisfied by the data.

It would be of interest to compute the seven unknown parameters in (14) from observed data, but unfortunately there are only six data. However, it is generally expected that the total cross-sections, viewed in the t-channel, should be non-exotic:

$$a^t_{27} = 0 \quad (25)$$

$$a^t_{10} = a^t_{\overline{10}} = 0 \quad (26)$$

and, that the exotic amplitudes in the s-channel should be equal.

$$a_{\overline{10}} = a_{27}. \quad (27)$$

The equality of a^t_{10} and $a^t_{\overline{10}}$ is just the result of time-reversal invariance. Putting them equal to zero, we obtain a relation among observed cross-sections

$$\sigma(\pi^-P) - \sigma(\pi^+P) = \sigma(K^-P) - \sigma(K^-n) + \sigma(K^+n) - \sigma(K^+P). \quad (28)$$

Similarly, from (27) we obtain

$$\sigma(K^+P) = \sigma(K^+n). \quad (29)$$

How well these relations are satisfied is illustrated in Fig. 1. In the following, we imagine these relations exactly satisfied, and make use only of four measured cross-sections.

Assuming (25) as well as (26) and (27), we may unambiguously compute the s-channel amplitudes a_1, $a_{10} = a_{27}$, a_α and a_β. They are shown, as a function of energy, in Fig. 2. That the positivity constraints are satisfied is manifestly true.

But, observe the remarkable coincidence of the α-octet with the decuplet. We do not know any simple explanation for this degeneracy. Note further that the remaining singlet and octet are not strongly excited, but keep close to the non-resonant background term. To understand the octet-decuplet

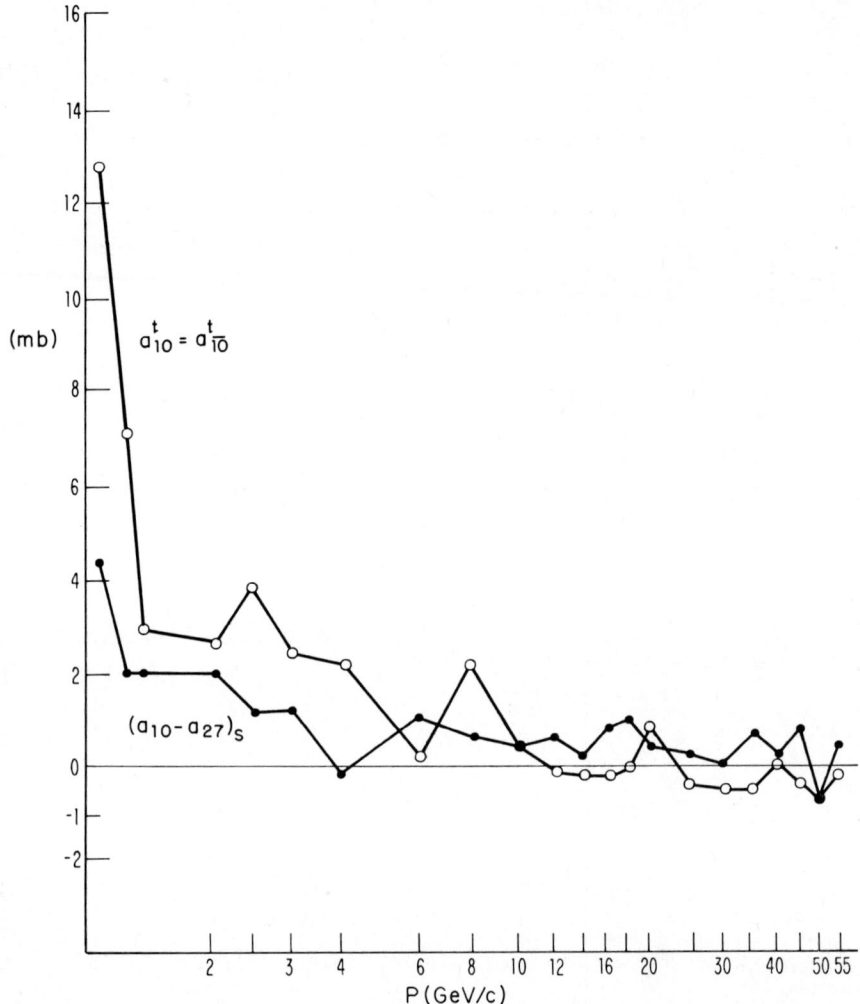

Fig. 1. – The s-channel exotic contributions to meson-baryon total cross-sections are about equal; the t-channel exotics are small.

degeneracy better, we show in Fig. 3 the d/f ratio of the excited α-octet as a function of energy. It is strikingly stable at an energy independent value of 1.5—very close to the known d/f ratio for ground state mesons and baryons

Let us return to $SU(2)$ and to the study of inclusive reactions. Imagine that the projection operator P in (9) is not isotopically invariant, but requires the existence of a particle of definite I^2 and I_z in the final state. Thus, we are

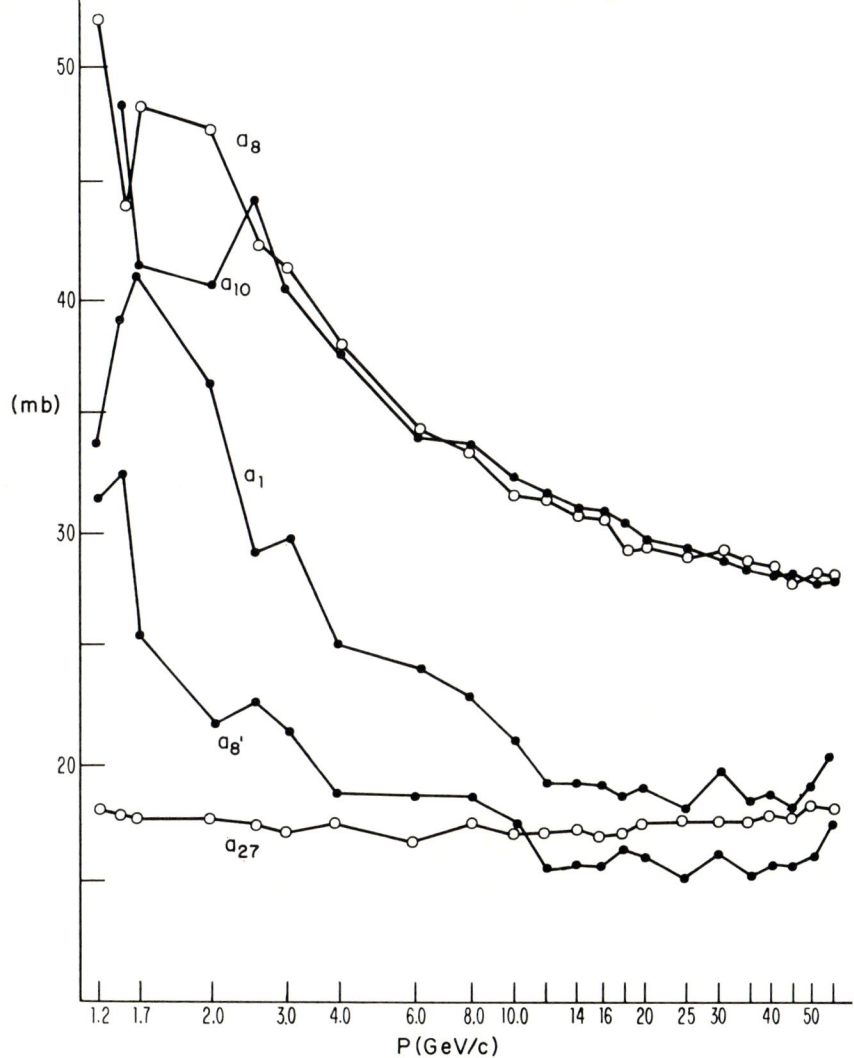

Fig. 2. – The four non-exotic s-channel contributions and the exotic background. Note the mysterious equality $a_{10} = a_8$.

considering inclusive reactions of the form

$$A+B \to C+\text{anything} \qquad (30)$$

where A, B and C have non-zero isospin. Let us consider the simplest situa-

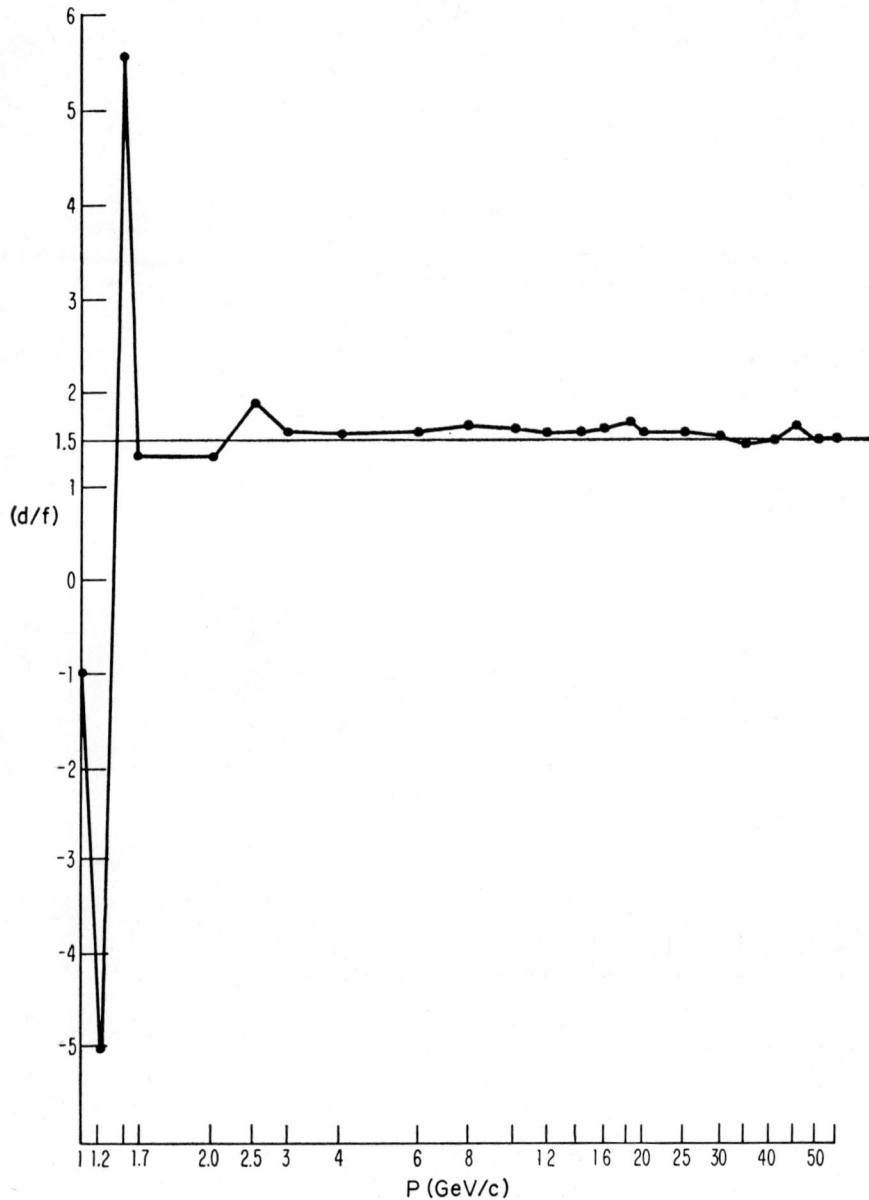

Fig. 3. – The *d/f* ratio for the dominant octet contribution: rapid oscillations at low energy, dead constant at higher energy.

tion where each particle has isospin $\frac{1}{2}$. Consider, as an example, kaon plus nucleon into kaon plus anything.

There are eight different cross-sections, which are equal in pairs by charge symmetry,

$$\left.\begin{aligned} \sigma_1 &= \sigma(uu \to u) = \sigma(dd \to d) \\ \sigma_2 &= \sigma(ud \to u) = \sigma(du \to d) \\ \sigma_3 &= \sigma(du \to u) = \sigma(ud \to d) \\ \sigma_4 &= \sigma(dd \to u) = \sigma(uu \to d) \end{aligned}\right\}, \quad (31)$$

where $i_j \to k$ stands for the reaction

$$A_i + B_j \to C_k + \ldots \quad (32)$$

and the indices take the values $u(\tau_3 = \frac{1}{2})$ and $d(\tau_3 = -\frac{1}{2})$. The problem we set is to determine the inequalities that must be satisfied by the σ_a.

Reaction (32) can be regarded as a total cross-section for the three-body collisions $A+B+\bar{C}$, with $\bar{C}$ having negative energy. Evidently, the corresponding 8×8 matrix must be positive semidefinite. The most general isotopically invariant expression for the cross-sections is

$$\sigma \sim a + b\tau_1 \cdot \tau_2 + C\tau_2 \cdot \tau_3 + d\tau_3 \cdot \tau_1 + e\tau_1 \cdot (\tau_2 \times \tau_3) \quad (33)$$

where τ_1, τ_2 and τ_3 refer to A, B and D. The last term corresponds to an antisymmetric matrix, and cannot be present if time-reversal invariance is required. It remains only to determine the conditions on a, b, c and d that ensure the positivity of σ, and to reexpress these conditions in terms of the four measurable cross-sections. The complete set of resultant inequalities is given below

$$\sigma_1 + \sigma_2 + \sigma_3 \geqslant \sigma_4 \geqslant 0 \quad (34)$$

$$(\sigma_1 + \sigma_2 + \sigma_3 - \sigma_4)^2 \geqslant (\sigma_1 + \sigma_2 - 2\sigma_3)^2 + 3(\sigma_1 - \sigma_2)^2. \quad (35)$$

At present, I know of no experimental data with which these inequalities may be compared.

We have computed the inequalities for the inclusive reactions (32) for any combination of isospins $\frac{1}{2}$ and 1. Among the relations, we quote only one which may directly be compared with experiment:

$$5\sigma(\pi^-p \to \pi^+ + ...) \geqslant \sigma(\pi^+P \to \pi^- + ...). \tag{36}$$

Unsurprisingly, it agrees with the data.

We conclude by considering some inclusive reactions under the hypothesis of exact $SU(3)$ invariance. Consider the reactions

$$\left.\begin{array}{l}\gamma+P \to \pi^+ + ... \\ \gamma+P \to K^+ + ... \end{array}\right\} \tag{37}$$

The photon is a U-spin singlet, the proton a member of a U-spin doublet, and π^+, K^+ comprise another doublet. We find directly

$$2\sigma(\gamma P \to K^+ + ...) \geqslant \sigma(\gamma P \to \pi^+ + ...). \tag{38}$$

This result is in violent disagreement with experiment. This is hardly surprising, since the heavy photo-produced systems are expected to decay by cascading to nearby resonances. The lower mass of the pion makes it kinematically favoured, so that $SU(3)$ comparisons of final state kaons and pions are unrealistic.

Fairer tests of approximate $SU(3)$ are given by such inequalities as

$$2\sigma(K^-P \to S + ...) \geqslant \sigma(\pi^-P \to S + ...) \tag{39}$$

where S is any U-spin singlet, like γ, x^0, or $\Lambda(1405)$, and

$$2\sigma(K^-P \to P \text{ or } \Sigma^+ + ...) \geqslant \sigma(\pi^-P \to P \text{ or } \Sigma^+ + ...). \tag{40}$$

But, we should always remember that exact $SU(3)$ invariance is a lie, and that its predictions should be regarded at best as approximate.

Finally, a word about the utility of the relations we consider. The $SU(2)$ results are all expected to be satisfied; the $SU(3)$ relations surprise nobody if they fail: why then are they useful? A possible answer lies in the current purely phenomenological approach to hadron scattering. Positivity and internal symmetry should be regarded as design requirements for model builders.

We thank Prof. A. Visconti for the hospitality we were shown at the Centre de Physique Theorique, Marseille, where this work was done.

DISCUSSION

Chairman: Prof. S. L. GLASHOW

Scientific Secretary: A. C. YAO

DISCUSSION

— GASIOROWICZ:

Some years ago people used positivity conditions not in direct s variable but in some other fashion. I would like to know if your work is connected with their works. In particular, is it connected with that of Martin, Van Hove etc.?

— GLASHOW:

I believe that the implications of positivity and internal symmetry are not adequately described in the literature.

— Ross G.:

The energies of comparison for your SU_3 inequalities are not defined. Could you explain what prescription you used?

— GLASHOW:

Yes. There is the usual problem at what energies to compare the π^+p, K^+p cross-sections. I would say these inequalities only apply at high energies. Once you go beyond 4 or 5 GeV, things vary slowly and it hardly matters whether you speak of center of mass momentum or s. In fact, we compare cross-sections at the same lab energy. At lower energies where the resonances appear I would not try to play this game.

— Ross G.:

I would like to make a comment about this point. I believe it is possible to make SU_3 comparisons at all energies provided the energies of comparison are related by a Gell-Mann Okubo type formula. For instance SU_3 would demand the equalities:

$$\tfrac{1}{3}\sigma(\pi^-p \to \Delta^-\pi^+) = \sigma(K^-p \to Y^{*-}\pi^+) = \sigma(\pi^-p \to Y^{*-}K^+) = \sigma(K^-p \to \Xi^{*-}K^+) \ .$$

Comparisons at the same Q (E—sum of all final particle masses) value and at $E < 3$ GeV satifies the first and the last equalities but the equality of the first and second set is violated by more than an order of magnitude. However, using a G-M-O energy formula gives good agreements for all the equalities. Furthermore, this prescription is working well even for relations involving exotic channels, for instance:

$$\sigma(\pi^+p \to K^+\Sigma^+)^{\frac{1}{2}} \geqslant [\sigma(\pi^+p \to \pi^+p)^{\frac{1}{2}} - \sigma(K^+p \to K^+p)^{\frac{1}{2}}] \ .$$

This is satisfied ($E <$ 4 GeV) using G-M-O formula, but is violated if comparison is made at equal Q values.

— GLASHOW:

I would insist on testing these SU_3 relations at high energies. It would be interesting to know examples of SU_3 violations at high energies that do not involve comparing kaons with pions in the final states. I do not know any gross violations of SU_3 at high energies by more than 30% or so. By the way, has anyone tried to make an SU_3 analysis at high energies of quasi two-body meson-baryon scattering or photoproduction? Now there are lots of data. Five years ago there were not.

— SAKURAI:

There is a violation of some SU_3 triangular relations in high energy photoproduction. You can find it in the Daresbury proceedings.

— GLASHOW:

What is the process? Are we comparing final state kaon and pion again? It is not fair to make this comparison because π leaks out of everything. Photoproduced resonances like all resonances, prefer pion decay modes.

— SAKURAI:

But we are looking at two-body processes where the π's are not leaking out of final states.

— COLEMAN:

If it is a two-body process, I would imagine that the only resonances relevant would be those near the center of mass energy. Now way up in the energy spectrum, and it is not inclusive therefore, it is not these resonances which make pions and do not have the muscles to produce kaons.

— GENSINI:

I remember someone had made an analysis combining SU_3 plus Regge behaviour. It seems all right from 4 to 7 GeV/c.

— SAKURAI:

That is something else. They use SU_3 for the vertices, but the trajectories violently violate SU_3. In this way you make good predictions. In fact it has been done for some time.

— MARTIN:

I just want to make a statement which is only vaguely connected with what Prof. Glashow said this morning. I want to report a work which has been done by Dass, S. M. Roy, Froyland, Halzen, Michael and to some extent myself. In the considerations that Prof. Glashow made this morning one can introduce a projection operator on a spin state. In this way you can get triangular inequalities between

$$\sqrt{\sigma_+(1\pm p_+)}, \qquad \sqrt{\sigma_-(1\pm p_-)}, \qquad \sqrt{2\sigma_0(1\pm p_0)}.$$

You get a picture like this:

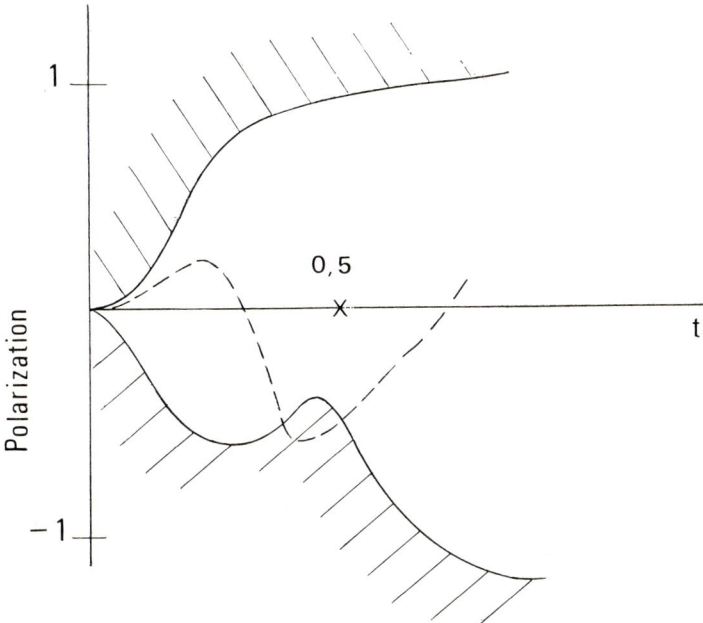

The shaded region is forbidden. The experimental measurement at 6 GeV of Guisan *et al.* fall in the allowed region, but the absorption cut calculated (dotted line) disagrees, which means that the calculation of the $\pi^-p \to \pi^0 n$ polarization has been done without paying attention to having a good simultaneous fit of $\pi^-p \to \pi^-p$ and $\pi^+p \to \pi^+p$.

We have also obtained an inequality on polarizations P^+P^-.

$$\left|\frac{P^+ - P^-}{2}\right| \leqslant \sqrt{\frac{\sigma_0(\sigma_+ + \sigma_- - \sigma_0) - \frac{1}{4}(\sigma_+ - \sigma_-)^2}{\sigma_+\sigma_-}}.$$

So far this inequality has only been tested in the forward direction. Typical numbers are $0.17\pm0.03 \leqslant 0.20\pm0.01$. Since it contains in the numerator a factor which vanishes when the triangular inequalities for some cross-sections are saturated, it will be still more interesting in the backward direction as indicated by the analysis of Ageel, Bareger and Sonderegger at Saclay from 200 MeV to 2 GeV, and also the work of Törnqvist (*Nuclear Physics*: B 6-8, (1968); *Physical Review*: 161 (1967)). Also see Korkea-Aho and Törnqvist in *Nuclear Physics* (in press).

— GLASHOW:

A lot of people like Michael have tried to apply positivity conditions on ordinary spin which are much more complicated than isospin. If you would combine spin and isospin, it stands to reason that you would get stronger inequalities than by simply putting the restrictions together. Michael and I talked about it for a while, but we felt it is too hard to work it out on the blackboard. But I am sure there is a lot of gold to be mined.

— CHEW:

The preceding remarks by Martin illustrate how unitarity affects both charge exchange and elastic scattering. At the risk of arousing the audience, I point out that the notion of « shadow scattering » or « diffractive scattering », normally reserved for elastic scattering, must correspondingly have relevance also for charge exchange scattering. This is one of the considerations that has made me loath to accept the widespread belief that the Pomeranchuk singularity is qualitatively different from the ρ.

— TÖRNQVIST:

I must say that I do not quite agree with Prof. Chew. In order for the Pomeron to contribute to the charge exchange process, the Pomeron must have quantum numbers different from the vacuum.

— NEFF:

It would seem equally possible in connection with the remark of Prof. Chew, that ordinary Regge singularities, including the ρ, may be simple, but the great number of such singularities, when fed back through the unitarity relation, may require a very complicated singularity structure for the Pomeron.

— GENSINI:

I want to make a point in connection with Neff's remark. I believe that Pomeron and ordinary Regge trajectories share the characteristics of being very complicated. This is evidenced in the polarization of πN scattering.

— JACOB:

There are many relations which correspond to duality. They might be able to explain the degeneracy of decuplet and octet in the direct channel. Consider a double charge exchange process like $\pi^+ \Sigma^- \to \pi^- \Sigma^+$. In the cross channel it is exotic. Therefore, the imaginary part of octet and decuplet in the direct channel must cancel out. It would also require a definite D/F ratio.

— GLASHOW:

In the SU_3 analysis of meson-baryon total cross-sections there are seven parameters. Putting 10 equal to 27 brings you down to six, *i.e.* background, 1, two 8's, 10 and D/F. Now, duality says there are no 27 and $10 + 10^-$ in the cross channel, which gives you two conditions on the six parameters. But these conditions are complicated and do not fix D/F ratio, nor do they imply the degeneracy of 8 and 10.

— ROY:

May I make a remark? Degenerate relations have been discussed (by Zweig et al., for instance) in an essentially different context, i.e. between baryon Regge trajectories. Absence of exotics in the s-, u-channel gives linear relations among the t-channel Regge trajectories. If the leading trajectories are assumed to be decuplet and a certain octet, then these relations give the degeneracy relation between 8 and 10. However, the situation Prof. Glashow discussed is a different situation.

Photon-Photon Collisions in Electron-Positron Storage Rings

P. KESSLER

1. Historical point 821
2. Background suppression and total cross-sections 823
3. Energy dependence and angular distributions 827
4. Effects of realistic experimental cut-offs 830
5. Conclusion 851
References 852
Discussion 854

Photon-Photon Collisions in Electron-Positron Storage Rings

P. Kessler

Collège de France, Laboratoire de Physique Atomique et Moleculaire
Paris, France

1. Historical point.

The history of this idea dates back to 1960, when the first electron-electron and electron-positron storage rings were planned. F. Low [1] suggested to study π^0 production in electron-electron or electron-positron collisions through the exchange of two virtual photons. A few months later, Calogero and Zemach [2] published a paper which covered a wider scope: they suggested to look for particle pair production in electron-electron collisions, and in particular for the process $e^-e^- \to e^-e^-\pi^-\pi^+$.

Strangely enough, this work was almost completely forgotten for about nine years. However, we must mention J. C. Le Guillou [3] who improved Low's calculation; and De Celles and Goehl [4] who suggested to study the production of the $\sigma(0^{++})$ resonance in electron-electron collisions.

In 1969, our group (N. Arteaga-Romero, A. Jaccarini, J. Parisi and myself; more recently, E. Calva-Tellez and C. Carimalo also entered this group) suggested to use the new and powerful—high energy, high luminosity—e^-e^+ storage rings planned or under construction for a systematic study of particle production in photon-photon collisions [5]. We were able to show:

— that the fundamental problem of background suppression can be solved by detecting both the outgoing electron and positron at small scattering angles;
— that the cross-sections are high enough to obtain reasonably large counting rates with future machines of beam energy $(2 \div 3)$ GeV and luminosity $\sim 10^{32}$ cm^{-2} s^{-1}.

One year later, Balakin, Budnev and Ginsburg [6] on the one hand, Brodsky, Kinoshita and Terazawa [7] on the other hand, also pointed out the importance of these reactions in colliding beam physics. Since that time, photon-photon collisions have become a very popular subject in high-energy physics, and quite a large number of papers have been published on that subject [8].

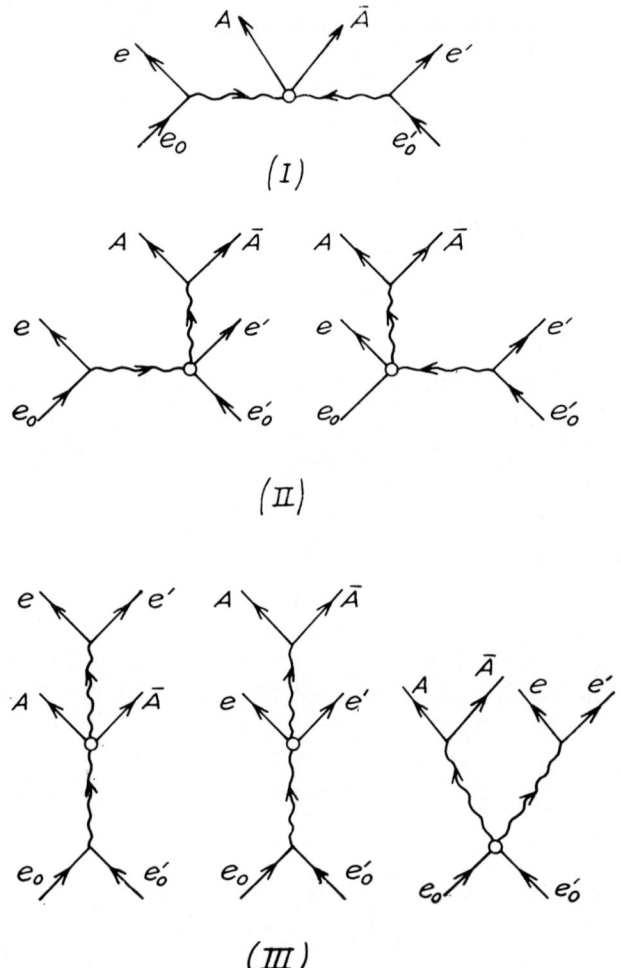

Fig. 1. – Feynman diagrams for $e^- + e^+ \to e^- + e^+ + A^- + A^+$, $e_0(e)$ is the incoming (outgoing) electron; $e_0'(e')$ is the incoming (outgoing) positron. (For convenience, the latter is represented like a particle, not an antiparticle).

2. Background suppression and total cross-sections.

Considering reactions of the type $e^-e^+ \to e^-e^+A^-A^+$, where A is any charged particle (e, μ, π, K, p), they are represented by the six diagrams of Fig. 1. What we want is to define an experimental situation where diagram (I) contributes alone, thus eliminating the background due to the five other diagrams.

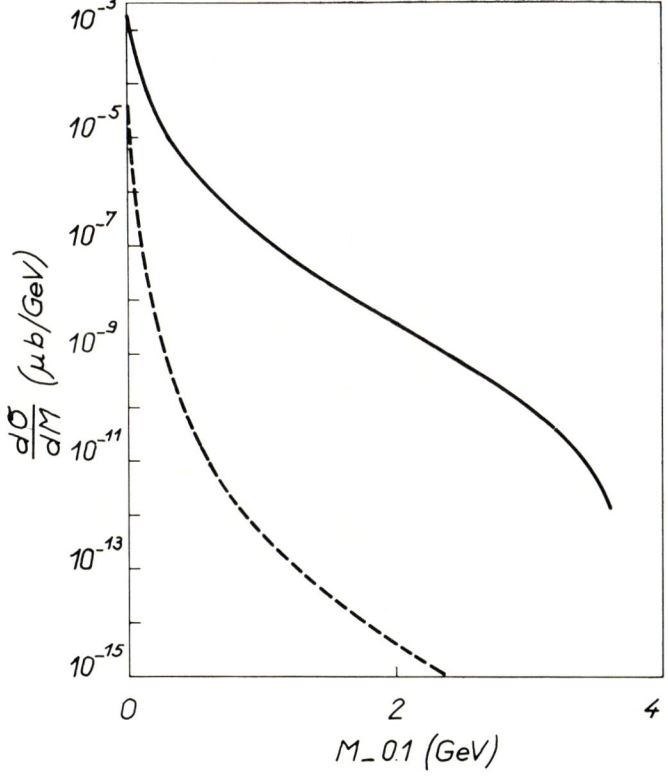

Fig. 2 a.

A priori, we may assume that such a situation can be realized by detecting both the outgoing electron and positron at extremely small scattering angles. Indeed, since in diagram (I) both the scattered electron and positron should tend to be very sharply peaked in their forward directions, it may be expected that the contribution of (I) will not be drastically affected by such an angular cut-off. In diagrams (II), only one of the outgoing e± particles will be sharply peaked at 0° scattering angle, whereas the other one will be (very roughly speaking) more or less isotropically distributed; thus, the angular cut-off, operating on both e± particles, should have a much more drastic

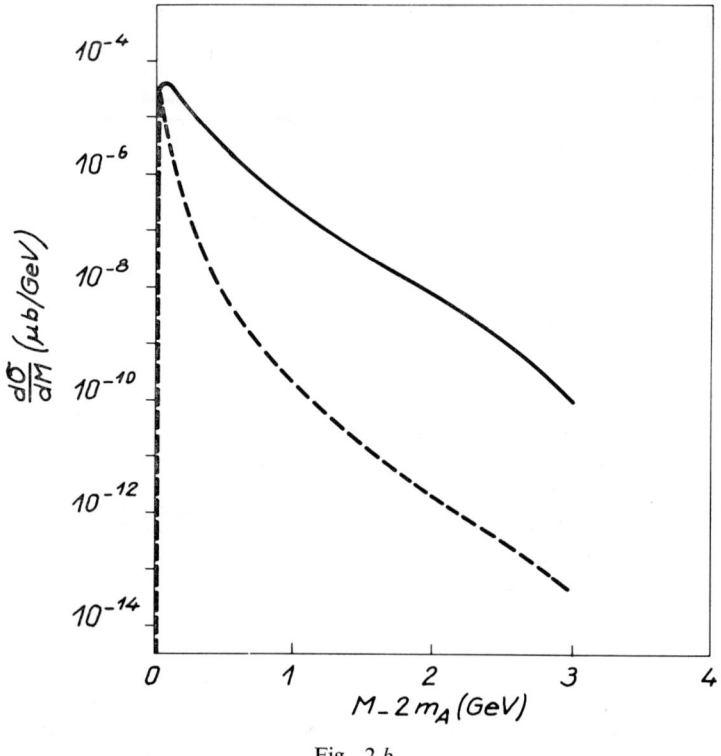

Fig. 2 b.

effect here. This suppression effect should be still much stronger on diagrams (III) where both e± particles should be (again roughly speaking) more or less isotropically distributed.

We were able to show numerically this effect of background elimination, at least as far as diagrams (II) were concerned. In Fig. 2, we show, for a beam energy $E_0 = 2$ GeV and a cut-off angle $\theta_{max} = 4$ mr (for both e± particles) the contribution of diagrams (I) and (II) separately (noticing that the interference between (I) and (II) is zero because of C-invariance), for the following cases: a) $A = e$; b) $A = \mu$; c) $A = \pi$; d) $A = K$. The curves represent the differential cross-sections $d\sigma/dM$, where M is the invariant mass of the pair A⁻A⁺. For the case A = e, only pairs with $M > 100$ MeV were considered. In the cases A = π and A = K, the contributions of diagrams (II) were calculated both in pure QED and with resonant enhancements. It can be noticed that—except for a very small region near threshold in the kaon

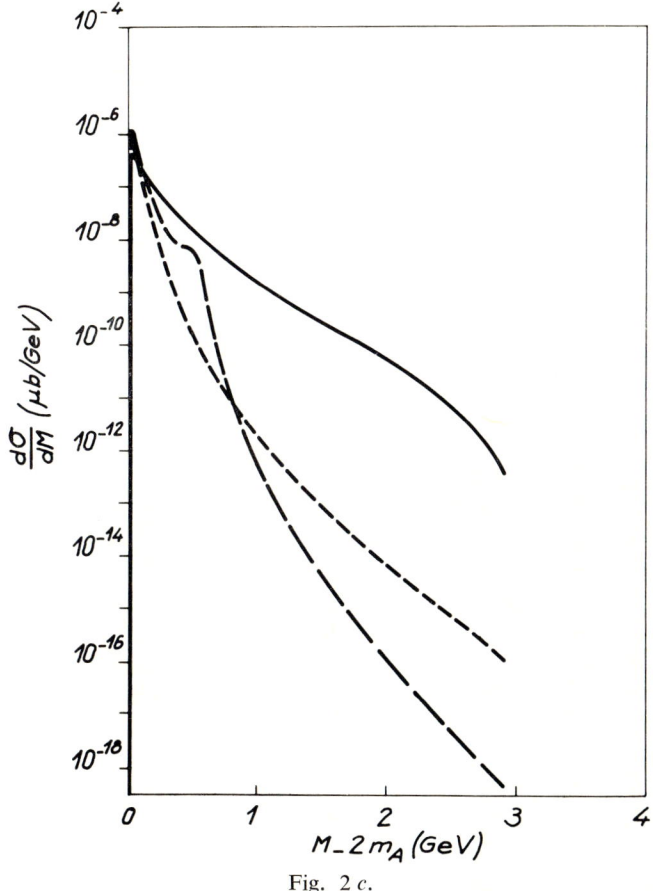

Fig. 2 c.

case—the contribution of (II) is always and everywhere totally negligible. We may then assume that the contribution of diagrams (III) may be neglected *a fortiori*.

The background problem being thus in principle solved, we may from now on consider diagram (I) alone. The table hereafter gives the total cross-sections at $E_0 = 2$ GeV, for the four types of particles A⁺ considered, as functions of the cut-off angle θ_{max}.

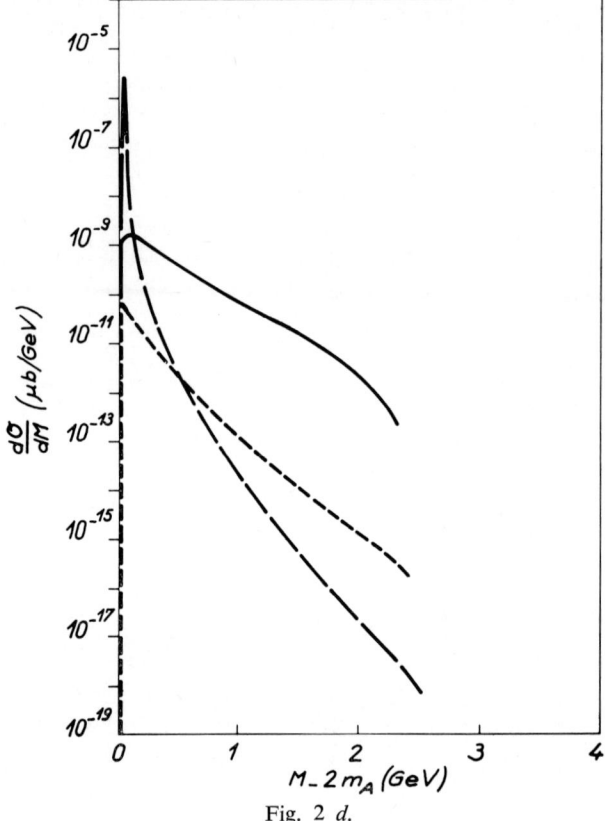

Fig. 2 d.

Fig. 2. – Differential cross-section $d\sigma/dM$ as a function of $M - 2m_A$ (M = invariant mass of the pair A^-A^+; m_A = mass of A) at beam energy $E_0 = 2$ GeV, cut-off angle $\theta_{max} = 4$ mr for both $e^\pm$. a) electron pair production (with lower cut-off $M_{min} = 0.1$ GeV): —— contribution of diagram (I), *divided by* 10^4; --- contribution of diagrams (II); b) muon pair production: —— contribution of diagram (I), *divided by* 10^4; --- contribution of diagrams (II); c) pion pair production: —— contribution of diagram (I), *divided by* 10^4; --- contribution of diagrams (II), according to QED; —— contribution of diagrams (II) with resonant (ϱ) enhancement; d) kaon pair production: —— contribution of diagram (I), *divided by* 10^4; --- contribution of diagrams (II), according to QED; —— contribution of diagrams (II) with resonant (Φ) enhancement.

TABLE I. – *Total cross-section in* μb.

$\theta_{max}=$	6°	3°	1°	4 mr	1 mr
$A = e$ ($M > 100$ MeV)	1.8	1.5	1.1	0.66	0.33
$A = \mu$	$3.0 \cdot 10^{-2}$	$2.4 \cdot 10^{-2}$	$1.7 \cdot 10^{-2}$	$0.90 \cdot 10^{-2}$	$0.38 \cdot 10^{-2}$
$A = \pi$	$2.2 \cdot 10^{-3}$	$1.7 \cdot 10^{-3}$	$1.2 \cdot 10^{-3}$	$0.62 \cdot 10^{-3}$	$0.26 \cdot 10^{-3}$
$A = K$	$3.2 \cdot 10^{-5}$	$2.5 \cdot 10^{-5}$	$1.5 \cdot 10^{-5}$	$0.62 \cdot 10^{-5}$	$0.15 \cdot 10^{-5}$

From these values, one may draw the following conclusions:

— The orders of magnitude of the total cross-sections are in no case substantially changed when reducing θ_{max} from a few degrees to a few milliradians; on the other hand, the smaller θ_{max} is, the better is the background rejection effect. $\theta_{max} \simeq 4$ mr seems a resonable value, also from the experimental point of view.

— The cross-sections are large enough, at least for electron, muon and pion pair production, to ensure that reasonably high counting rates will be obtained with storage rings of luminosity $\sim 10^{32}$ cm^{-2} s^{-1}. This statement will remain valid when additional experimental cut-offs are taken into account (see Chapter 4, hereafter).

Two remarks must be made about our calculation:

i) To calculate $\gamma\gamma \to A^-A^+$, the Born terms were systematically used by us. For lepton pairs, this is quite legitimate; for boson pairs, such a procedure can only be expected to give a rough approximation (its justification is that no better model is presently available).

ii) A double Williams-Weizsäcker (equivalent photon spectrum) approximation was used, resulting in considerable simplifications. This approximation is perfectly justified here, since—due to our angular cut-off— the q^2 values of both photons are constrained to remain extremely small (they range from a few (KeV)^2 to a few (GeV)^2, with the lower values predominating) and since it can be shown that the errors involved in this procedure are essentially of the order of q^2/M^2.

3. Energy dependence and angular distributions.

Figure 3 shows the behaviour of the total cross-sections (with $\theta_{max} = 4$ mr) of the process $e^-e^+ \to e^-e^+A^-A^+$ (A = e, μ, π or K) as a function of beam energy. It is seen that all cross-sections increase with E_0. This fact is easily understandable, since—for any value of the invariant mass M of the pair A^-A^+ produced—more and more photons become available when the beam energy is increased. This phenomenon is to be connected with the quite general effect—familiar to the experimentalists—that the multiplicities of secondaries are strongly increased when the energy of the primary beam becomes higher.

In Fig. 3, we also show the energy dependence of the total cross-sections (with $\theta_{max} = 4$ mr) for $e^-e^+ \to e^-e^+ X$ ($X = \pi^0, \eta$ or η'). The following values were used: $\Gamma(\pi^0 \to 2\gamma) = 11$ eV; $\Gamma(\eta \to 2\gamma) = 1$ keV; $\Gamma(\eta' \to 2\gamma) = 5$ KeV. Here also, it is seen that the cross-sections increase with E_0.

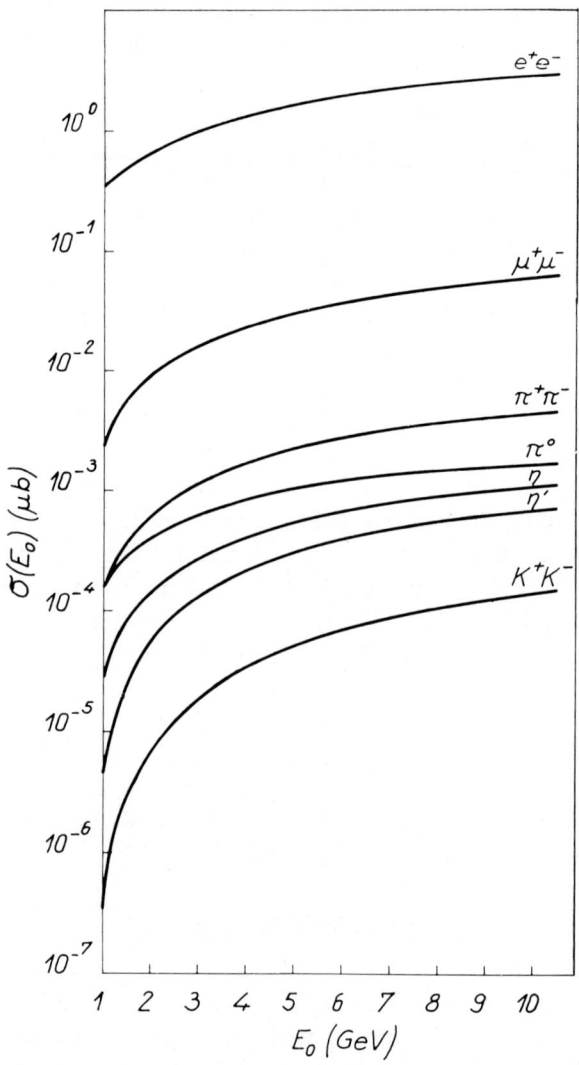

Fig. 3. – Variation of the total cross-section σ with the beam energy E_0, the $e^\pm$ cut-off angle being fixed at $\theta_{max} = 4$ mr. The reactions considered are: $e^- + e^+ \to e^- + e^+ + A^- + A^+$, where: $A^-A^+ = e^-e^+$ (with $M_{min} = 0.1$ GeV), $\mu^-\mu^+$, $\pi^-\pi^+$, K^-K^+; $e^- + e^+ \to e^- + e^+ + X$, where: $X = \pi^0, \eta, \eta'$.

However, we shall see in Chap. 4 that such a systematic increase of the cross-sections with energy does no longer occur when realistic experimental conditions are taken into account in view of fourfold coincidence experiments.

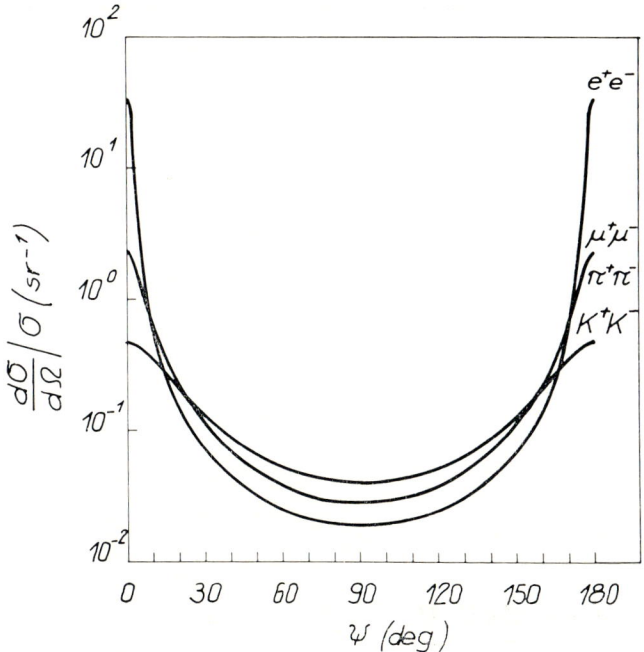

Fig. 4. – Angular distribution in the lab frame for a particle $A^{\pm}$ emitted in the process $e^- + e^+ \to e^- + e^+ + A^- + A^+$, where: $A^- A^+ = e^- e^+$ (with $M_{\min} = 0.1$ GeV), $\mu^- \mu^+ \pi^- \pi^+$, $K^- K^+$. Beam energy: $E_0 = 2$ GeV; cut-off angle: $\theta_{\max} = 4$ mr.

Going over now to the angular distributions of the particles produced, these distributions are shown in Fig. 4 for $A = e, \mu, \pi$ and K. The abscissa ψ is the lab emission angle, with respect to the beam axis, of the particle $A^{\pm}$ considered. The curves are normalized in such a way that one obtains 1 in all cases after integration over the solid angle Ω of the particle $A^{\pm}$.

It is seen that all curves are forward and backward peaked; this peaking is sharper where the mass of $A^{\pm}$ is lower (for muons and pions, however, the difference between their angular distribution curves calculated was so small that we could not distinguish them in the figure). We shall see in Chap. 4 how these angular distributions will affect the integrated cross-sections, once realistic angular cut-offs are taken into account.

Figure 5 shows, for the process $e^-e^+ \to e^-e^+ X$, the angular distribution of one photon, assuming that the particle X ($= \pi^0$, η or η') will be identified, thanks to its decay, into 2 photons. Again, the curves are normalized in order

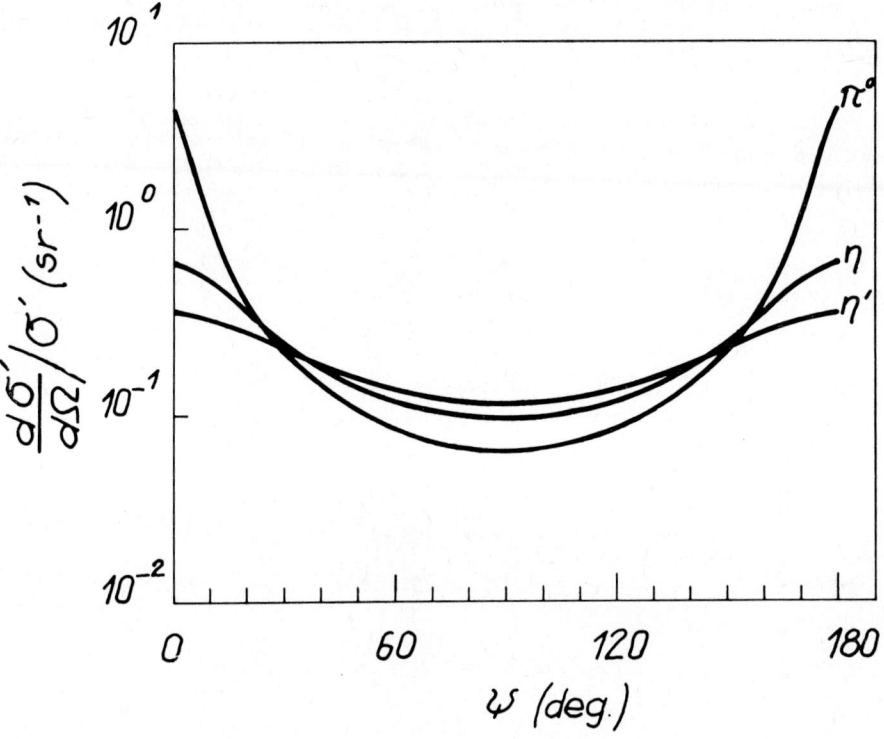

Fig. 5. – Angular distribution in the lab frame for a photon emitted in the process $e^- + e^+ \to e^- + e^+ + X$ (where $X = \pi^0$, η, η') followed by the decay $X \to 2\gamma$. Beam energy: $E_0 = 2$ GeV; cut-off angle: $\theta_{\max} = 4$ mr.

to obtain 1 when integrating over the solid angle of the photon considered. Forward and backward peaking occurs again here (it is sharper where the mass of X is smaller).

4. Effects of realistic experimental cut-offs.

We shall now consider more in detail the experimental conditions, taking into account the realistic cut-offs in phase-space which will occur in an experiment. The reason why we did these calculations — instead of leaving them to be performed by the experimentalists—is that these processes are of a very peculiar nature, in the sense that a small cut-off in phase-space may in some cases reduce the measured cross-section by several orders of magnitude. So it is important to tell the experimentalists what counting rates they will *really* obtain. On the other hand, these calculations are quite difficult, since they involve cut-offs on non-independent parameters.

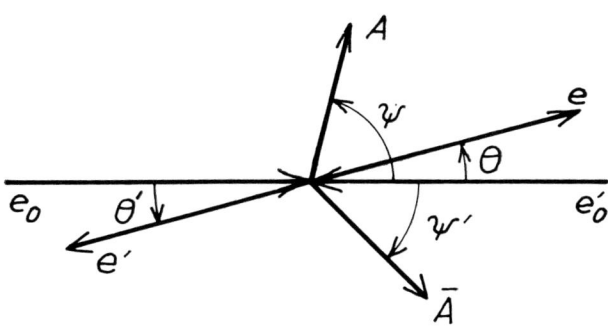

Fig. 6. – Kinematic scheme for $e^-+e^+ \to e^-+e^++A^-+A^+$ (for simplicity, azimuthal angles were left out).

Considering the kinematic scheme of Fig. 6, we introduce—in addition to θ_{max} which was already mentioned before—the following cut-off parameters:

i) A minimal emission angle ψ_{min} for A^- and A^+, so that $\psi_{min} \leqslant \psi$, $\psi' \leqslant \pi - \psi_{min}$. It is indeed well known that—for geometrical reasons related to the shortness of the region of interaction—the detection device for the particles produced cannot be set up too near to the beam axis.

ii) A minimal relative energy loss χ_{min} for both scattered $e^\pm$ particles; one has: $\chi, \chi' \geqslant \chi_{min}$ where we define:

$$\chi = (E_0-E)/E_0, \qquad \chi' = (E_0-E')/E_0,$$

E_0 being the beam energy and E, E' the energies of the scattered $e^\pm$ particles. We must introduce χ_{min} because, in order to separate itself from the beam and thus be detectable, the (practically forward) scattered electron or positron must have lost part of its energy.

iii) A maximal relative energy loss χ_{max}, such that: $\chi, \chi' \leqslant \chi_{max}$.

We shall show that ψ_{min} and χ_{min} play a quite fundamental role, whereas χ_{max} and θ_{max} have relatively little effect on the cross-sections.

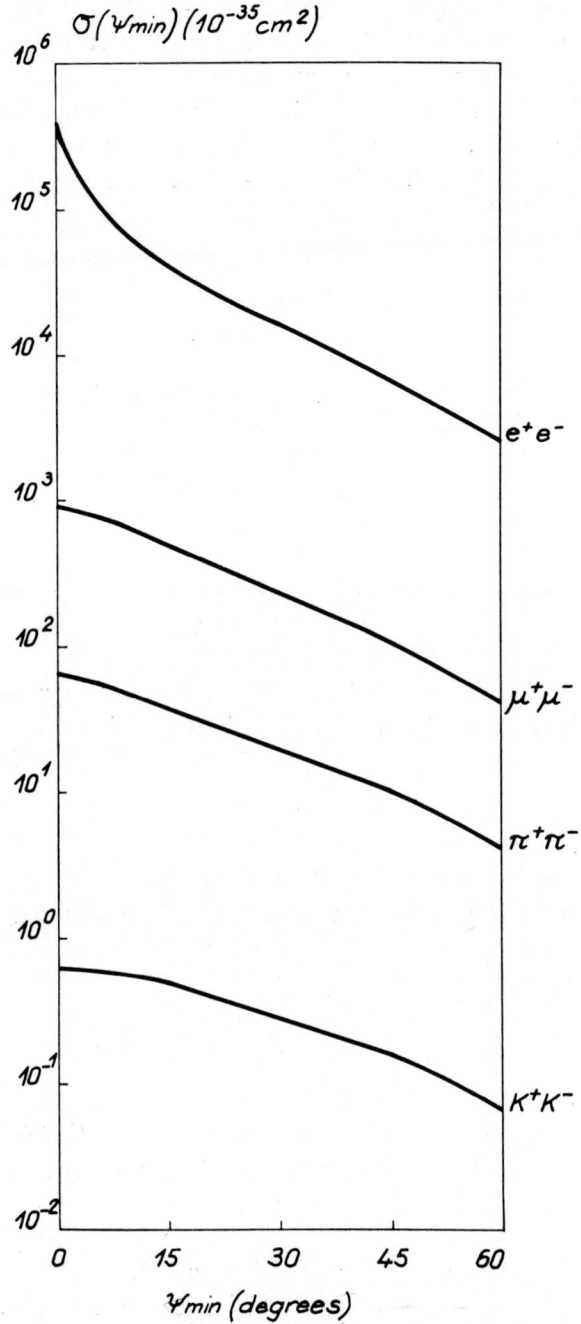

Fig. 7. – Effect of ψ_{min} on the total cross-section, at $E_0 = 2$ GeV, $\theta_{max} = 4$ mr, for the process $e^-e^+ \to e^-e^+ A^- A^+$, where: A = e ($M > 50$ MeV), μ, π, K.

Figure 7 shows the effect of ψ_{min} on the integrated cross-section (at $E_0 = 2$ GeV, $\theta_{max} = 4$ mr). It is seen that this effect is quite drastic,

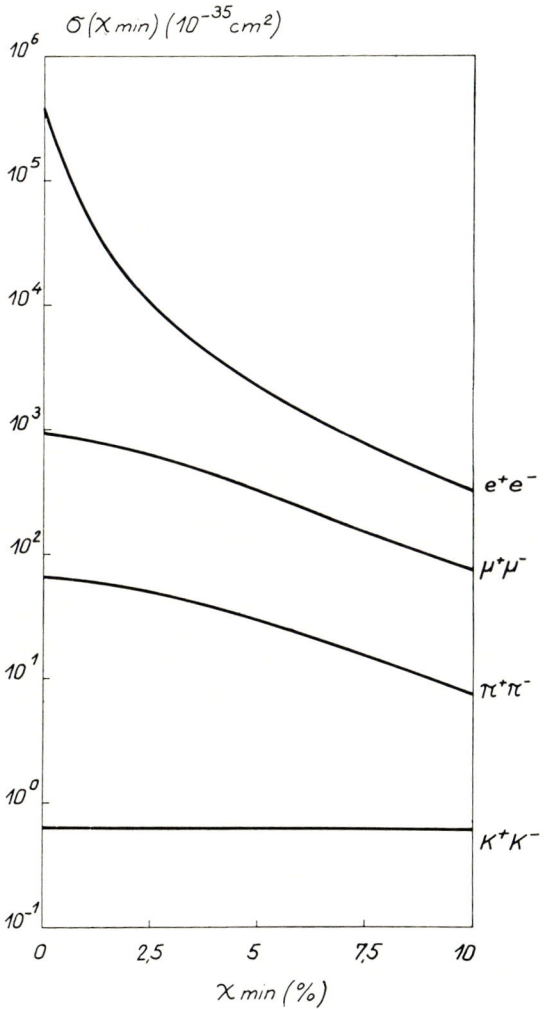

Fig. 8. – Effect of χ_{min} on the total cross-section, at $E_0 = 2$ GeV, $\theta_{max} = 4$ mr, for the process $e^-e^+ \to e^-e^+A^-A^+$, where: $A = e$ ($M > 50$ MeV), μ, π, K.

especially where the mass of particle $A^\pm$ is small (this fact could have been foreseen from the angular distributions of the $A^\pm$ particles, see Fig. 4).

Figure 8 shows the effect of χ_{min} (at $E_0 = 2$ GeV, $\theta_{max} = 4$ mr). Here again, the effect depends on the mass of the particles $A^{\pm}$ produced: it is very violent for electrons, still strong for muons and pions, and uneffective for kaons.

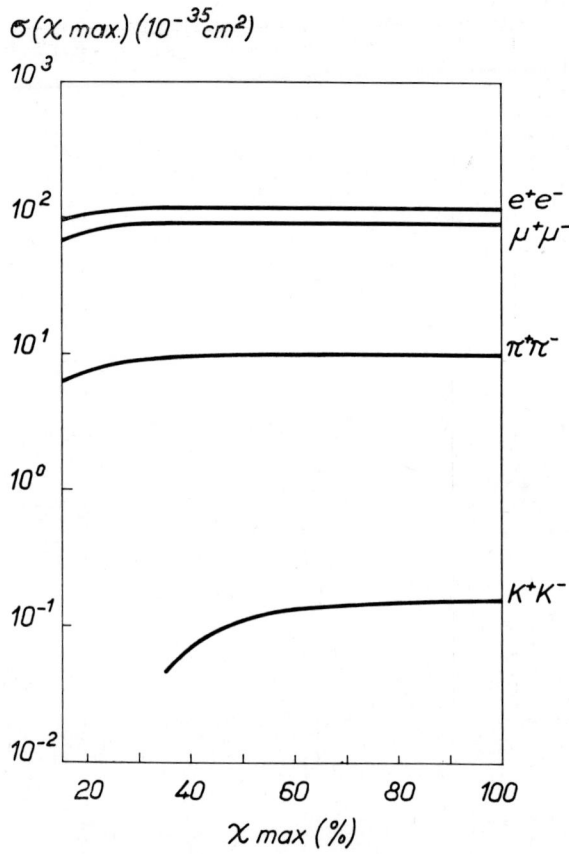

Fig. 9. – Effect of χ_{max} on the total cross-section, at $E_0 = 2$ GeV, $\theta_{max} = 4$ mr, $\psi_{min} = 45°$, $\chi_{min} = 5\%$ for the process $e^- e^+ \to e^- e^+ A^- A^+$, where $A = e, \mu, \pi, K$.

Figure 9 shows the effect of χ_{max} (at $E_0 = 2$ GeV, $\theta_{max} = 4$ mr, $\psi_{min} = 45°$, $\chi_{min} = 5\%$). It is seen that, except for kaons, all curves are practically flat between $\chi_{max} = 20\%$ and 100%. This means that it is not worthwhile, for the experimentalists, to make an effort in order to set the value of χ_{max} near to 100% (they would just include a large amount of empty phase-space).

Figure 10 shows the effect of θ_{max} (at $E_0 = 2$ GeV, $\psi_{min} = 45°$, $\chi_{min} = 5\%$, $\chi_{max} = 70\%$). As already noticed (see Table in Chap. 2), the cross-sections increase only very weakly with θ_{max} above a few milliradians.

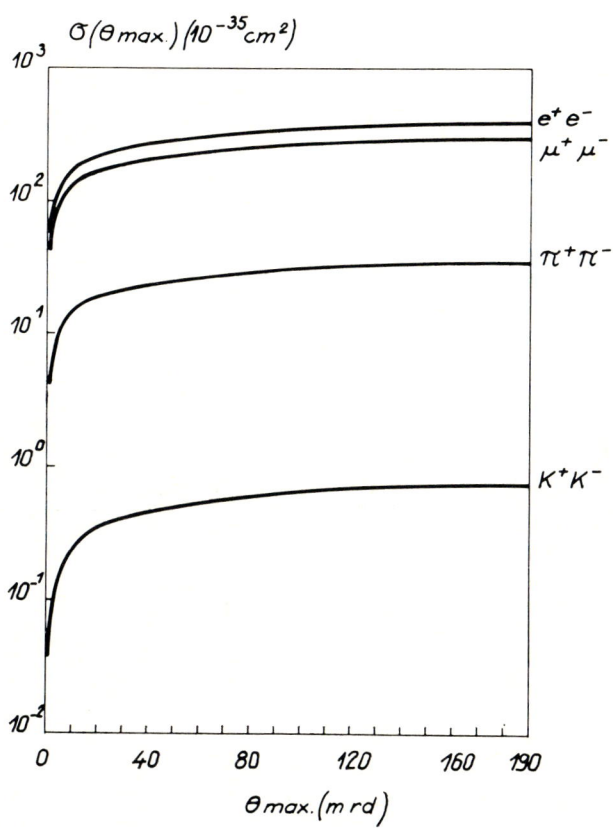

Fig. 10. – Effect of θ_{max} on the total cross-section, at $E_0 = 2$ GeV, $\psi_{min} = 45°$, $\chi_{min} = 5\%$, $\chi_{max} = 70\%$, for the process $e^-e^+ \to e^-e^+A^-A^+$, where $A = e, \mu, \pi, K$.

In Figs. 7-10, as well as in the following ones (Figs. 11-14), a minimal invariant mass of 50 MeV was set for the pair A^-A^+ in the case $A = e$.

Figure 11 shows the effect of various values chosen for ψ_{min} on the invariant mass distributions $d\sigma/dM$ (at $E_0 = 2$ GeV and $\theta_{max} = 4$ mr). It is seen that this cut-off effect is more or less of the same importance at any value of M.

Figure 12 shows the effect of various values chosen for χ_{min} on $d\sigma/dM$

(at $E_0 = 2$ GeV and $\theta_{max} = 4$ mr). It is seen that the main effect of χ_{min} is to cut the threshold region away, especially where the threshold is low. The

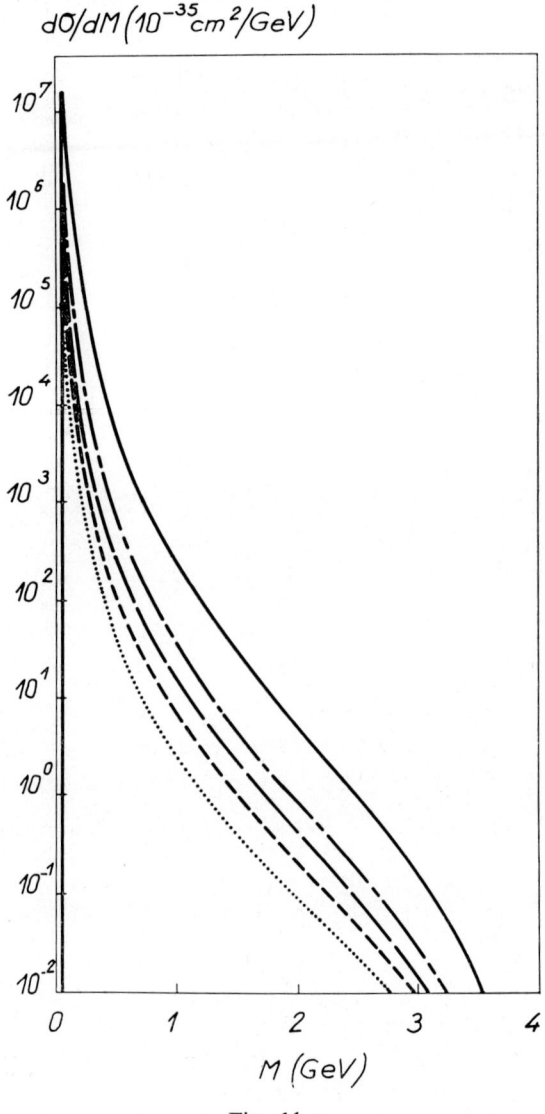

Fig. 11 a.

explanation is obvious, since one has: $M \geqslant 2\chi_{min} E_0$. No curves are shown for the case A = K, since there—due to the high mass of the K—no threshold effect appears up to $\chi_{min} = 10\%$.

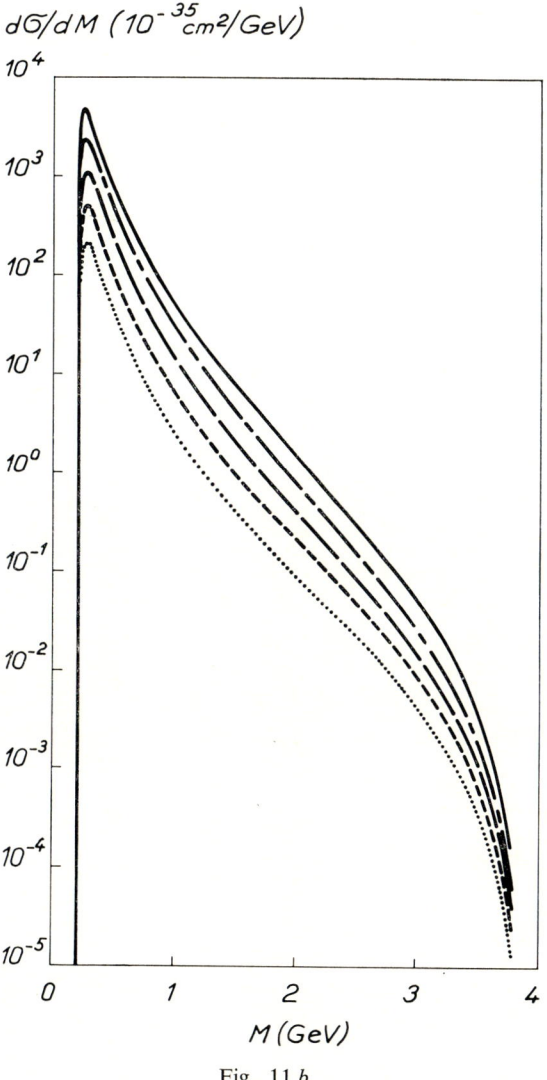

Fig. 11 b.

Figure 13 shows the separate and combined effect of ψ_{min} and χ_{min}, for which the values of 45° and 5% were taken (at $E_0 = 2$ GeV, $\theta_{max} = 4$ mr). Again, no curves are shown for A = K, since in that case only ψ_{min} is effective.

Figure 14 shows the effect of realistic cut-offs ($\theta_{max} = 4$ mr; $\chi_{max} = 70\%$; $\psi_{min} = 30°$ or $45°$; $\chi_{min} = 2.5\%$, 5% or 10%) on the energy behaviour of

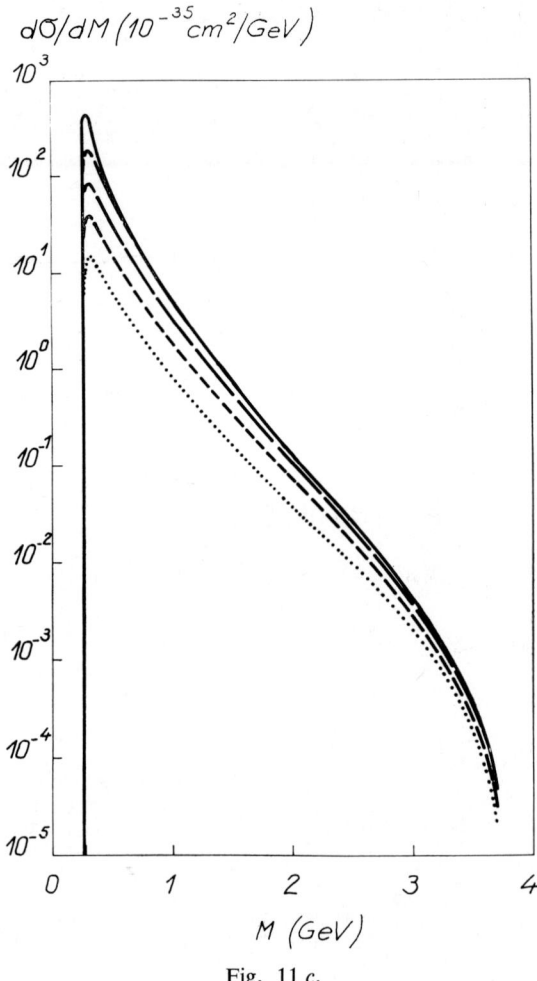

Fig. 11 c.

the cross-section. For reference, we also show the curves obtained with $\theta_{max} = 4$ mr and no other cut-off. It is seen that—except to some extent for A = K—the energy behaviour is completely modified by introducing realistic cut-offs (it is mainly χ_{min} which is responsible for this modification, due to the relation $M \geqslant 2\chi_{min} E_0$). For electron pairs, $\sigma(E_0)$ is now systematically and strongly decreasing. For muon and pion pairs, one notices that there is

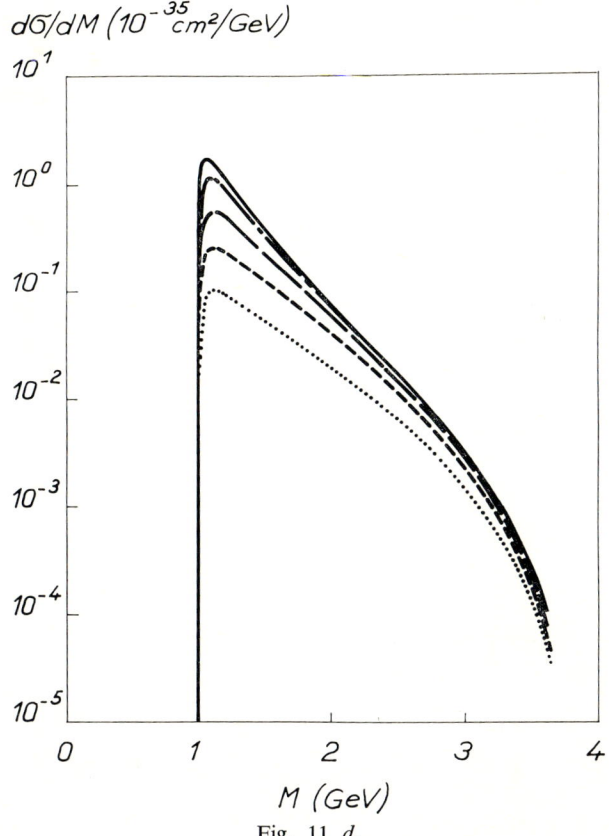

Fig. 11 d.

Fig. 11. – Effect of ψ_{min} on the invariant mass distribution $d\sigma/dM$ in the process $e^-e^+ \to e^-e^+A^-A^+$ at $E_0 = 2$ GeV, $\theta_{max} = 4$ mr. a) $A = e$ ($M > 50$ MeV); b) $A = \mu$; c) $A = \pi$; d) $A = K$. —— $\psi_{min} = 0$; –·–· $\psi_{min} = 15°$; ——— $\psi_{min} = 30°$; – – – $\psi_{min} = 45°$; ··· $\psi_{min} = 60°$.

an optimum around $E_0 \sim (2 \div 3)$ GeV. This is a very fortunate circumstance, since the beam energy of the e^-e^+ storage rings should precisely lie in this region. For kaon pairs, a similar optimum should occur, but at higher beam energies.

If we consider now the processes $e^-e^+ \to e^-e^+ X \to e^-e^+\gamma\gamma$ ($X = \pi^0, \eta, \eta'$), similar experimental conditions should be envisaged, the two outgoing photons taking the place of the $A^\pm$ particles. Choosing again realistic cut-offs ($\theta_{max} = 4$ mr; $\chi_{max} = 70\%$; $\psi_{min} = 30$ or $45°$; $\chi_{min} = 2.5\%$ or 5%), we show the energy behaviour of the cross-section in Fig. 15. The branching ratios used for $X \to 2\gamma$ were: 100% for $X = \pi^0$, 40% for $X = \eta$, 10% for $X = \eta'$.

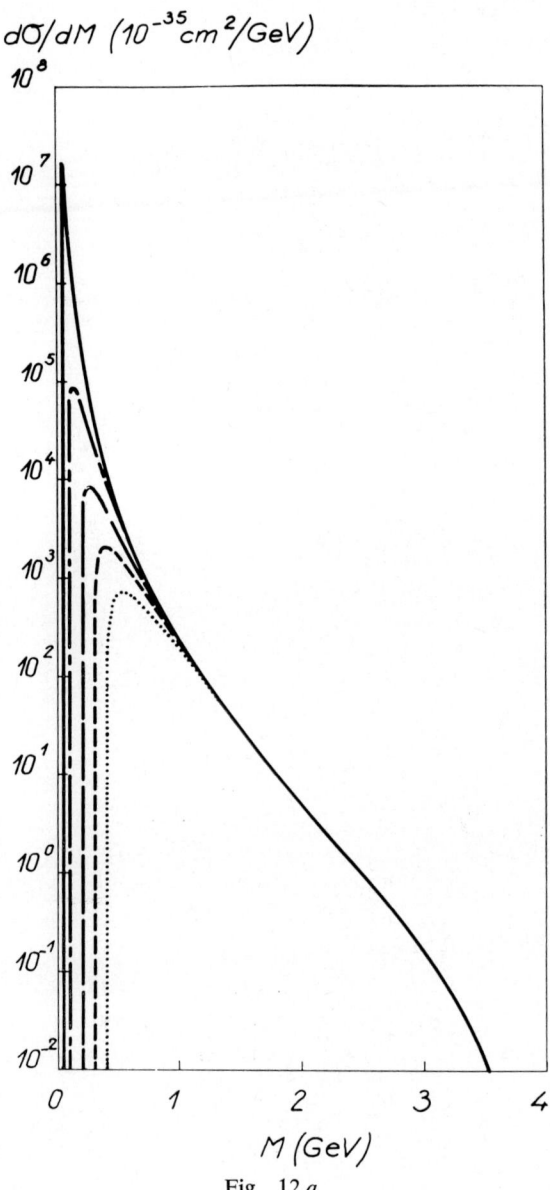

Fig. 12a.

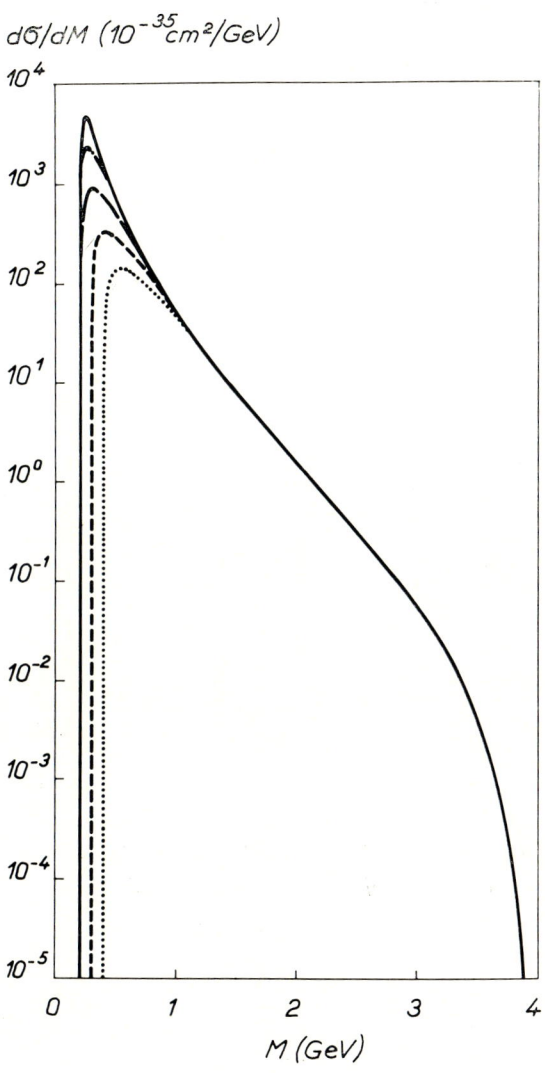

Fig. 12 b.

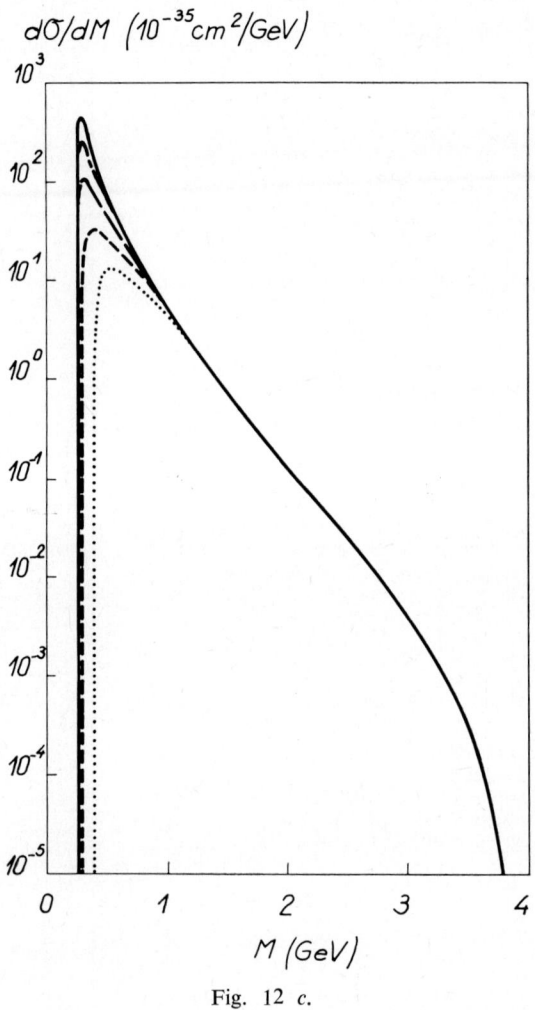

Fig. 12 c.

Fig. 12. – Effect of $\chi_{\min}$ on the invariant mass distribution $d\sigma/dM$ in the process $e^-e^+ \to e^-e^+A^-A^+$ at $E_0 = 2$ GeV, $\theta_{\max} = 4$ mr. a) $A = e$ ($M > 50$ MeV); b) $A = \mu$; c) $A = \pi$; --- $\chi_{\min} = 0$; --- $\chi_{\min} = 2.5\%$; --- $\chi_{\min} = 5\%$; --- $\chi_{\min} = 7.5\%$; $\cdots$ $\chi_{\min} = 10\%$.

Photon-photon collisions in electron-positron storage rings 843

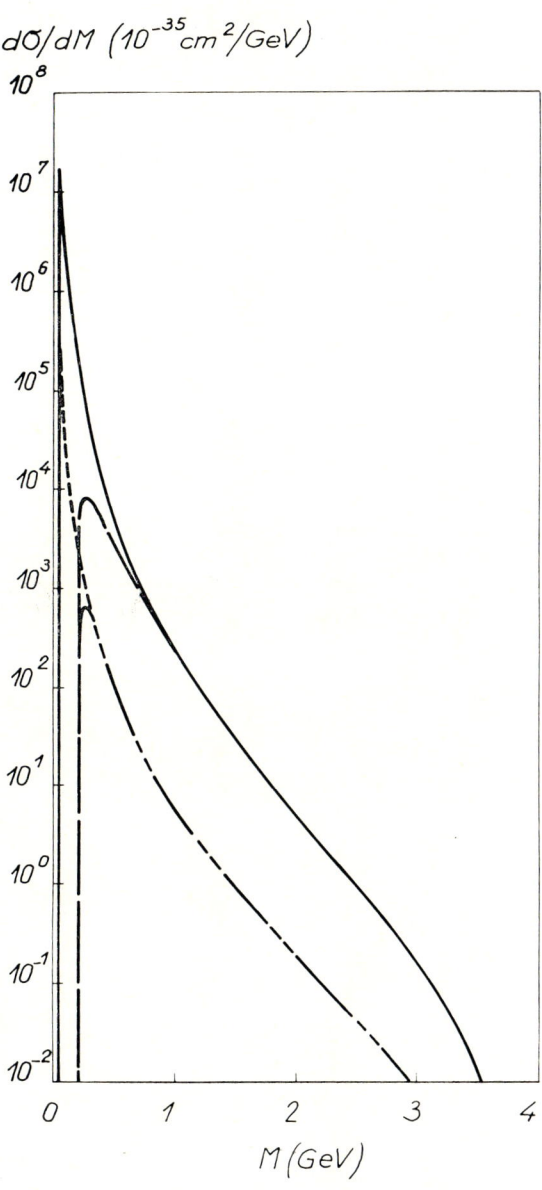

Fig. 13 a.

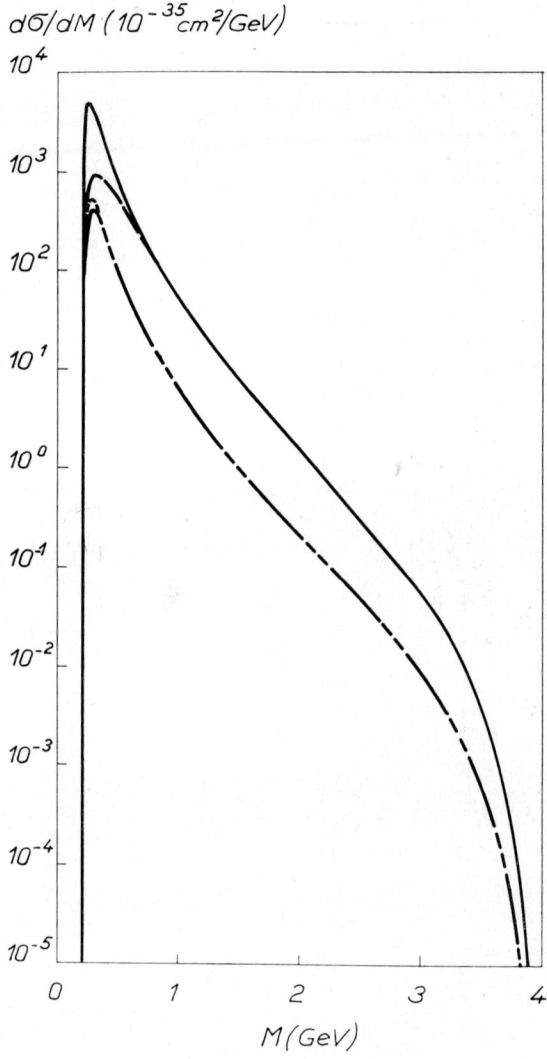

Fig. 13 b.

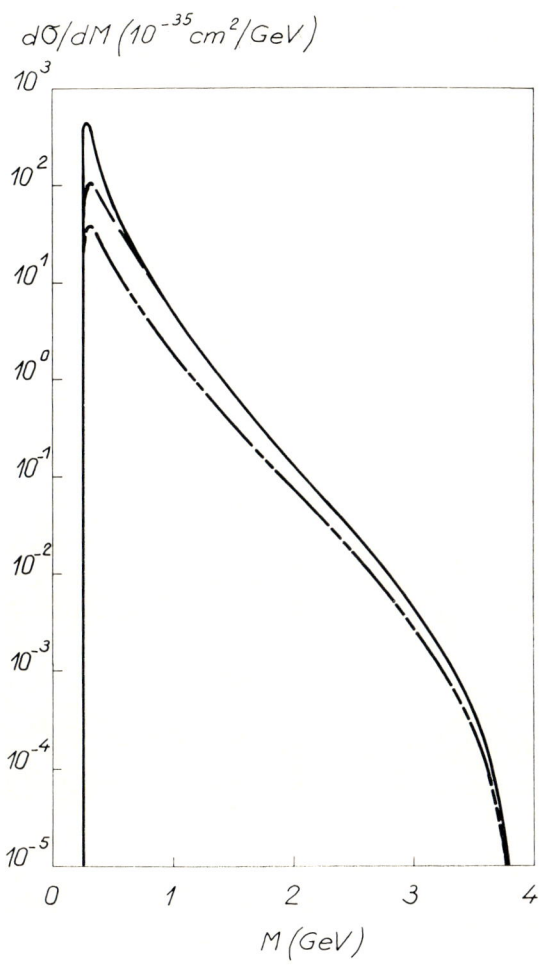

Fig. 13 c.

Fig. 13. – Combined effect of ψ_{min} and χ_{min} on the invariant mass distribution $d\sigma/dM$ in the process $e^-e^+ \to e^-e^+A^-A^+$ at $E_0 = 2$ GeV, $\theta_{max} = 4$ mr. a) $A = e$ ($M > 50$ MeV), and b) $A = \mu$ --- $\psi_{min} = 0$, $\chi_{min} = 0$; --- $\psi_{min} = 0$, $\chi_{min} = 5\%$; --- $\psi_{min} = 45°$, $\chi_{min} = 0$; ---- $\psi_{min} = 45°$, $\chi_{min} = 5\%$; c) $A = \pi$; --- $\psi_{min} = 0$, $\chi_{min} = 0$; --- $\psi_{min} = 0$, $\chi_{min} = 5\%$; ---- $\psi_{min} = 45°$, $\chi_{min} = 0$ or 5%.

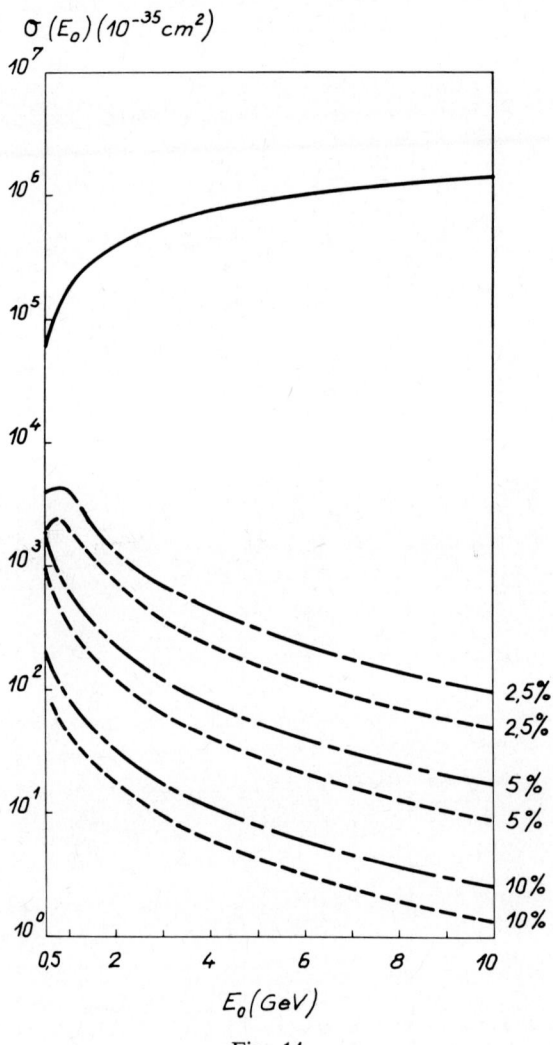

Fig. 14 a.

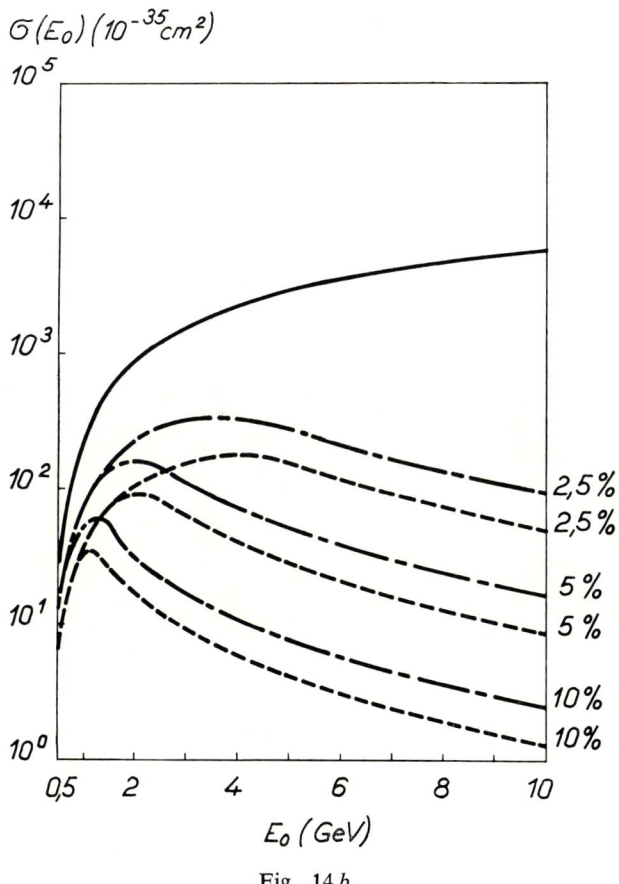

Fig. 14 b.

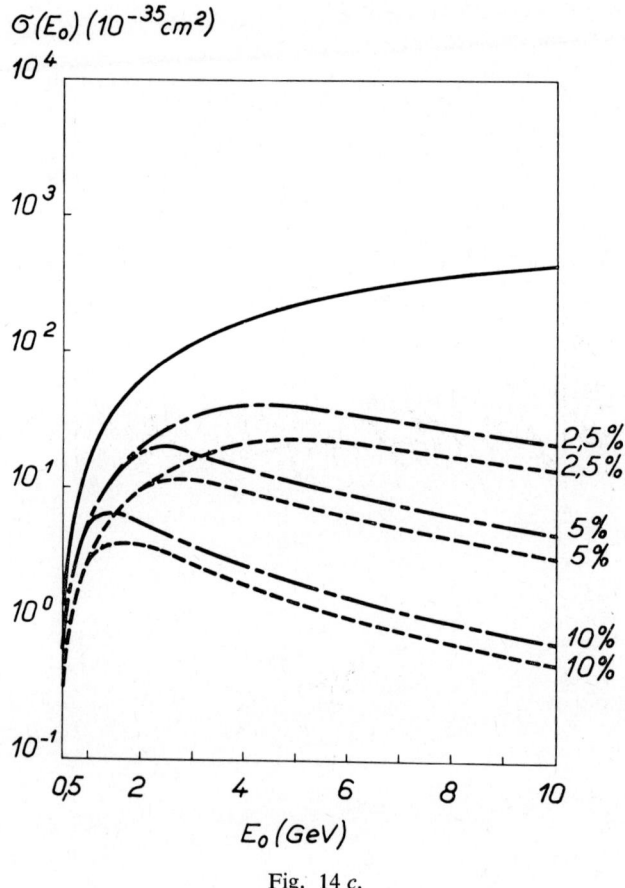

Fig. 14 c.

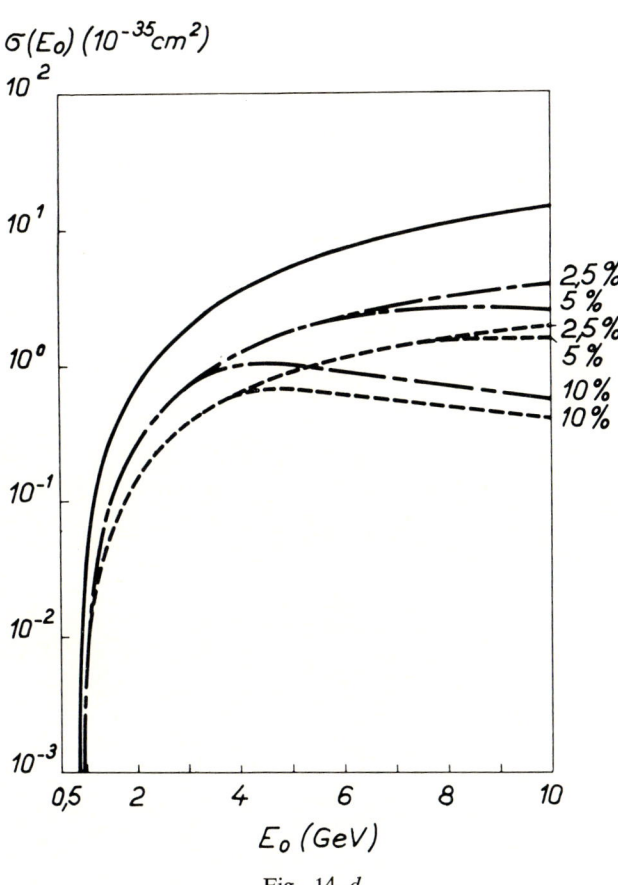

Fig. 14 d.

Fig. 14. – Combined cut-off effect on the total cross-section as a function of beam energy, for the process $e^-e^+ \to e^-e^+A^-A^+$. *a)* $A = e$ ($M > 50$ MeV); *b)* $A = \mu$; *c)* $A = \pi$; *d)* $A = K$; --- $\theta_{max} = 4$ mr, no other cut-off. All other curves: $\theta_{max} = 4$ mr, $\chi_{max} = 70\%$, χ_{min} as indicated; --- $\psi_{min} = 30°$; --- $\psi_{min} = 45°$.

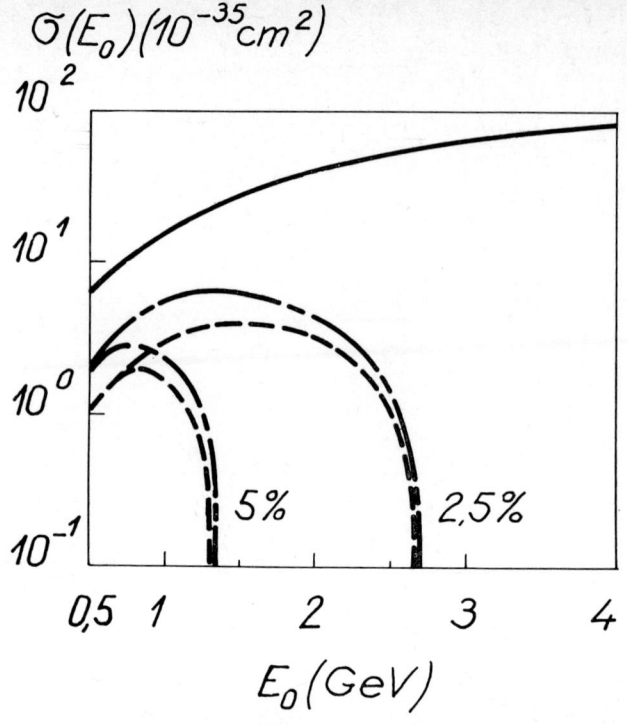

Fig. 15a.

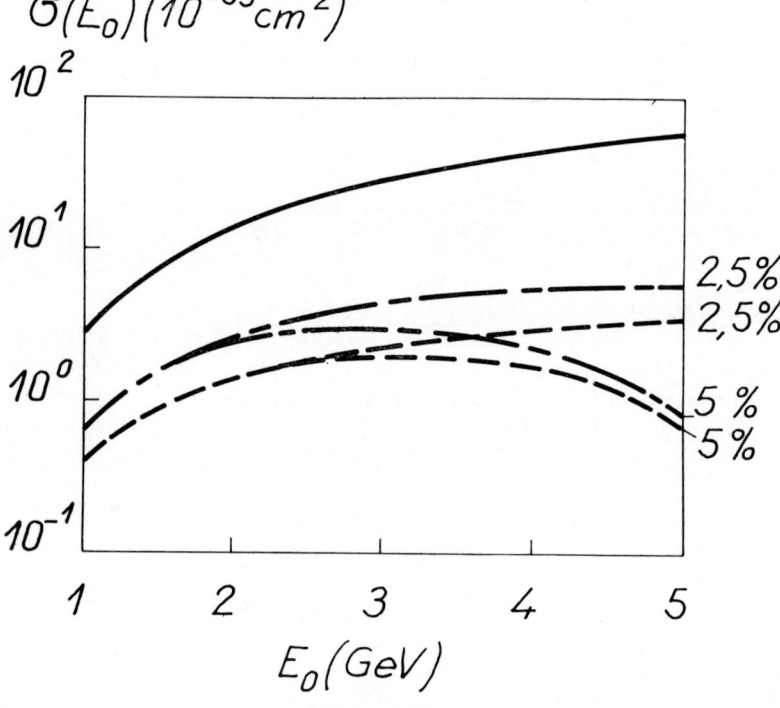

Fig. 15b.

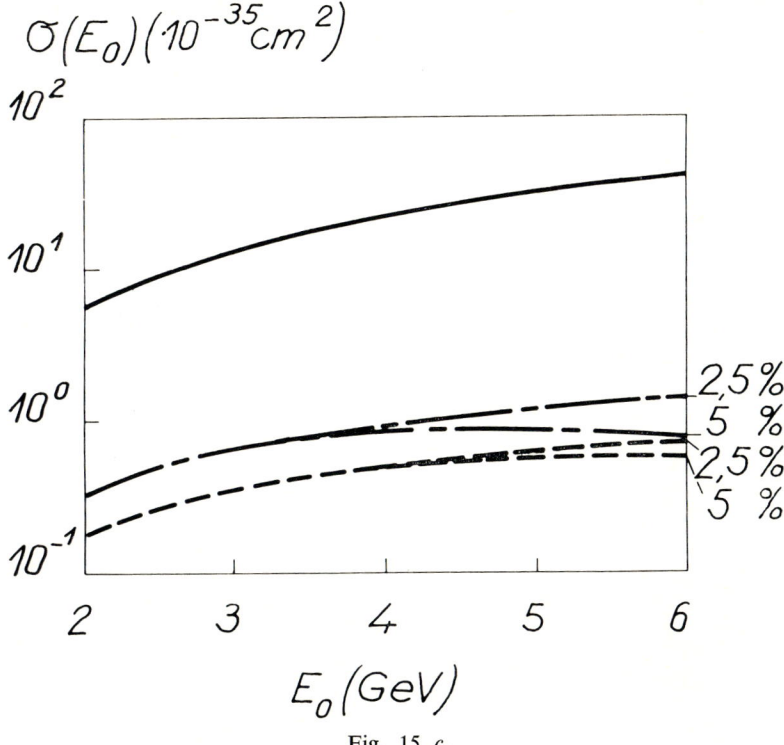

Fig. 15 c.

Fig. 15. – Combined cut-off effect on the total cross-section of beam energy, for the process $e^-e^+ \to e^-e^+X \to e^-e^+\gamma\gamma$. a) $X = \pi^0$; b) $X = \eta$; c) $X = \eta'$. - - - $\theta_{max} = 4$ mr, no other cut-off (process $e^-e^+ \to e^-e^+X$). All other curves: $\theta_{max} = 4$ mr, $\chi_{max} = 70\%$, χ_{min} as indicated; - - - $\psi_{min} = 30°$; - - - $\psi_{min} = 45°$.

It is seen that (due to the influence of χ_{min}, through the relation $M \geq 2\chi_{min} E_0$) the cross-section for $X = \pi^0$ goes rapidly to zero with E_0; a similar vanishing of the cross-section should also occur, but at much higher beam energies, for $X = \eta$ and $X = \eta'$.

5. Conclusion.

In the following table, we give the numerical values of the cross-sections expected, at $E_0 = 1$, 2 and 3 GeV, for processes $e^-e^+ \to e^-e^+A^-A^+$ and $e^-e^+ \to e^-e^+X \to e^-e^+\gamma\gamma$ under realistic conditions: $\theta_{max} = 4$ mr, $\psi_{min} = 45°$, $\chi_{min} = 5\%$, $\chi_{max} = 70\%$.

TABLE II. $\sigma(E_0)$ in 10^{-35} cm^2.

E_0 (GeV)	A = e ($M >$ 50 MeV)	A = μ	A = π	A = K	X = π^0	X = η	X = η'
1	343	38	3	0.01	1.68	0.39	0.07
2	119	91	10	0.15	0.00	1.36	0.18
3	63	63	11	0.4	0.00	1.98	0.34

There is no doubt that it will be possible to investigate, with reasonably high counting rates, the production of electron, muon and pion pairs at least, once the electron-positron storage rings of the next generation (SPEAR at SLAC, DORIS at DESY and the machine planned at Orsay) with luminosities $\sim 10^{32}$ cm^{-2} s^{-1} will become available. The first and the most interesting experiment to be performed will then be the investigation of the 0^{++} pion-pion resonance called σ or ε, presumably located near 700 MeV. It is an immense advantage to be able here to produce this resonance without any ϱ contribution, and without any spectator hadron. Electron and muon pair production may serve either for checking QED or for calibration of the pion pair production experiment.

With existing storage rings (ADONE at Frascati, VEPP-3 at Novosibirsk and BYPASS at CEA) which have much weaker luminosity, it seems unreasonable to try any hadron production through photon-photon collisions. It may be worthwhile, on the other hand, to use these machines for investigating lepton pair production, with the purpose of clearly defining the conditions of measurement to be applied in this entirely new type of experiment.

REFERENCES

1) F. Low: *Phys. Rev.*, **120**, 582 (1960).
2) F. Calogero and C. Zemach: *Phys. Rev.*, **120**, 1860 (1960).
3) J. C. Le Guillou: Thèse de troisième cycle, Paris (1965); *Compt. Rend.*, **261**, 326 (1965).
4) P. C. De Celles and J. E. Goehl jr., *Phys. Rev.*, **184**, 1617 (1969).
5) N. Arteaga-Romero, A. Jaccarini and P. Kessler: *Compt. Rend.*, **269** B, 153, 1129 (1969); *Proceedings of the IV International Symposium on Electron and Photon Interactions at High Energy* (Liverpool, 1969), p. 290; *Photon-photon collisions with electron-positron colliding beams*, Internal report PAM 70-02 (April 1970); J. Parisi and P. Kessler: *Proceedings of the IV International Symposium on Electron and Photon Interactions at High Energy* (Liverpool, 1969), p. 289-290; *Study of ee → ee(0⁻)*, Preprint (Oct. 1969); J. Parisi: Thèse de troisième cycle, Paris (Febr. 1970); A. Jaccarini: Thèse de troisième cycle, Paris (July 1970); N. Arteaga-Romero, A. Jaccarini, P. Kessler and J. Parisi: *Lett. Nuovo Cimento*, **4**, 933 (1970); **1**, 935 (1971);

Phys. Rev. D, **3**, 1569 (1971); *On the experimental investigation of photon-photon collisions in electron-positron storage rings*, Preprint (May 1971), submitted to *Phys. Rev. D*; J. PARISI and P. KESSLER: *Study of the vertices $\pi^0\gamma\gamma$, $\eta\gamma\gamma$ and $\eta'\gamma\gamma$ with almost real photons* and *Study of the vertices $\pi^0\gamma\gamma$, $\eta\gamma\gamma$ and $\eta'\gamma\gamma$ with one almost real and one highly virtual photon*, Preprints (July 1971), submitted to *Lett. Nuovo Cimento*.

6) V. E. BALAKIN, V. M. BUDNEV and I. F. GINSBURG: *JEPT Lett.*, **11**, 388 (1970).
7) S. J. BRODSKY, T. KINOSHITA and H. TERAZAWA: *Phys. Rev. Lett.*, **25**, 972 (1970).
8) V. G. SERBO: *JEPT Lett.*, **12**, 39 (1970); M. GRECO: Internal report LNF 71/1 (Jan. 1971); V. N. BAYER and V. S. FADIN: *Lett. Nuovo Cimento*, **1**, 481 (1971); *Phys. Lett.*, **35** B, 156 (1971); H. TERAZAWA: *Phys. Rev. Lett.*, **26**, 591 (1971). D. H. LYTH: *Nucl. Phys.*, B **30**, 195 (1971). In addition, a large number of preprints are presently circulating on this subject.

DISCUSSION

Chairman: Prof. P. KESSLER
Scientific Secretary: E. CALVA-TELLEZ

DISCUSSION

— KLEINERT:

You said there are many $\sigma \to \gamma\gamma$ couplings floating around, so you can not estimate the contribution of a σ graph to $\rho^+\rho^- \to \rho^+\rho^-\pi^+\pi^-$ at small angles. As much as I know, only two values are considered at present. One corresponds to $\Gamma_{\gamma\gamma} \approx 20$ KeV, the other (obtained from Ward identities) is zero. The first estimate will increase the total cross-section at 3 GeV by a factor of about two. Will your accuracy be enough to kill one of the predictions?

— KESSLER:

There has been a work by Sarker who estimated this coupling by superconvergence relations. He arrived at a value of the coupling $\sigma \to \gamma\gamma$ which finally will give about the same contribution as the Born term.

— KLEINERT:

Will your accuracy be sufficient to resolve a factor two in cross-section predictions?

— KESSLER:

Yes, I think so.

— SAKURAI:

You presented the approach from the point of view of experimentalists who are really looking for this two photon effect. There are experimentalists and there are also theorists to whom this kind of effect is a nuisance, for instance, in Frascati experiments (Adone experiments); how important is this effect? My impression is that unless $\eta'(960)$ going into two γ has an enormous width the effect is not terribly important.

— KESSLER:

I must say that in contradistinction with other people like Brodsky who specially looked at these processes from the point of view of contamination, we were always interested by these processes *as such* (I mean by experiments on these processes) rather than by their negative aspect as background. They can be of course a background in the Adone experiments. I would not like to interfere with experimental questions. From the theorist's point of view there can be two kinds of background, namely: Two particle emission in e^+e^- collisions, let us say $\pi^+\pi^-$ can be contaminated by our processes (in the sense that in our processes, if the experimentalists do not measure the outgoing electron and positron, you just have $\pi^+\pi^-$ or other pairs). In fact what is dangerous is l^+l^- because the counting rates are higher. So the question is how far the experimentalists are in danger to take low energy leptons for high energy pions. Now, an argument against this is that pairs from our processes are coplanar but not collinear. However, we found in our calculations that there is a certain tendence to collinearity, namely 10 to 15 % of our events are collinear within 5°; this is not negligible. To state it clearly: Pion pairs from our processes are negligible as a contamination; muon pairs are more dangerous, and electron pairs are even more (because there are much more of them). Now, the experimentalists would probably say that there is no danger of taking low-energy electron pairs for high-energy pion pairs, because electrons « shower ». However, this is an experimental question.

I must say that we have not pushed all these questions to the end. Another background effect that we have not studied, at least quantitatively, is the multipion production, especially the case where (see Silvestrini paper in *Nuovo Cimento*) the experimentalists have found many events which are not collinear in the transverse plane, which means not coplanar; so our processes should not explain this type of events. However, they are coplanar only in the approximation of order zero, to some extent they are not coplanar and so there may be some contamination from them (Brodsky would say about 25 %). However, I must say there is no precise calculation up to now on this point. So, in conclusion for both 2-body and many-body events, there exists a certain danger of contamination; but perhaps Prof. Zichichi will tell you that the danger is not so big because the experimentalists are able to distinguish between low-energy lepton background and high-energy pions.

— ZICHICHI:

Yes, using the Kinoshita-Brodsky diagrams we calculated the special troubles from photon-photon collisions and for our experiment it was negligible. The experimental results are perfectly in agreement with everything which is expected: The acoplanarity of the 50 e^+e^- pairs observed is fully accounted for by removing the peaking approximation in radiative corrections. The muon pairs do not show any contradiction to the acollinearity, which is not accounted for again by removing the peaking approximation, so I would consider for example the muon as our monitor. For the pion case it is out of the question. The pions can not be contaminated by this kind of background. Considering the probability of simulation of low energy leptons against pions, we have now a detection power of 10^{-5} lepton; so, according to our estimates, this number at 1 GeV is not important.

— KESSLER:

The energies of the pairs from our processes are essentially low (near the threshold), so they are extremely different from the energies of the annihilation pairs, so that if you are able to separate these two energy regions there can be no trouble.

— ZICHICHI:

In fact, a rough check about this hypothesis by studying the correlation between acollinearity and the energy of the emitted electron pair (despite the fact that this is not a precise measurement) is again in good agreement with these predictions. The angular and energy correlation of the electrons from $\gamma\gamma$ processes is totally different from the radiative correction, and we do not see anything like this.

Coherent Interactions

A. Pevsner

1. Introduction 857
2. Kinematics 859
3. Coherence 861
4. Experimental detection of coherent reactions 866
5. Discussion on some experimental results 867
6. Coherent pion production from complex nuclei 875
References 879
Discussion 880

Coherent Interactions

AIHUD PEVSNER (*)
Johns Hopkins University
Baltimore, Maryland, USA

1. Introduction.

Interpretation of data obtained from experiments using targets heavier than nucleons is complicated by corrections due to the « nuclear physics » of the target. What are the compensatory advantages for an elementary particle experimentalist? There are many in the use of high energy (several GeV to several hundred GeV) incident beams (such as π, K, p_s, $\bar{p}$) that interact coherently with nuclei.

1) Copious production of resonances is possible since the cross-section for production is proportional to A^2 where A is the atomic number of the target. (In practice the effect is smaller due to absorption effects).

2) Selection rules restrict the spin parity of the produced particles. This allows assignment of unknown quantum numbers, as well as facilitating study of overlapping resonances by reducing the background production of disallowed quantum numbers.

3) There is a large signal to noise ratio in the production of allowed resonances. Spin analyses are then much simpler.

4) Isotopic spin determination is exceedingly straightforward for $T = 0$ targets. Any produced resonance in a diffraction process must have the I-spin of the incident particle. No numerical comparisons are necessary.

5) Cross-sections for diffractive processes are relatively constant with energy so that at the new super machine energies probably only diffractive individual channels will be produced copiously enough for study.

6) Primakoff effect production of resonances by virtual gammas increases at high energies, and for high Z targets allows study of radiative widths as well as γ couplings.

7) Cross-sections of produced systems in matter may be measured and used to differentiate particles from kinematical enhancements.

(*) John Simon Guggenheim Memorial Foundation Fellow.

Coherent reactions between two particles have been extensively studied. Usually one particle retains its identity (most often, but not necessarily the target particle in the laboratory, a nucleus or nucleon) and the incident particle diffraction dissociates into a system of higher mass in the same spin-parity series but with other quantum numbers unchanged. An excellent summary of this work for hadrons as well as electromagnetic reactions may be found in ref. ([1]).

Here, we will review some of the guiding principles in such reactions and illustrate them with a few examples.

In a given experiment with an incident particle of fixed momentum there are limitations on the possible produced masses and recoil momenta for diffraction production. This arises since the conservation of energy and momentum kinematically determines the value for the target's longitudinal recoil momentum, q_{11},

$$q_{11} = \frac{M_3^2 - m_1^2}{2P_1} \qquad (1)$$

where a particle of mass m, and incident laboratory momentum P_1 dissociates into a system of mass M_3. The dynamical requirement of coherence over the target sets an upper limit for reasonable cross-sections to the target's recoil momenta:

$$q < \text{order of } \frac{140}{A^{1/3}} \text{ MeV/c} \qquad (2)$$

where A is the atomic number of the nucleus. There is advantage in using large values of A if the kinematic requirement can be met as the cross-section for production of M_3 increases with A (A^2 in zeroth order before absorption is considered). Further, a large nucleus allows us to study the traversal of nuclear matter by the system M_3. However, eq. (2) shows that even for a proton target, q is less than 140 MeV/c, so that if we wish to produce a heavy resonance M_3 we may have to go to very high momenta. For example, if in a p-p collision we consider one proton as the target and the other dissociating into three quarks (there are, of course, more efficient diagrams for producing a quark), M_3 is three times a quark mass. Then $M_3^2 \simeq 2P_1 q$ or $9m_q^2 < (2P_1 \times 140) \text{ GeV}^2$. Even for an equivalent incident laboratory momentum of 1500 GeV, diffraction production of quarks of mass greater than about seven GeV will already have a decreasing cross-section.

2. Kinematics.

Consider (Fig. 1a) particle 1 of mass m_1 incident on particle 2 of mass $m_2 = A$ at rest in the laboratory. Let m_2 recoil after the interaction with

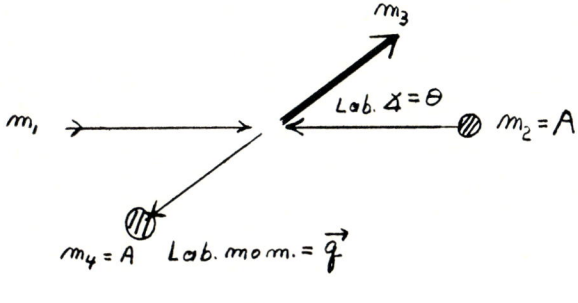

Fig. 1a

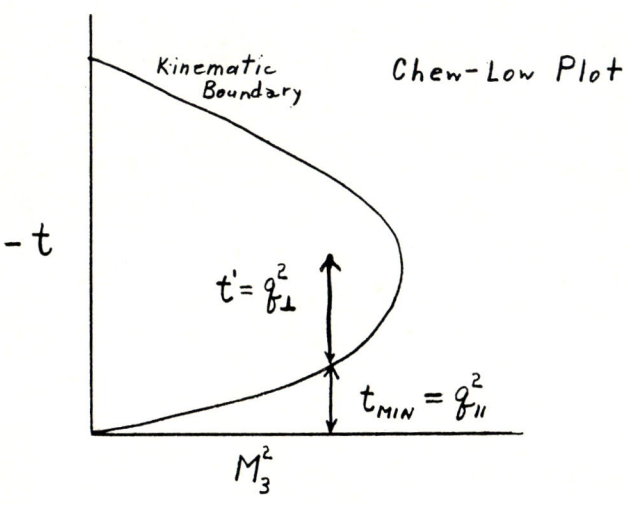

Fig. 1b

laboratory momentum q and the same mass $m_4 = A$. Let m_3 represent the system into which m_1 dissociates emitted at an angle θ with respect to m_1's line of flight:

$$1 + 2 \to 3 + 4.$$

The 4-momentum transfer t, is an invariant. From its definition we have

$$t =_{\text{def}} (p_3^\mu - p_1^\mu)^2 = (p_2^\mu - p_4^\mu)^2$$

where $p^\mu = (E, i\mathbf{P})$. Then

$$t = m_3^2 + m_1^2 - 2E_1 E_3 + 2P_1 P_3 \cos\theta. \tag{3}$$

If we evaluate this for m_2 and m_4 in the laboratory where m_2 is at rest, we see that

$$t = -q^2 = -(q_{11}^2 + q_\perp^2) \tag{4}$$

where the parallel and perpendicular components are with respect to m_1's line of flight. Applying the conservation of energy and momentum, we find in the approximation that $|q| \ll |P_1|$ where P_1 is the laboratory momentum of the incident particle that:

$$q_{11} = \frac{M_3^2 - m_1^2}{2P_1}. \tag{1}$$

The term neglected is proportional to q^2 which is quite small in our approximation. We do not consider here the case of elastic scattering where $M_3 = m_1$, $q_{11} = 0$ in our approximation, so that the next term in the approximation must be considered. Attention should be paid to the fact that we focus on a definite final mass $M_3 = M^*$ (e.g. in the reaction $K+A \to Q+A$ or $K+A \to L+A$ where the Q is a $K\pi\pi$ resonance with $M_3 \simeq 1.3$ GeV, and the L is a $K\pi\pi$ resonance with $M_3 \simeq 1.7$ GeV.). Then in a given experiment such as a bubble chamber run with set incident momentum P_1, the value of q_{11} is fixed for all events as shown in Table I.

TABLE I.

M^*	P_1 GeV/c	q_{11} GeV
$Q = 1.3$ GeV	5	0.145
Q	13	0.052
Q	30	0.027
Q	200	0.0040
$L = 1.7$ GeV	5	0.265
L	13	0.10
L	30	0.048
L	30	0.048
L	200	0.0071

This is reasonable if we recall that if the system of particles comprising M_3 is considered as a single entity, we are dealing with a two body reaction that is specified by two parameters such as energy s, and momentum transfer or related angles t. Here q_{11} specifies the energy through its relation to the incident momentum P_1 (eq. (1)). The other parameter can be taken as $q_\perp$ which varies with the scattering angle. The minimum value of the magnitude of t (eq.(3)) is called t_{min} and occurs for forward scattering, $\theta = 0$, $q_\perp = 0$, and $\cos\theta = 1$. Therefore by (3)

$$t_{min} = q_{11}^2. \tag{5}$$

Figure 1b represents a typical « Chew-Low » plot that depicts the allowed kinematic range for t as a function of the mass M_3. It is advantageous to introduce the variable t'

$$t' =_{def} |t| - t_{min}$$

as shown in Fig. 1b. Then cuts in t' do not artificially discriminate against higher masses as would a cut in t. Also, plots of $d\sigma/dt'$ are not dependent on the mass M_3, so that when necessary for experimental reasons, it is easy to extrapolate to $t'=0$. From the definition of t' and (3) we see that

$$t' = 2P_1 P_3 (1-\cos\theta)$$

so that for small θ, $P_1 \sim P_3$

$$t' = P_1^2 \theta^2 = q_\perp^2 \tag{6}$$

and

$$t = -(q_1^2 + q_\perp^2) = -(t_{min} + t'). \tag{7}$$

3. Coherence

In the last paragraph we treated kinematic effects. The cross-section for production of a given M^* will only be appreciable if the coherence condition is satisfied. This is considered below from two points of view.

a) In any diffraction process of the type considered here or in X-ray scattering, coherence occurs when the phase shift due to scattering from two different local centers in the medium is such that there is constructive addition of the contributions to the scattering amplitudes. Thus, if the incident and outgoing waves have wave numbers k and k', and $q =_{\text{def}} k - k'$ in appropriate units, and if the typical distance between scattering centers is given by the radius of the medium R, then the phase shift in $\exp[i(k-k')\cdot x]$ between incident and outgoing wave is given by qR. For constructive addition in the amplitude function we require

$$qR < \text{order of 1 to } \pi.$$

Using the formula for nuclear radii we see that $q < 1/R$ or

$$q < \frac{140}{A^{1/3}} \text{ MeV/c}. \qquad (2)$$

Some authors use $q < 1/R$, others use the diameter for R or add a π in the numerator. Thus the « 140 » may be varied between seventy and five hundred according to taste. We note that the allowed momenta for q are the order of fermi momenta in nucleii. If an individual nucleon tried to take up this amount of recoil momentum, it would have difficulty due to the presence of other nucleons and the Pauli principle. The nucleus as a whole would recoil. For much higher momentum the nucleon could escape and result in an incoherent interaction.

The restriction (2) applies to all components of q, q_{11} and $q_\perp$. If we combine (2) with the kinematic requirement (1) we find an approximate upper limit for copious production,

$$M_3 < \sqrt{\frac{\cdot 3 P_1}{A^{1/3}}} \text{ GeV } (P_1 \text{ in GeV/c}).$$

The formula is only approximate. Higher masses may be produced (see Bemporad et al. ([2])) but with falling cross-sections. Absorption of the incoming and outgoing systems will alter the expectations. For particles with high absorption and Pb target only a small ring around the edges should be considered. Use of the coherence condition (2), with « 140 » replaced by « 280 », would increase the expected masses by the $\sqrt{2}$. As the deuteron radius is larger than that given by the nucleon radius formula applicable to all other nucleii, it is convenient to use an effective value for A equal to about 4 in this case. The approximate validity of these considerations is demonstrated in the K^- production of the L meson with $M^* \simeq 1.77$ GeV. The L « resonance » is seen in deuterium experiments with incident momentum of 13 GeV but not at 7 GeV. At 13 GeV the L is not seen with a neon target as expected. The Q is seen in all cases.

b) A more rigorous criterion for coherent production can be derived if we consider the amplitude for diffraction production from a nucleus $f_N(t)$ in terms of the A point nucleon amplitudes $f(t)$ and where we again consider a plane wave of momentum $\boldsymbol{k}$ incident, and $\boldsymbol{k'}$ scattered, and $\boldsymbol{q} = \boldsymbol{k} - \boldsymbol{k'}$,

$$f_{\text{nucleus}}(t) = \sum_1^A f(t) \exp[-i\boldsymbol{q} \cdot \boldsymbol{x}j].$$

The jth nucleon is located at $\boldsymbol{x}$, and spin and isospin differences are ignored. If the distribution of nucleon matter is given by $\varrho(\boldsymbol{r})$ the summation may be transformed to an integral and

$$f_N(t) = Af(t) \int \exp[(\boldsymbol{q} \cdot \boldsymbol{r})] \varrho(\boldsymbol{r}) \, d\boldsymbol{r} \tag{8}$$

where $f(t)$ is the average amplitude for scattering off a single nucleon. To see the significance of (8) we assume for ease of calculation that nucleii have a gaussian shape $\exp[-r^2/2a^2]$ where a is related to the nucleon radius formula $r = 1.12 A^{1/3}$ fermi. We find then that

$$\frac{d\sigma}{dt} = A^2 f(t)^2 \exp[\cdot 25 a^2 q^2]$$

$$\frac{d\sigma}{dt} = A^2 f(t)^2 \exp[11 A^{2/3} t]$$

$$\frac{d\sigma}{dt} \simeq A^2 \exp[Bt] \tag{9}$$

where we have assumed a simple exponential shape for $f(t)$ and absorbed it into the $\exp[Bt]$ term. Experiments on single nucleon result in B's of the order of 3 to 15, eight to ten being most common. We note that the experimental cross-sections observed follow this exponential fall-off very well at small t's. Only in very high statistic experiments at higher angles are deviations observed [2].

Figure 2 is taken from D. Fournier's thesis [3] and shows for the mass region around the Q meson $d\sigma/dt'$ for neon, deuterium, and hydrogen. The

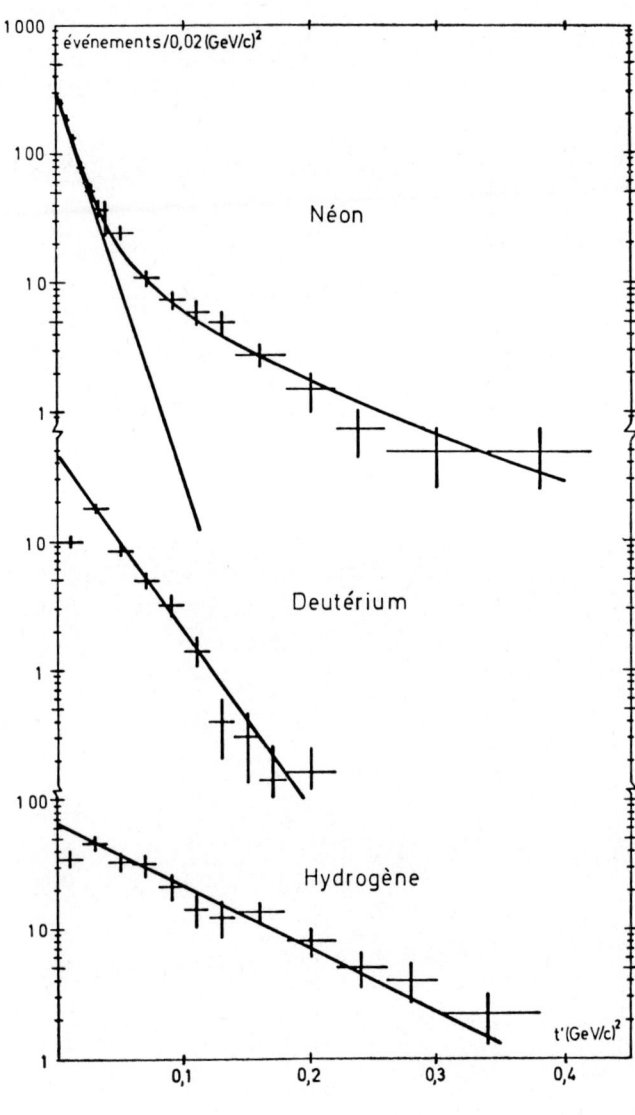

Fig. 2

slopes are in excellent agreement with the expression $B=11A^{2/3}$. In the case of D_2, coherent events can be easily differentiated from background as discussed below in the Johns Hopkins 12.6 GeV/c K^--deuterium experiment ([4]). When heavier targets are used the definite break in the slope of $d\sigma/dt'$ at small t' allows separation of the coherent events from the break-up events. The latter have the same slope as production on hydrogen, about $\exp[10t]$. At small t the ratio of coherent events to background is quite large, as Fig. 2 is a logarithmic plot. For very heavy elements slopes of several hundred have been seen ([2]) at very low t'.

It can be seen from eq. (9) that the measured slope is a combination of the form factor of the target and of the individual nucleon. In some processes the incident particle π, K, nucleon, or anti-nucleon does not break up, but continues on its trajectory with a momentum transfer q, while the target, a nucleon, dissociates into a $N^*_{\frac{1}{2}}$. At some values of the $N^*_{\frac{1}{2}}$ mass the slope of $d\sigma/dt$ is very small. It would be interesting to compare at high energies and identical N^* masses, the experimental slopes obtained with different incident particles to study form factor differences.

In deriving eq. (8), no account was taken of the absorption of the incoming and outgoing plane waves. Absorption effects introduce a factor into the integral of eq. (8)

$$\exp\left[-\int \frac{\sigma_j}{2}(1-i\alpha_j)\varrho(r')\,dZ'\right]$$

due to the incident and outgoing waves ([3]). Where σ_j is the cross-section of system j, Z' is the beam direction, b is perpendicular to Z, and $\alpha_j = f_r/f_i$ is the ratio of the real part to the imaginary part of the elastic scattering of the particle. Details are given in Daugeras' thesis ([3]). Integrating over the angle φ, the result can then be put in the form:

$$\frac{d\sigma}{dt}\bigg|_{coh} = \frac{d\sigma}{dt}\bigg|_{nucleon} \bigg| 2\pi \int J_0(q_1 b)\exp[iq_{11}Z]\exp\left[\left(-\frac{\sigma_i}{2}(1-i\alpha_i)\int_{-\infty}^{z}\varrho(b,Z')\right)\right].$$

$$\cdot \exp\left[-\frac{\sigma_f}{2}(1-1\alpha_+)\int_z^{\infty}\varrho(b,Z')\,dZ'\right]\varrho(b,Z)\,b\,db\,dZ\bigg|^2\bigg] \tag{10}$$

where i and f refer to the incident and outgoing particle and J_0 is the Bessel function.

4. Experimental detection of coherent reactions.

a) Most coherent reactions reported in the literature use an indirect method of establishing the coherence of a reaction. Reference to Figs. 2 and 10 shows that $d\sigma/dt'$ from production of a system with a target recoil has essentially two linear slopes on a semi-logarithmic plot. $d\sigma/dt'$ is given approximately by $\exp[Bt]$ in each region, with the value $B = 10$ in the high $|t|$ region as is characteristic of interactions with a single nucleon. In the small $|t|$ region the slope experimentally observed is characteristic of the target particle, varying from $B = 30$ in D_2, $B = 80$ for neon, and up to $B =$ several hundred in the heavier elements. This difference in observed slope is used in many experiments to differentiate the coherent events from the incoherent by taking a cut that eliminates all events with $|t|$ greater than an appropriate value. The slope of $d\sigma/dt'$ is so steep at small $|t|$ that only a small background of incoherent events usually remains. The background can be estimated by extrapolating the straight line in the $B = 10$ region to $t' = 0$ and counting the events of each type with $|t'|$ less than the chosen cutoff value. Typical estimates of background reported are 5% to 20%.

b) *Deuterium case.* In deuterium bubble chamber experiments a more positive identification of the coherent events is usually possible since the deuteron recoil is often visible. In many cases of M^* decay all particles form visible tracks, so a four constraint reconstruction of the event is possible. The question may still be asked as to how many deuteron break-up events simulate the $4-c$ events. The break-up events, however, do not have the proton and neutron emitted parallel to each other ($\cos\theta = 1$). Also, the mass of the p-n system for break-up events does not peak at the characteristic mass of deuteron events. (If in a real deuteron event the visible recoil particle is assumed to be a proton and a neutron is fitted to the event, the mass of the assumed p-n system is slightly different than the deuteron-mass). In Fig. 3 the angle between the p-n and the p-n mass is shown for the Hopkins K^--d experiment [4] at 13 GeV. This curve is typical of most deuterium experiments. The shaded events are those that have a four constraint fit to a deuteron recoil. The number of background events, as estimated by extrapolating the break-up events under the large deuteron peak, is quite small. The slope parameter for the deuteron events has the characteristic $B = 30$, while $B \simeq 10$ for the break-up events.

c) *Other targets.* We will just mention briefly here other means of identifying a target recoil. A group at CERN [2] has experimented with the

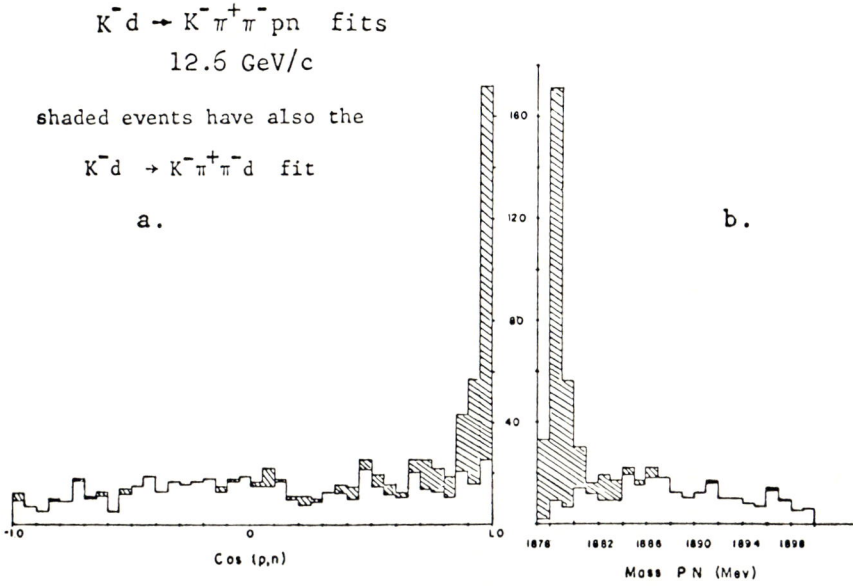

Fig. 3

use of walled gaseous helium targets in which the angle of recoil as well as the energy are measured. A Washington-Orsay group has proposed a helium streamer chamber experiment at N.A.L. The helium nucleus is tightly bound and has no stable excited state, so that detection of the α particle is evidence of a coherent reaction.

Other attempts at reducing incoherent background have been made by a Milan-CERN group using silicon detectors that determine when the target nucleus has not broken up. Nuclear emulsions have been used to differentiate coherent reactions by selection of « clean events » in which the heavy evaporation prongs usually present in break-up events are missing.

5. Discussion on some experimental results.

Diffraction production is more difficult to establish on hydrogen or nucleon targets as the identity of the recoil does not provide an automatic indication. Further, the slope of $d\sigma/dt$ is of no aid here either. It is expected however, that the cross-section would be constant for production of a system off a nucleon target with Pomeron of 0^+ exchange. On a Regge picture we expect

$$\sigma \propto p_{\text{beam}}^{2\alpha(0)-2}$$

where $\alpha(0) = 1, \frac{1}{2}, 0$ for the Pomeron ω^0, and π respectively, and the cross-section falls as a constant, $1/p_{\text{beam}}$ and, $\dfrac{1}{p_b^2}$ respectively. Thus, at high energies, production of resonances by exchange of particles should have smaller and smaller cross-sections. Only diffraction processes may be expected to have substantial cross-sections in a single channel. This should make it possible to study diffraction dissociation of nucleon targets into $N_{\frac{1}{2}}^*$ resonances, with use of the constancy of the cross-section as the indicator of the diffraction process.

It should be remarked that, as neither the nucleon nor the nucleus is in an eigenstate of C or G, a virtual particle with odd C or G can be emitted and still leave the target in its ground state yielding a coherent reaction. However, the cross-section for such non-Pomeron or dissociation reactions is suppressed both by the $p^{2\alpha(0)-2}$ factor mentioned above and in heavy targets by any cancellation of neutron and proton amplitudes.

We will illustrate some of the above principles with a small selection of experimental results: the L meson, mainly a $K\pi\pi$ resonance at 1770 MeV, was discovered in a 10 GeV K^-p bubble chamber experiment. The background beneath the very clean L signal in this experiment was quite copious. The Q meson (1300 MeV region) had a much larger signal. There also was considerable background in the region of the well established K*(1420).

In diffraction production of the Q and L from incident K's, we expect a better signal-noise ratio. Production by 0^+ exchange implies production only of particles in the spin parity series $0^-, 1^+, 2^-, \ldots$. This excludes production of the K*(1420). Further, observation of production of a particle by the diffraction process immediately restricts the spin parity to this series. In the particular case of deuterium (or other $T = 0$ nucleii) the isotopic spin of any particle produced by a $T = \frac{1}{2}$ incident beam is immediately determined to be $T = \frac{1}{2}$ independently of the magnitude of the cross-section in different channels. In the Johns Hopkins K^-d experiment ([4]) Fig. 4 shows clear Q and L production even with small statistics. *I*-spin of $T = \frac{1}{2}$ is thus established. Further, there is no shoulder on the Q in the 1420 MeV region since the spin of the 1420 is known to be 2^+ in the unallowed spin parity series. The K*(1420) is known to copiously decay to $K\pi$ as well as to $K\pi\pi$.

In the K⁻d experiment there is only one candidate for K⁻d → K⁰π⁻d in the 1420 MeV region. Since the Kπ channel is dominant in K*(1420) decay we can be sure there is no K*(1420) contribution in Fig. 4. Clearly, future higher statistic experiments in this channel should offer a better chance to study the possible splitting of the Q.

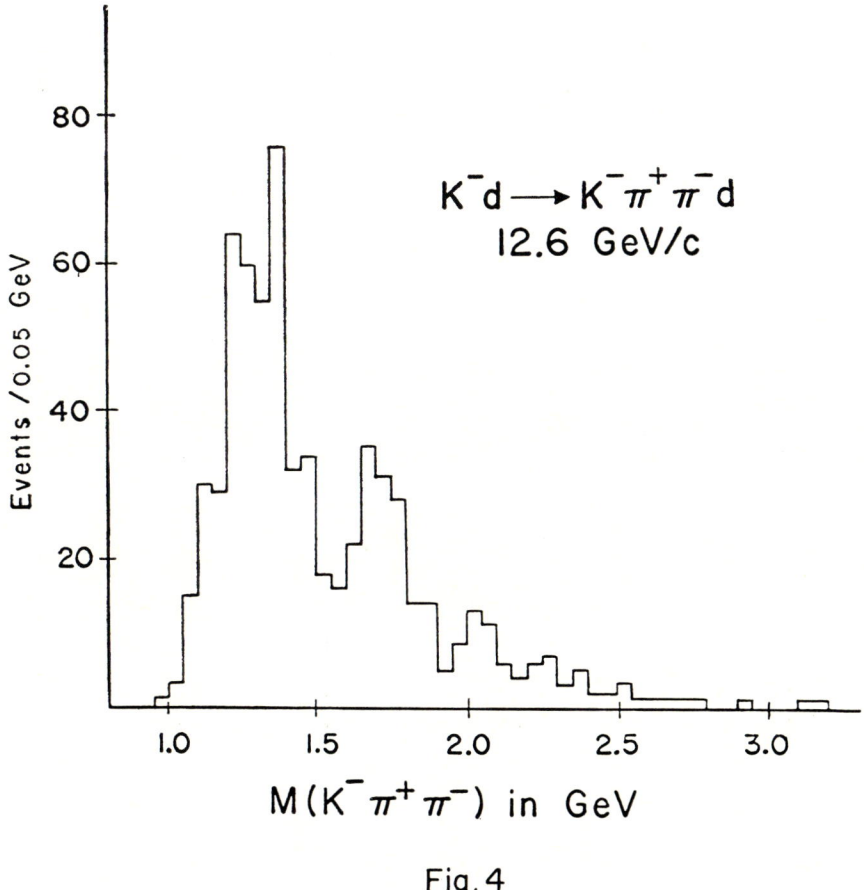

Fig. 4

The high signal noise ratio in the Q-region is exemplified in Fig. 5, taken from ref.([4]), in which we see that in a spin analysis using angular distributions, where the theoretical 1⁺ distribution is expected to reach 0, it indeed nearly does so.

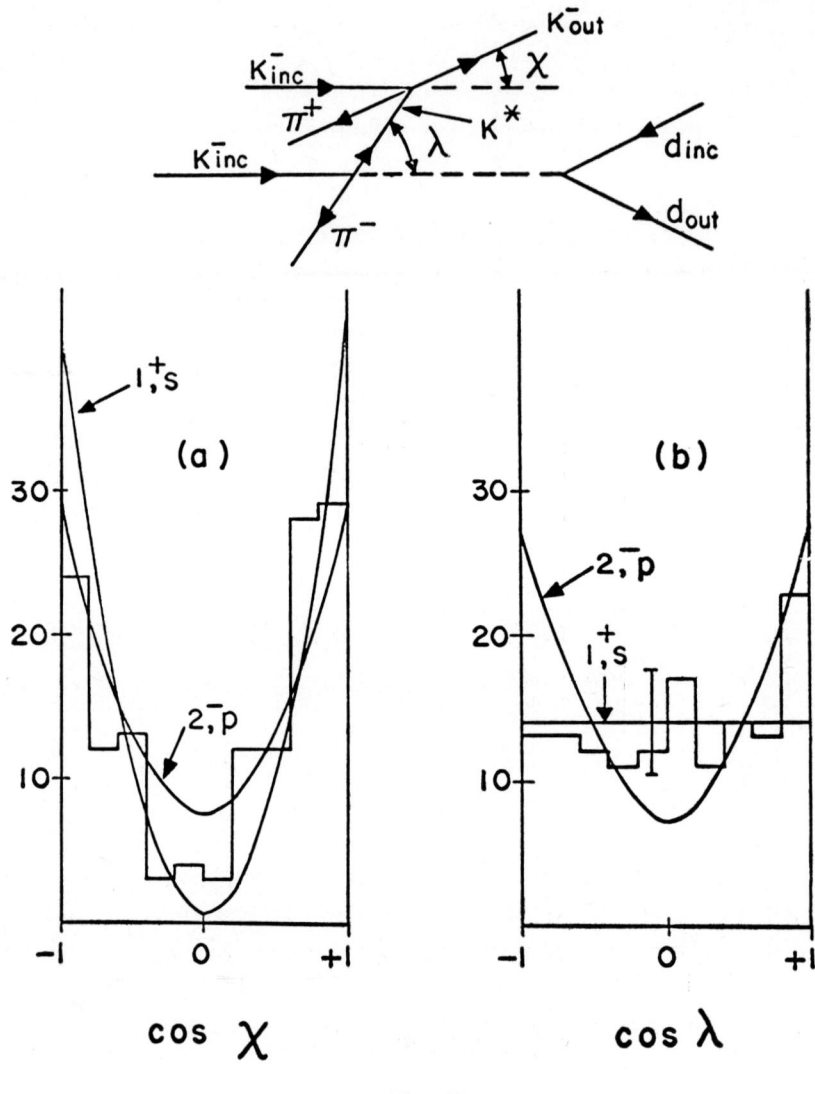

Fig. 5

The constancy of the cross-section for K⁻d, Q production is shown in Fig. 6 where the cross-section for Q production is plotted as a function of the incident beam momentum. This constancy is expected for Pomeron exchange production of a spin 1^+ system. On the other hand, the $K^*(890)$ of spin 1^- is forbidden by Pomeron exchange. Production of the $K^*(890)$

by ω^0 exchange is possible, but the cross-section is then expected to fall with incident momentum. K*(890) production is also plotted in Fig. 6, and indeed falls very rapidly as predicted.

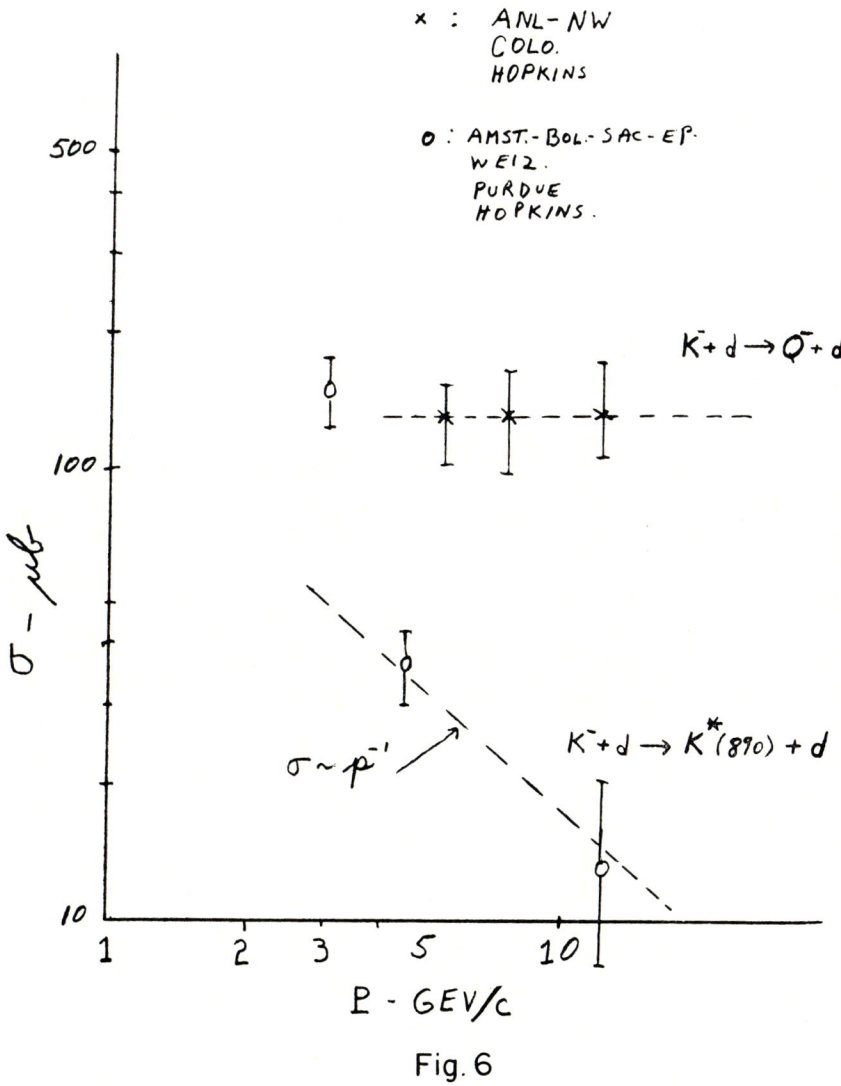

Fig. 6

In the L region, in this same experiment, there are about twenty events of the type $K^-d \to K^+K^-K^-d$. Eleven of the forty-four double plotted events are in the φ region, of which nine form a $K\varphi$ of mass in the L region. Thus there is an indication of this new L decay mode.

Coherent events without deuteron break-up have also been studied by a Berkeley group ([5]) in a high statistics study of 12 GeV K^+ on deuterium. Figure 7 shows their $K\pi\pi$ mass distribution. The Q-region is peaked as expected. However, it is clear that the L-meson region is different than that

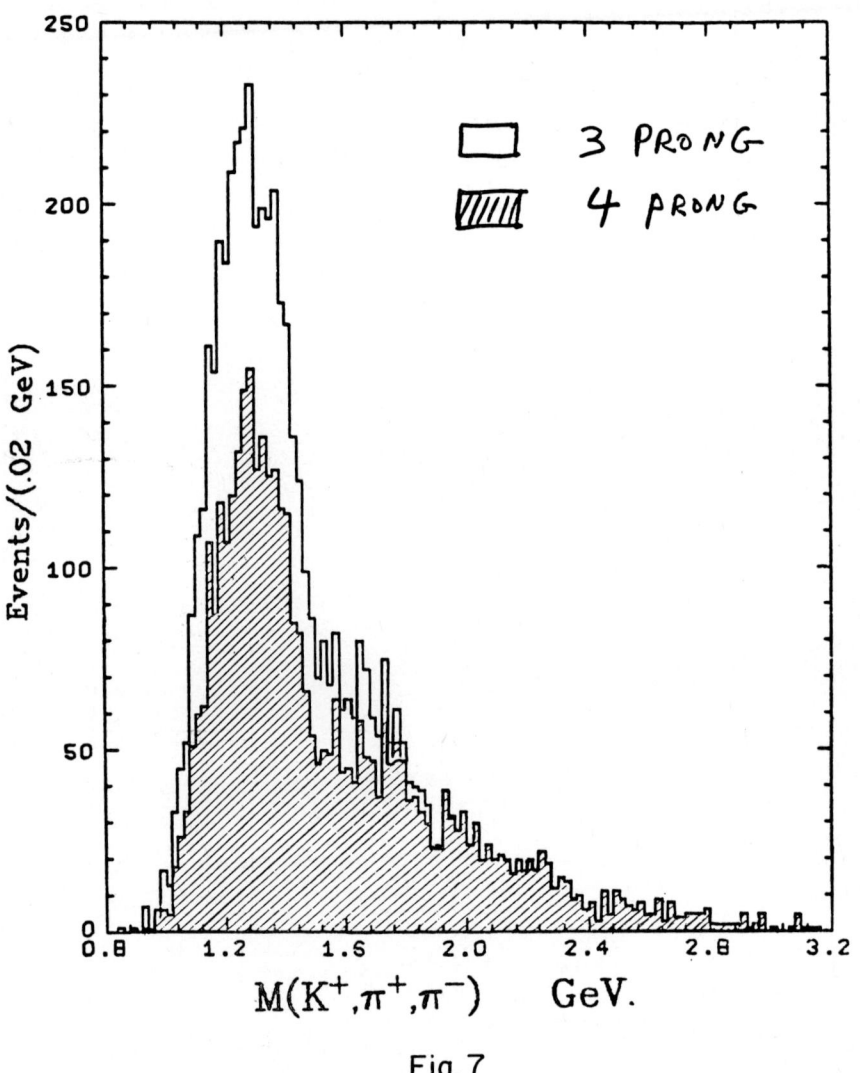

Fig. 7

Coherent interactions 873

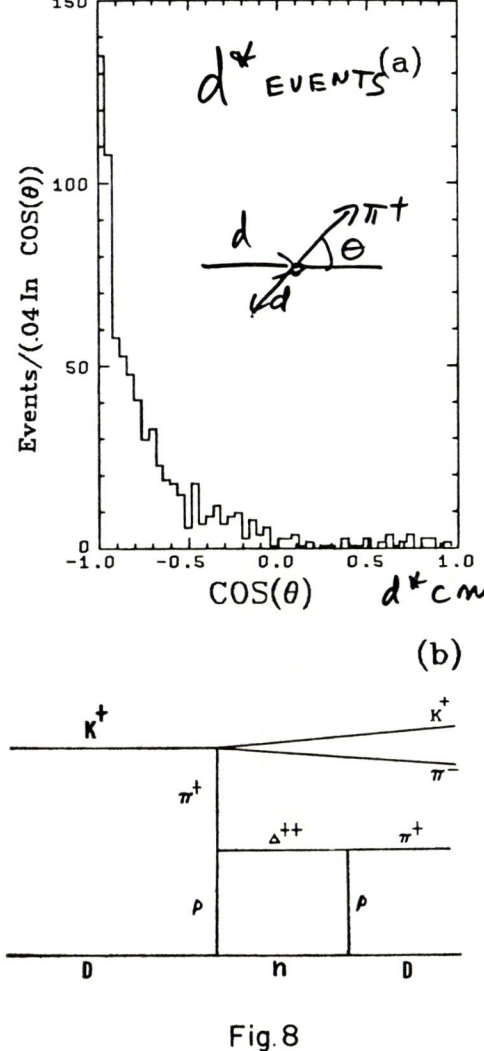

Fig. 8

of the K⁻-d experiment at 12.6 GeV. The difference could be due to a statistical fluctuation favouring the L-region in the smaller K⁻d experiment. If the difference is real, it is quite unexpected as the predicted distributions for Pomeron exchange are the same for K⁺ and K⁻ incident. Differences could arise from ω^0 exchange but we saw that at least in the particular channel favored by ω^0 exchange, production of the K*(890), the cross-section had dropped considerably at 12 GeV. If ω^0 exchange were responsible for the differences, then from the known cross-over at $t = -2$ for ω-exchange, we would expect identical results. Unfortunately, the number of events at this high t is much too small, as expected in a diffractive process. The Berkeley

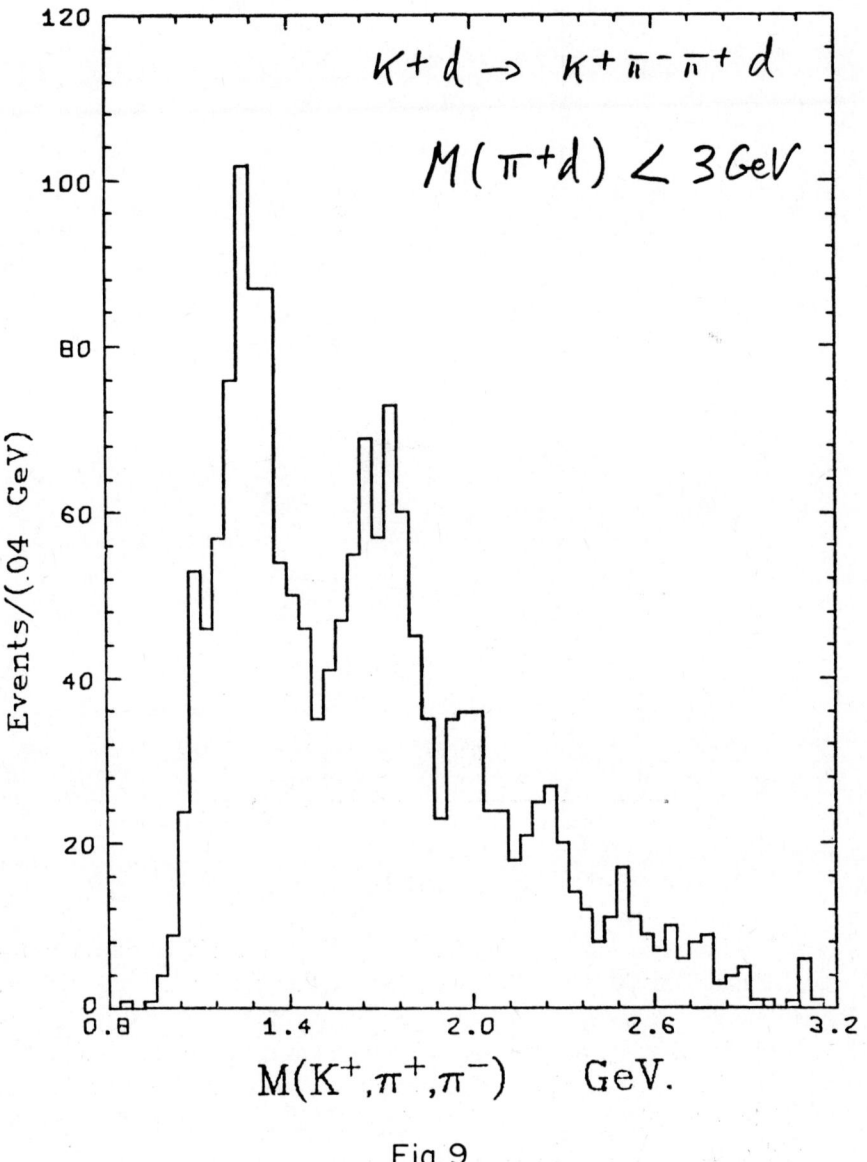

Fig. 9

group has also seen a much stronger d* signal than in the K⁻d experiment.

The d* comprises a well-known bump in the d* mass spectrum. It has been « explained » in many deuterium experiments as arising from a π resonating with one nucleon of the deuterium, with subsequent recombination and emission of a d and a π. Figure 8 shows this diagram for the Berkeley K^+ experiment with the asymmetric angular distribution that indicates lack of a resonance. As π exchange is involved, the strength of the d* should fall off as $1/p^2$ and ought not to be strong at high energies. In looking for a cut that might explain the K^+ and K^- difference in the L region, the Goldhaber group found the surprising enhancement of events in the L region shown in Fig. 9, where the events plotted were those in the region of strong d*. This is under further study. The K^- experiment is being continued to determine if the above K^+-K^- differences are due to statistics or to surprising physical differences.

6. Coherent pion production from complex nuclei.

In order to establish whether mass bumps such as the A_1 for three pions, and the Q for $K\pi\pi$ are threshold enhancements or else indeed real particles, it has been suggested that their cross-section in nucleon matter be measured. For kinematical mass enhancement, cross-sections typical of three particles traversing the nucleus might be expected. Detailed consideration takes into account that the A_1 is comprised mainly of a ρ and π and that there may be correlations due to their proximity. Cross-sections in nuclear matter of the order of 45 mb are predicted for this case, while for single particles, cross-sections of the order of 20—25 mb are expected. Twenty-five millibarn cross-sections have been found from production of A's and Q's in heavy liquid chambers. It has been claimed that this establishes these enhancements as real particles. However, recently a careful high statistics experiment has been reported ([2]) which calls for re-examination of the above conclusion. Measurements were made for about ten target nuclei from Be to Pb with several thousand coherent events collected for each element. The reactions studied were:

$$\pi + A \rightarrow (3\pi) + A \quad \text{and} \quad \pi + A \rightarrow (5\pi) + A$$

each π meson being charged.

As an example, Fig. 10 shows the cross-section as a function of t' for one particular target and demonstrates the flat fall-off due to incoherent events ($B \simeq 10$) as well as the steep fall-off at low t'. The solid curve is an optical model fit that combines the expected shape for incoherent events with the coherent expectation given in formula (10) above. Similar excellent fits are obtained for every element and mass region. In the intermediate $|t'|$ region the quantitative fit is poorer, but in all cases the theoretical maxima and minima

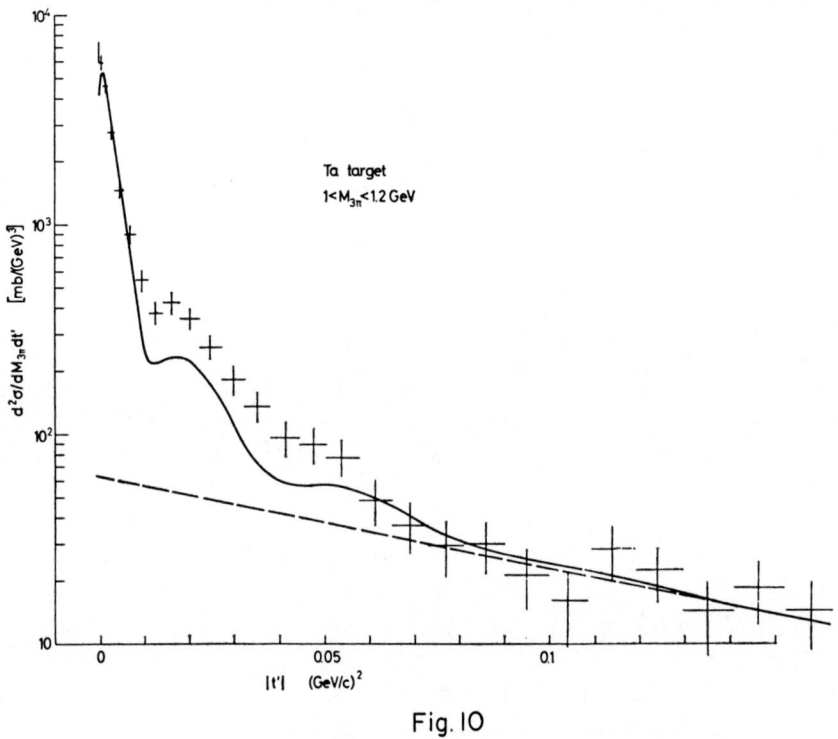

Fig. 10

reproduce the data. The three pion mass spectrum is shown in Fig. 11. This is a preliminary result submitted to the Dubna conference. We may note here that the hopes of using diffraction production to sharpen the A_1 bump as seen in hydrogen experiments have not been realized. Next, the authors use the enormous quantity of data available to determine σ_2 as it appears in eq. (10). σ refers to the interaction cross-section in nuclear matter of the produced system, σ_1, to that of the incident particle. These terms are inserted in the theory (eq. (10)) to account for the interaction of the particles in

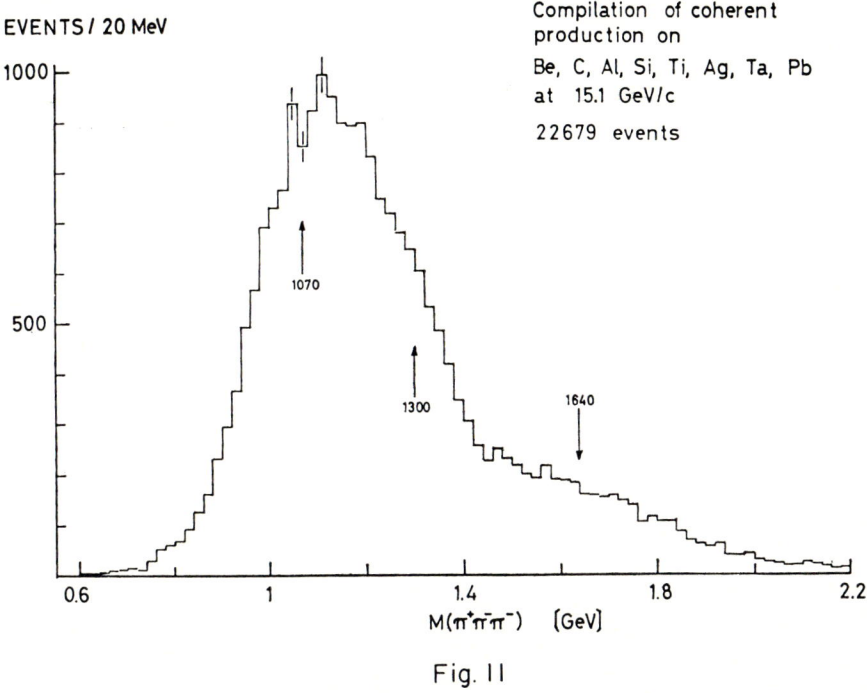

Fig. 11

nuclear matter. As the theoretical fit of Fig. 10 was quantitatively poor in the intermediate region of t', the analysis was limited to only smaller values of t'. The density of nucleon matter appearing in eq. (10) was well approximated by a two parameter Fermi distribution, the constants being known from other experiments. The incident π's cross-section are also well known. For each mass interval of the final 3π or 5π system, best fits were obtained to the data by varying the unknown σ_2. The fit is typified by the black line in Fig. 10 at small t'. The cross-section for the outgoing system was determined along with the variations in σ_2 for reasonable change of the input parameters. The results for the cross-section, σ_2, of the (3π) system in the mass region of the A_1 was about 25 mb. The behaviour of the observed coherent cross-section for production of a 3π system as a function of target mass number A was exactly as predicted by the model. However, the 200 MeV wide mass region both below and above the A region, gave identical results. Thus raising a question as to the significance of the 25 mb result in the A_1 region, 45 mb is the theoretical prediction for the cross-section of several particles. Similarly, the cross-section in nuclear matter, σ_2, for (5π) systems was determined. The points in Fig. 12 represent the coherent cross-section

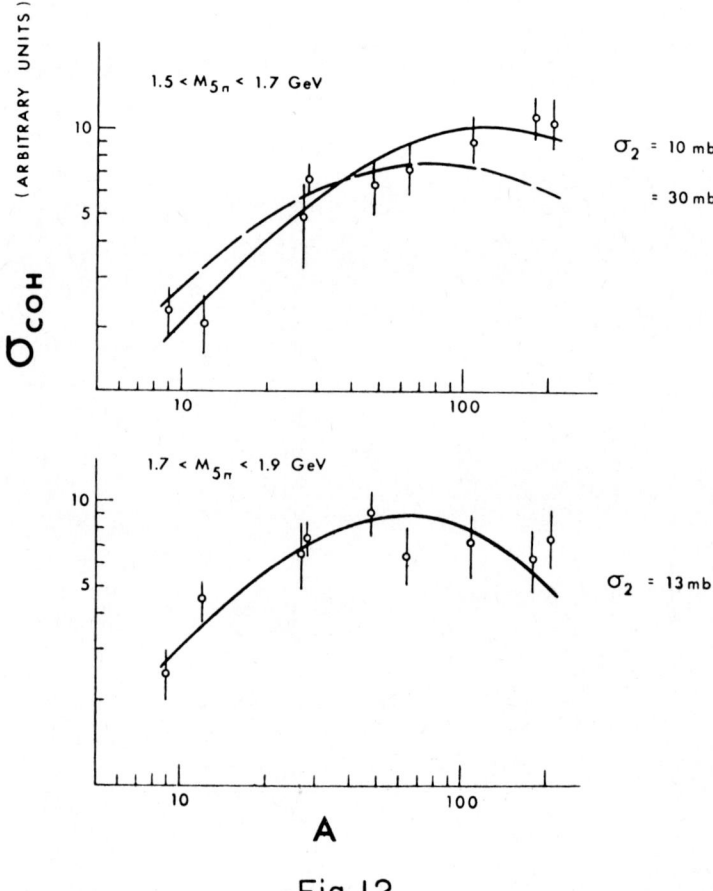

Fig. 12

measured for each target element of mass number A. The solid black curve in Fig. 12 is the expected experimental result using the model. Best fits were obtained for the 5π cross-section in a nuclear matter of 17 mb, 10 mb and 13 mb! The errors on these (5π) curves are much greater than in the (3π) case since there are only a total of 13.000 5π events compared to 90.000 three π events.

Clearly, we must be cautious as to the interpretations of the σ_2 determined in these models.

REFERENCES

1) Proceedings of the Topical Seminar on: *Interactions of Elementary Particles with Nuclei*, (Trieste, 1970).
2) BEMPORAD et al., CERN, ZURICH, IMPERIAL COLLEGE and MILANO COLLABORATION: *Coherent Production of Pions on Nuclei Determination of Unstable Boson-Nucleon Total Cross-Sections*, submitted to *Nucl. Phys.*
3) D. FOURNIER: *Thesis*, Universite de Paris, Centre Orsay; *Etude de la Production Coherent sur Noyer du Systeme* $K^-\pi^+\pi^-$ *per des* K^- *de* 5.5; 10.0; *et* 12.7 GeV/c, Unpublished. See also the thesis of B. DAUGERAS at Orsay.
4) P. ANTICH, A. CALLAHAN, R. CARSON, C. Y. CHIEN, B. COX, D. DENEGRI, L. ETTLINGER, D. FEIOCK, G. GOODMAN, J. HAYNES, R. MERCER, A. PEVSNER, L. RESVANIS, R. SEKULIN, V. SREEDHAR and R. ZDANIS: *Nucl. Phys.*, B **28**, 13 (1971).
5) FIRESTONE, GOLDHABER, LISSAUER and TRILLING: Preliminary and unpublished.

DISCUSSION

Chairman: Prof. A. PEVSNER
Scientific Secretary: Z. SEKERA

DISCUSSION

— CABIBBO:

I have a comment on the cross-sections. The analysis of total cross-sections for mesonic states which you mentioned at the end of your lectures is based on a method which is not in general satisfied. Consider for example the process

$$\pi + A \to X + A \qquad \text{(X being a mesonic state)}.$$

The method assures that the elementary processes are ($\mathcal{N}$ being a nucleon)

1) $\pi + \mathcal{N} \to X + \mathcal{N}$
2) $X + \mathcal{N} \to X + \mathcal{N}$ (elastic scattering)
3) $X + \mathcal{N} \to Y + \mathcal{N}$ (inelastic scattering)

2) and 3) are used to compute an optical potential for X in nuclear matter. The method describes this process in two steps

a) X is created at some point;
b) X propagates through the nucleus.

The amplitude for process 1) is then obtained by letting the creation point vary within the nucleous. The total $X + \mathcal{N}$ cross-section appears in the second step. It determines the imaginary part of the optical potential for the propagation of X in nuclear matter and is determined by studying the A dependence of the process 1). Now in the case you have discussed we do not have a single state X, but a continuum. For simplicity let me consider the case of a discrete number of states X, Y, Z. We should compute (1) in a more complex way. In step *a)* any of the states can now be produced, while during propagation any state can turn into any other. In other words, the optical potential is now a matrix, elements of which could only be obtained by a much more complex analysis which would consider all channels at once. The total $X + \mathcal{N}$ cross-section would enter as the imaginary part of the appropriate diagonal element of the optical potential. To do a single channel analysis where a multi-channel one is appropriate could lead to gross errors. If for example a particular state Y is not directly produced by pions, it would appear in three steps:

i) $\pi \to X$
ii) $X \to Y$
iii) Y propagates and leaves the nucleus.

If in this case we apply a single channel analysis, the total $Y + \mathcal{N}$ cross-section would be underestimated. A single channel analysis can be justified in certain cases such as analysis of $\rho \mathcal{N}$ cross-section from coherent $\gamma + A \to \rho + A$, since **VMD** guarantees in this case that ρ would be the dominant state. The funny results you have quoted, especially on the 5π states, suggest that it is not applicable there.

— CHEW:

Has the Deck model been applied to the conditions of the heavy nucleus experiment that you described? This model gives a reasonable fit to many of the corresponding experiments with a proton target, so it is interesting to know whether it works also for heavy target nuclei.

— PEVSNER:

I do not know of any Deck model being applied directly to this experiment. But in general these bumps do fit the Deck model that is Reggeized today.

— CHEW:

Do you remember what widths the Deck model calculation gives, does it fit also very narrow peaks?

— PEVSNER:

To my knowledge I have never seen a Deck model to fit something very narrow.

— MORPURGO:

I have also a comment in connection with the Deck effect mentioned by Chew. I believe that in fact there are two interfering amplitudes which are important in the coherent production process. Consider, to be definite, the 3π production process. Then the first diagram is the Deck effect diagram (amplitude A) as follows:

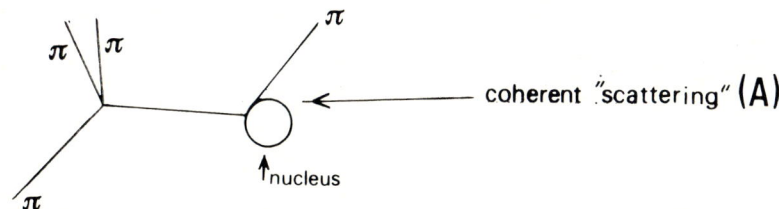

The second diagram is the coherent production of the three pion state from the nucleus by short range interactions on each individual nucleon:

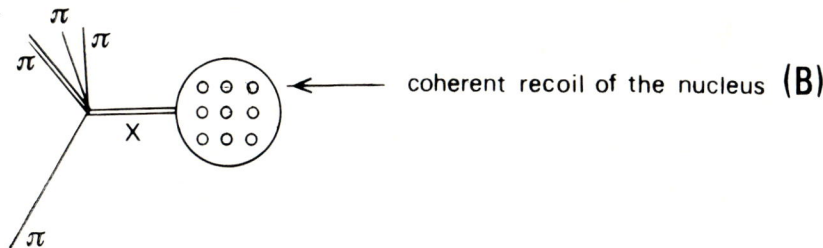

where three pions are produced as indicated (amplitude B). Then the total cross-section is proportional to

$$|A + B|^2$$

and I believe that this makes the analysis, which has to be performed in order to extract the B amplitude (which is the one interesting), rather complicated. Such an analysis should however be performed to get useful information from this kind of experiment. For the calculations of the B part all the uncertainties which Cabibbo just noted of course arise.

Photoproduction of Vector Mesons-Experimental

A. H. ROSENFELD

1. Introduction 883
2. Polarized photon beams 884
3. Polarization properties of the reaction $\gamma p \to \rho^0 p$ 888
   A. Helicity conservation 891
   B. Exchange of natural vs. un-natural J^P 895
   C. Does natural exchange imply helicity conservation? . 899
   D. Rho mass shape and the interference model 900
4. Polarization properties of the reaction $\gamma p \to \omega p$ 904
5. Polarization properties of the reaction $\gamma p \to \varphi p$ 907
6. Cross-sections of the reactions $\gamma p \to V^0 p$ 908
   A. Difficulties and uncertainties. 908
   B. Results 911
7. Test of the vector dominance model 918
8. Vector meson photoproduction on the deuteron 920
9. The reaction $\gamma A \to V^0 A$ on complex nuclei 927
10. The phase of the ρ, ω and φ forward elastic scattering . 933
11. Photoproduction of heavy (vector) mesons; the $\rho'(1500)$. 936
Acknowledgement 941
References 941
Discussion 946

Photoproduction
of Vector Mesons - Experimental

A. H. ROSENFELD

Department of Physics, Lawrence Berkeley Laboratory
University of California - Berkeley, Cal., USA

P. SÖDING

Deutsches Elektronen-Synchrotron, DESY
Hamburg, Germany

Preface.

During the summer of 1971, one of us (P. S.) lectured on Vector Mesons at the Topical Seminar on Electromagnetic Interactions in Trieste, and the other (A. H. R.) at Erice in July on this topic and the laser-beam bubble-chamber experiment of the SLAC-Berkeley-Tufts collaboration. When we met at the Amsterdam Conference, we discovered that we had prepared very similar reviews, both trying to emphasize the physics and not the formalism. Since we have enjoyed collaborating for many years, we decided to collaborate on these notes, hoping that the product would be both more efficient for us, and more readable.

1. Introduction.

As the quantum numbers of the vector-mesons equal those of the photon, it is not surprising that vector-meson photoproduction is related to hadronic elastic scattering. More precisely, the current-field identity ([1])

$$-j_\mu(x) = \frac{m_\varrho^2}{2\gamma_\varrho} \varrho_\mu^0(x) + \frac{m_\omega^2}{2\gamma_\omega} \omega_\mu(x) + \frac{m_\phi^2}{2\gamma_\phi} \phi_\mu(x) + \ldots ?$$

(where j_μ is the hadronic electromagnetic current; ϱ_μ^0, ω_μ and ϕ_μ are the vector meson fields, m_V the vector-meson masses and γ_V the coupling parameters) leads us to consider the photon-hadron interaction to be mediated by the vector mesons, with a direct photon-vector meson coupling

$$\gamma \;\;\rightsquigarrow\!\!\bullet\!\!\rightsquigarrow\;\; V^0$$

$$-\frac{e m_V^2}{2\gamma_V} \quad (e^2/4\pi = 1/137).$$

In the limit of unbroken $SU(3)$, ideal $\omega\phi$ mixing, and zero mixing with other possible vector states, the couplings are in the famous ratio

$$\frac{1}{\gamma_\rho} : \frac{1}{\gamma_\omega} : \frac{1}{\gamma_\phi} = 3:1:(-\sqrt{2});$$

this is changed somewhat by symmetry-breaking ([2]) (see Sect. 9).

The data on photoproduction of vector mesons allow some rather direct tests of the vector-meson dominance model of the electromagnetic current ([2]). They may also reveal some of the general properties of hadronic processes. On first sight vector-meson photoproduction at high-energies is a particularly pure example of a diffractive production process. Helicity conservation has already been discovered here and has suggested itself as perhaps a new principle for certain types of reactions ([3]).

On closer examination however, the data do not always follow our expectations. And vector dominance, although doing surprisingly well in some respects, apparently fails in others.

We will concentrate in this presentation on some of the newer and (supposedly) more important experimental results, and we shall try to discuss them in terms of physical arguments rather than density matrix elements. Because of the many good recent reviews ([4-11]) we make no attempt to be complete.

2. Polarized photon beams.

a) Coherent bremsstrahlung from a diamond monocrystal ([12,13]).

In the bremsstrahlung of high-energy electrons on the atoms of a regular lattice, one observes a strong enhancement if the momentum transfer coincides with a vector of the reciprocal lattice. The photons under this condition

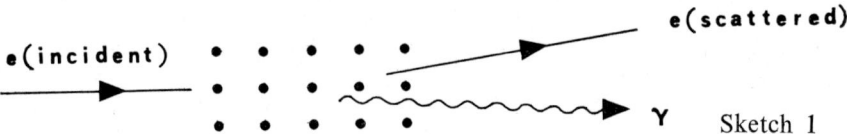

Sketch 1

turn out to be linearly polarized, with a polarization of up to ~ 70%. This method to polarize photons has been used in vector-meson production experiments at Cornell, DESY, and SLAC. Rather intense beams can be produced. Large polarization is, however, achieved only at $E_\mu \leqslant \frac{1}{2} E_{\text{incident}}$, which limits the usable photon energy E_γ to $\leqslant 5$ GeV at Cornell and $\leqslant 3.5$ GeV at DESY. Furthermore, there is a large, flat, unpolarized photon background extending up to $E_\gamma^{\max} = E_{\text{incident}}$.

b) « *Acceleration* » *of polarized light* ([14,15]).

Light from a laser is Compton-scattered under $\approx 180°$ on high-energy electrons. The backscattered photons thereby achieve high energy in the laboratory system. As Compton scattering is a two-body process, the final-state photon energy E_γ depends only on the scattering angle. One can therefore obtain a nearly monocromatic photon beam by sufficiently collimating the electron and photon beams. The polarization (linear or circular) of the laser light is essentially retained in the scattering process. This method has been

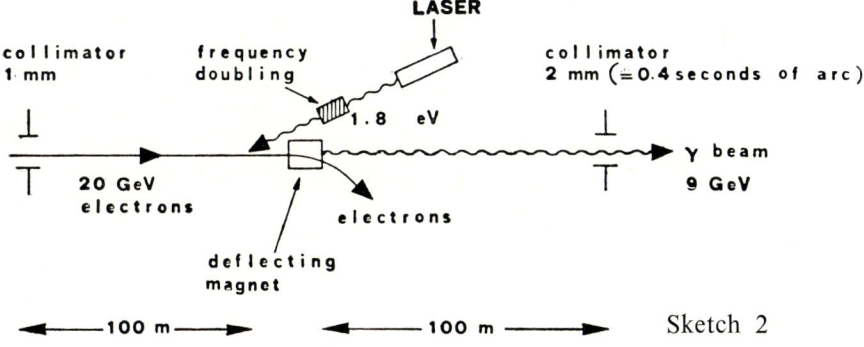

Sketch 2

used to study vector-meson photoproduction by linear polarized photons of $E_\gamma = 2.8$ GeV, 4.7 GeV and 9.3 GeV at SLAC ([16-19]). The polarization was 94% at 2.8 and 4.7 GeV, and 77% at 9.3 GeV. The small intensity and short pulse length of the photon beams so obtained limit their use to bubble chamber experiments.

A comparison of the spectra of a coherent bremsstrahlung beam used recently at Cornell ([20]), with the one from the laser Compton scattering ([17]), is shown in Fig. 1.

Figure 1.1 is a bubble chamber picture taken with 2.8 GeV γ. About 50 photons enter the chamber through a thin window off the bottom of the picture. This flux is limited by the fact that we find it hard to scan and measure with more than 5-10 pairs per picture. The pair cross-section is 20 mb, so the mean free path for pair production in liquid hydrogen is about 50 ft. In a 5 ft. visible length of hydrogen this means that about one photon in ten converts, and hence we limit the flux to 50 photons.

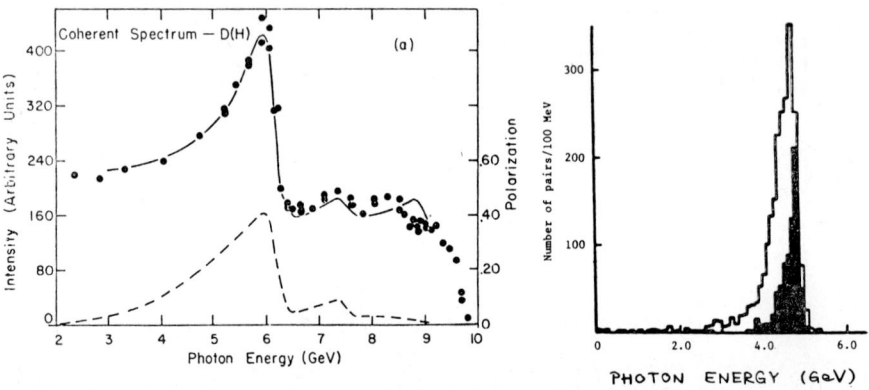

Fig. 1. – Comparison of photon beam spectra. On the left, the coherent bremsstrahlung intensity (= number of photons × photon energy) (full curve) and the calculated polarization (dashed curve) from a recent Cornell experiment are shown ([20]). The right hand figure shows the measured e^+e^--pair energy spectra (white histogram), and the energy spectra of fitted $\gamma p \to \pi^+\pi^- p$ events (black histogram), produced by the laser backscattered beam at SLAC ([17]).

The comparison between pairs and hadronic events is as follows (based on 50 photons/frame and 5 ft. of hydrogen).

	e^+e^-	Hadrons
σ	20 mb	120 µb
Events/frame	5	0.03

Our scanners can scan about 200 frames, thus finding about 6 hadronic events, per hour.

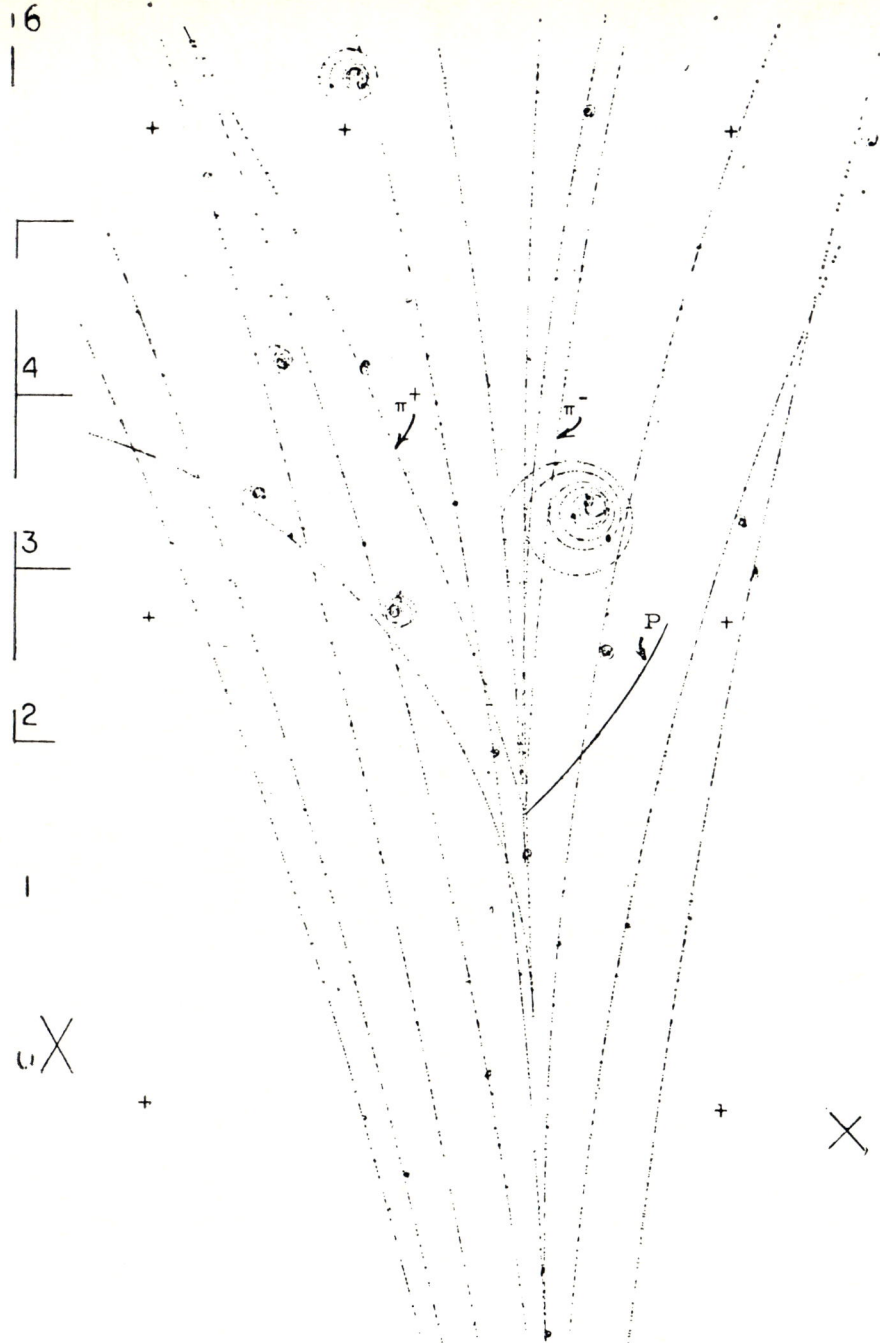

Fig. 1.1. – Photograph of the 82-inch HBC, showing an event of the reaction $\gamma p \to \omega p$, $\omega \to \pi^+\pi^-\pi^0$, at 2.8 GeV. About half of the frame is shown. The high-energy background tracks are electrons and positrons from pair production; the low-energy (curled) tracks are delta rays or Compton electrons. Note that the reaction and pair vertices lie along a narrow beam line. Hadronic events are easily distinguished from electron pairs with zero opening-angle. This is Fig. 4 in the thesis of W. J. Podolsky, UCRL 20128 (1971).

c) *Photon absorption in highly oriented graphite* ([21]). If a beam of high-energy photons is passed through oriented single crystals of graphite, photons with different directions of their polarization vector will be absorbed differently. This is due to the fact that the cross-section for coherent e^+e^- pair production depends on the relative orientation of the polarization vector and the crystal axis. In a recent experiment at Cornell, a polarization of 6% was achieved at a beam energy of 9 GeV. Higher degrees of polarization are expected when E_γ becomes higher, so that the method could be useful at the new accelerators.

3. Polarization properties of the reaction $\gamma p \to \rho^0 p$

Assume the incident photon beam to be linearly polarized, with degree of polarization P_γ. Let ϕ be the angle between the photon polarization vec-

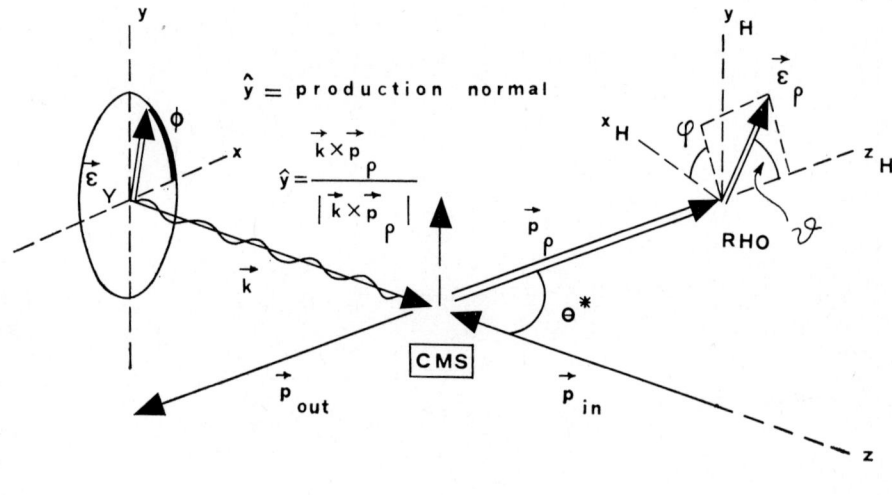

Sketch 3

tor $\boldsymbol{\varepsilon}_\gamma$ and the production plane. Then the helicity density matrix ([22]) of the ρ^0 meson depends on ϕ in the following way:

$$\varrho_{\lambda\lambda'} = \varrho_{\lambda\lambda'}^{(0)} - P_\gamma \cos 2\phi \, \varrho_{\lambda\lambda'}^{(1)} - P_\gamma \sin 2\phi \, \varrho_{\lambda\lambda'}^{(2)} . \qquad (1)$$

The ϕ dependence cannot be more complicated because the spin of the photon is only 1. $\varrho_{\lambda\lambda'}^{(0)}$ is the density matrix for the unpolarized case.

In the sketches, we have drawn an unobservable vector called $\boldsymbol{\varepsilon}_\varrho$ to indicate the polarization of the ρ^0. We *measure* $\boldsymbol{p}_\pi$, the momentum of say, the π^+, in the ρ rest frame (call its helicity angles θ and φ), and assume a decay matrix element

$$T_\varrho = \langle \pi^+\pi^- | \boldsymbol{\varepsilon}_\varrho \cdot \boldsymbol{p}_\pi | \rho^0 \rangle . \tag{2}$$

Thus in all the sketches, instead of $\boldsymbol{\varepsilon}_\varrho$, one can read $\boldsymbol{p}_\pi$.

It turns out ([23]) that from observation of the ρ^0 decay angular distribution $W(\cos\vartheta, \varphi; \phi)$ using linearly polarized photons, one can determine a total of 9 independent (real or imaginary parts of) elements of the density matrices $\varrho_{\lambda\lambda'}^{(0)}$, $\varrho_{\lambda\lambda'}^{(1)}$ and $\varrho_{\lambda\lambda'}^{(2)}$. Therefore, one gets 10 times as much information (differential cross-section plus 9 density matrix elements) as from a mere differential cross-section measurement.

The determination of the 9 density matrix elements has been done only in the bubble chamber, since one needs the full (or at least a large part of the) decay angular distribution $W(\cos\vartheta, \varphi; \phi)$ to separate the various matrix elements.

We do not want to discuss here the general expression for the decay angular distribution $W(\cos\vartheta, \varphi; \phi)$ in terms of the density matrix. We mention only *two simple properties*. As in Sketch 3, we take ϑ and φ to be the polar and azimuthal angles of the π^+ from the $\rho^0 \to \pi^+\pi^-$ decay, measured in the ρ^0 rest system in the s-channel helicity frame $(x_H y_H z_H)$. This frame is defined by a z_H axis parallel to $-\boldsymbol{p}_{\text{out}}$ and a y_H axis parallel to the normal to the production plane.

The first property has to do with the question of helicity conservation. We can have the helicities

$$\lambda_\gamma = \pm 1 \quad \text{for the photon,} \quad \lambda_\gamma = 0, \pm 1 \quad \text{for the } \rho^0 .$$

The question arises: Are there « helicity flip » transitions into the $\lambda_\varrho = 0$ state? This can be answered from the $\cos\vartheta$ distribution alone, even with unpolarized photons, since

$$W(\cos\vartheta) = \begin{cases} \text{const}\,|Y_1^{\pm 1}|^2 = \text{const}\cdot\sin^2\vartheta \\ \\ \text{const}\,|Y_1^0|^2 = \text{const}\cdot\cos^2\vartheta \end{cases} \text{for } \lambda_\varrho = \begin{cases} \pm 1 & (3) \\ \\ 0 & (4) \end{cases}$$

in the *s*-channel helicity frame.

The second property relates the exchange of natural *vs.* un-natural spin-parity in the *t*-channel, with the correlation of the photon and the ϱ^0 polarization planes. To make it plausible we use a simple mnemonic. Imagine the photon-rho meson transition at small cms angles θ^*, with exchange of a $J^P = 0^+$ or 0^- object. The matrix elements are ([24])

$(\varepsilon_\gamma \cdot \varepsilon_\varrho)k$ and $(\varepsilon_\gamma \times \varepsilon_\varrho)\cdot k$ Sketch 4

(e.g. for 0^- remember the perpendicular polarization planes of the photons from π^0 decay). For exchange of higher spins, the mnemonic is

Sketch 5

can combine to total exchange of $J^P = 0^+, 1^-, 2^+ \ldots$ ($=$ natural series)

can combine to total exchange of $J^P = 0^-, 1^+, 2^- \ldots$ ($=$ un-natural series)

Let $\psi(=\varphi-\phi)$ be the angle between $\boldsymbol{\varepsilon}_\gamma$ and the projection of $\boldsymbol{\varepsilon}_\varrho$ onto a plane perpendicular to **k**. Then we have from the square of the matrix elements

$$W(\Psi) \propto \cos^2 \psi \quad \text{(natural exchange)} \tag{5}$$

$$W(\Psi) \propto \sin^2 \psi \quad \text{(un-natural exchange)}. \tag{6}$$

At large cms production angles θ^* it turns out still to be true that for natural (un-natural) exchange the ψ distribution peaks at 0 and 180 deg (90 and 270 deg) ([23]).

A) *Helicity conservation.* Experimental evidence for the tendency of the ρ^0 in the reaction $\gamma p \to \rho^0 p$ to emerge with helicities $\lambda_\varrho = \pm 1$ like the photon, was first reported by the ABBHHM bubble chamber collaboration with data obtained at DESY ([25]). The most convincing evidence is provided by the bubble chamber data of the SLAC-Berkeley-Tufts Collaboration ([17,19]). In Fig. 2 we show some of their recent unpublished data on the reaction $\gamma p \to \pi^+ \pi^- p$ at 9.3 GeV, obtained with the Compton backscattered

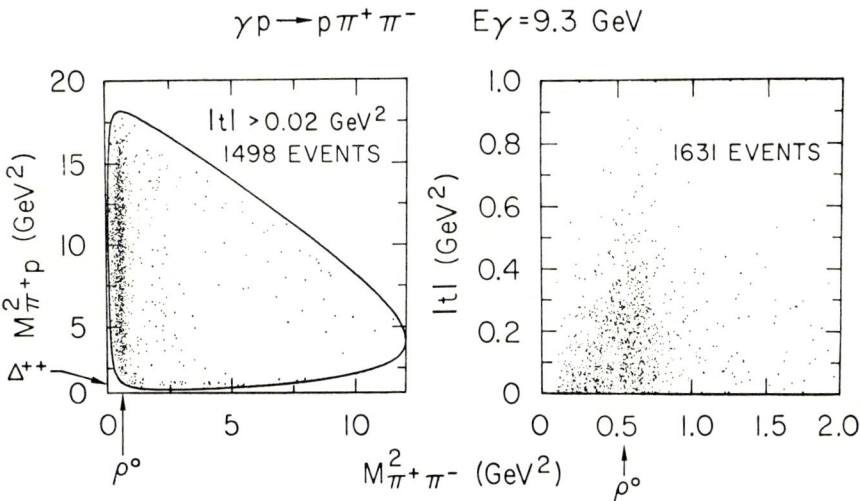

Fig. 2. – Dalitz plot, and part of Chew-Low plot, for the reaction $\gamma p \to \pi^+\pi^- p$ at $E_\gamma = 9.3$ GeV ([19]).

polarized photon beam ([19]). The left part of the figure shows the Dalitz plot $M^2_{\pi^+\pi^-}$ vs. $M^2_{p\pi^+}$. One sees the ρ^0 and the $\Delta^{++}(1236)$ bands, and perhaps an indication of $\Delta^0(1236)$ production. Note that there is some additional background, outside the ρ^0 and $\Delta(1236)$ bands. On the right hand side of Fig. 2 is part of the Chew-Low plot, $M^2_{\pi^+\pi^-}$ vs. $|t|$, where $t = (p_\gamma - p_{\pi^+\pi^-})^2$ is the square of the four-momentum transfer from the photon to the mesons. Small $|t|$ are strongly preferred. The slope of the t distribution is seen to vary with $M^2_{\pi^+\pi^-}$, or put differently, the form of the $M_{\pi^+\pi^-}$ mass distribution is seen to change with t. This causes difficulties in determining the ρ^0 production cross-section since obviously it cannot have a simple Breit-Wigner resonance form.

The decay angular distributions of the $\pi^+\pi^-$ system for events in the ρ^0 mass region and for small momentum transfer ($|t| < 0.4$ GeV^2) from this experiment are shown in Fig. 3. The polar angle distribution is compatible with $\sin^2\vartheta$, consistent with complete helicity conservation at the $\gamma\varrho$ vertex. The ψ data show clear evidence for overwhelming natural J^P exchange. The

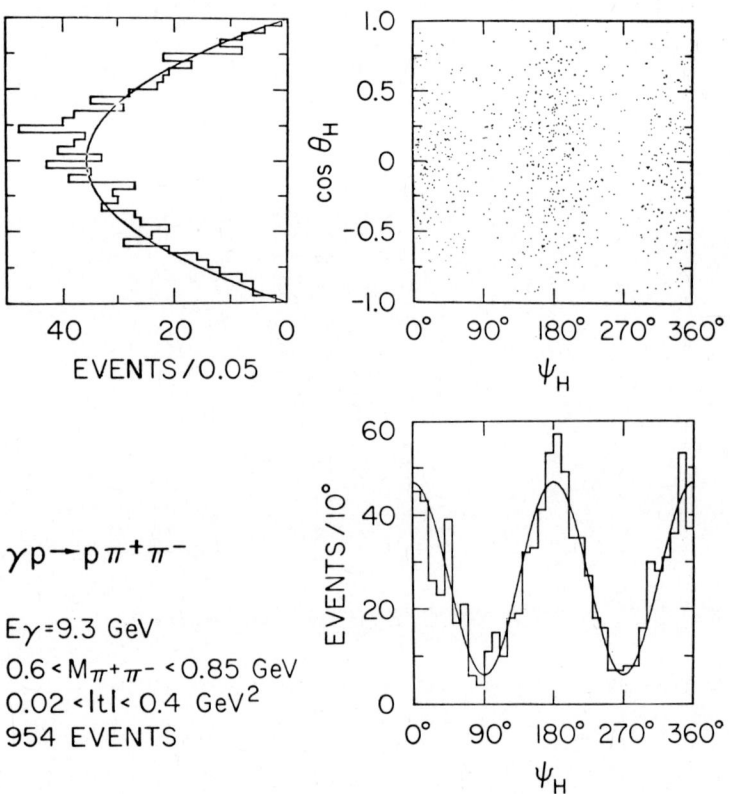

Fig. 3. – Distribution of the dipion angles ϑ_H, ψ_H (in the helicity frame) in the reaction $\gamma p \to \pi^+\pi^- p$ at $E_\gamma = 9.3$ GeV, with cuts 0.6 GeV $< M_{\pi^+\pi^-} < 0.85$ GeV and 0.02 GeV$^2 <$ $< |t| < 0.4$ GeV^2 in the ρ^0 region ([19]). The curves are the angular distributions expected for s-channel helicity-conserving ρ^0 production.

distribution is not expected to go exactly to zero at 90° and 270°, since the photons polarization P_γ was only 77%. Taking $P_\gamma < 1$ into account eq. (5) really becomes

$$W(\psi) = 1 + P_\gamma \cos 2\psi = 1 + 0.77 \cos 2\psi \tag{7}$$

which is what we see in Fig. 3.

The most concise way to visualize the apparent conservation of helicity in ρ^0 photoproduction is presented in Fig. 4, also from the SLAC-Berkeley-Tufts experiment ([19]). Consider a coordinate frame, in the rest system of the ρ^0, in which the ρ^0 density matrix most closely resembles that of the initial photon (*i.e.* pure transverse polarization, same polarization plane). Then let β be the angle of rotation, around the normal to the production

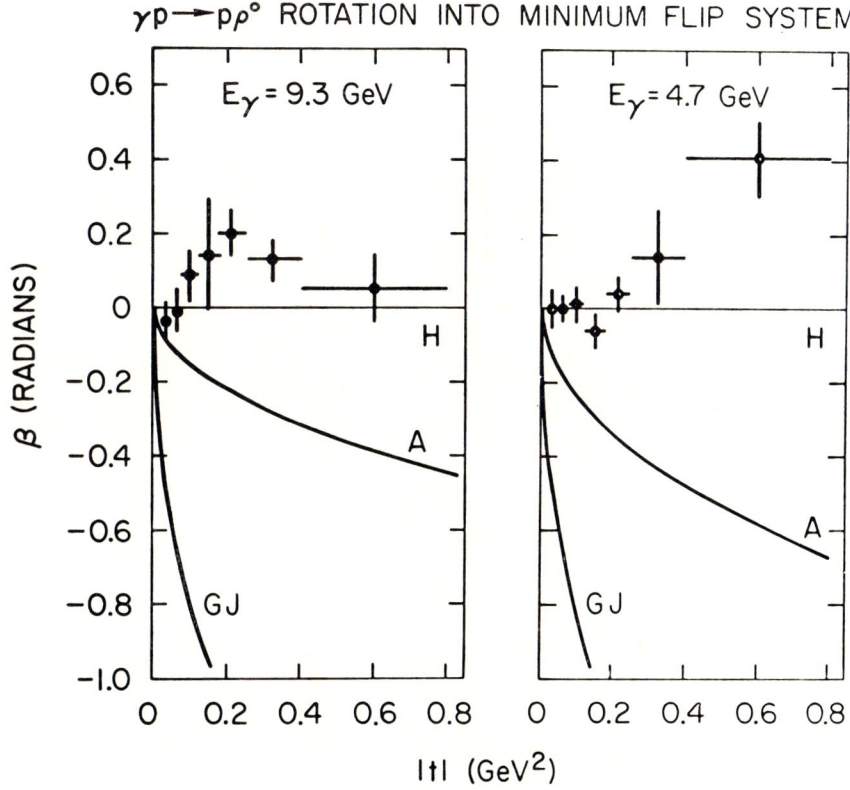

Fig. 4. – Angle β for rotation from the helicity frame into the «minimum-flip system» (see text) as a function of $|t|$, for the reaction $\gamma p \to \rho^0 p$ at $E_\gamma = 9.3$ GeV and 4.7 GeV ([17,19]). The curves marked H, A and GJ show where the data points should be if the minimum flip system were the helicity, Adair and Gottfried-Jackson frame, respectively.

plane, that transforms the *s*-channel helicity frame into this minimum-flip system. It is seen in Fig. 4 that at 9.3 GeV, β is not far from zero up to $|t| = 0.8$ GeV^2. Also shown in Fig. 4 are the angles of rotation from the helicity frame ([22]) into the Adair frame ([26]) (Curve A), and into the Gottfried-Jackson frame ([27]) (Curve GJ). These frames differ from the *s*-channel helicity frame only by a rotation around the normal to the production plane. The helicity frame has its z axis parallel to $\boldsymbol{p}_\varrho$ in the cms, the Adair frame parallel to $\boldsymbol{p}_\gamma$ in the cms, and the Gottfried-Jackson frame parallel to $\boldsymbol{p}_\gamma$ in the ϱ^0 rest system; the y axes are always perpendicular to the production plane. Zero flip in the Adair system would imply « spin direction conservation », while zero flip in the Gottfried-Jackson frame would hold if no spin was exchanged in the *t* channel:

« helicity conservation »

« Spin direction conservation » (ruled out)

No spin transfer in *t* channel (ruled out)

One sees from Fig. 4 that the latter two possibilities are definitely ruled out for $|t| < 0.8$ GeV^2. Contrast this with the situation in the reactions, also believed to be diffractive,

$$\pi^\pm p \to A_1^\pm p, \qquad K^\pm p \to Q^\pm p$$

where the data are more or less consistent with zero flip in the Gottfried-Jackson frame, and incompatible with *s*-channel helicity conservation ([28]). The reason for this difference in behaviour is not clear. These reactions differ however from photoproduction of neutral vector mesons in two respects:

i) The J^P quantum numbers of the bosonic system *change* from 0^-(K, or π) to 1^+(A$_1$ or Q).

ii) The A$_1$ and Q may not be genuine resonances. In any case we conclude from Fig. 4 that for ϱ^0 photoproduction, helicity conservation at the $\gamma\varrho$ vertex may hold up to $|t| \sim 1$ GeV^2 at *high* energy.

B) *Exchange of natural vs. un-natural J^P.* We already saw from the $\cos 2\psi$ distribution of Fig. 3 and eq. (7) that ρ^0 production is consistent with 100% J^P = Natural exchange (see Sketches 4 and 5).

We next discuss this question more quantitatively. Without resorting to density matrix elements, we can combine eqs. (5), (6) and (7) to yield

$$W(\psi) = 1 + P_\gamma \frac{\sigma^N - \sigma^U}{\sigma^N + \sigma^U} \cos 2\psi. \tag{8}$$

Here σ^N (or σ^U) means the cross-section for $J^P = N$ (or U) exchange. Equation 8 is often written

$$W(\psi) = 1 + P_\gamma P_\sigma \cos 2\psi \tag{9}$$

where we have defined the « Parity Asymmetry »

$$P_\sigma \equiv \frac{\sigma^N - \sigma^U}{\sigma^N + \sigma^U}. \tag{10}$$

Bubble chamber experiments could evaluate P_σ from $W(\psi)$, as given in Fig. 3. The SBT results are given in Fig. 6 and the bottom of Fig. 7.

The actual evaluation of P_σ is usually done via $\varrho_{\lambda\lambda'}$ elements, using the relation (to leading order in E_γ ([23,29]))

$$P_\sigma = 2\varrho^{(1)}_{1,-1} - \varrho^{(1)}_{00}. \tag{11}$$

To make eq. (11) plausible, compare eqs. (1) and (9).

Counter experiments report, instead of P_σ, an « asymmetry ratio »

$$\Sigma \equiv \frac{\sigma_\parallel - \sigma_\perp}{\sigma_\parallel + \sigma_\perp}$$

$$= \frac{(\varrho^{(0)}_{11} + \varrho^{(0)}_{1-1})^N - (\varrho^{(0)}_{11} + \varrho^{(0)}_{1-1})^U}{(\varrho^{(0)}_{11} + \varrho^{(0)}_{1-1})^N + (\varrho^{(0)}_{11} + \varrho^{(0)}_{1-1})^U} = \frac{\varrho^{(1)}_{11} + \varrho^{(1)}_{1-1}}{\varrho^{(0)}_{11} + \varrho^{(0)}_{1-1}}.$$

Here, the superscripts N and U mean natural and un-natural J^P exchange; $\sigma_\parallel(\sigma_\perp)$ is the cross-section for the case where the ρ polarization vector $\boldsymbol{\varepsilon}_\varrho$ is orthogonal to the production plane and the γ polarization vector $\boldsymbol{\varepsilon}_\gamma$ parallel (orthogonal) to $\boldsymbol{\varepsilon}_\varrho$, as illustrated below:

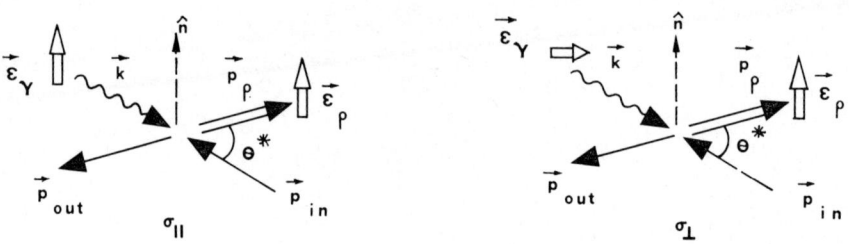

Loosely speaking Σ is the relative contribution of natural vs. un-natural J^P-exchange, to the production of helicity ± 1 vector meson states. For diffraction production one expects $P_\sigma = \Sigma = 1$.

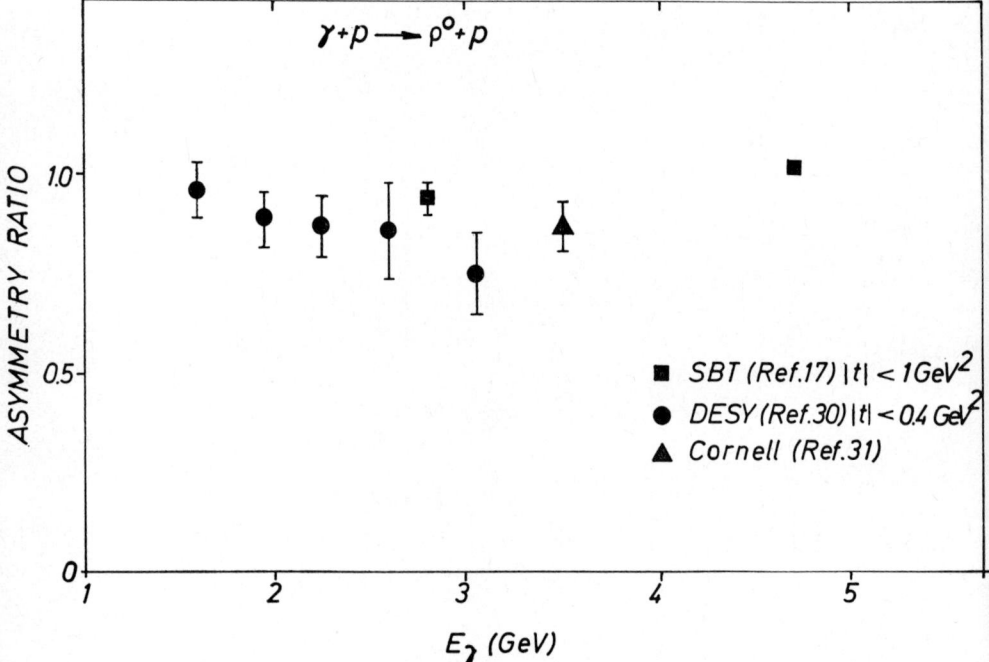

Fig. 5. – Asymmetry ratio Σ in the reaction $\gamma p \to \rho^0 p$ as a function of the photon energy E_γ

Figure 5 shows the measured values (^{17,30,31}) of Σ as a function of the photon energy E_γ. They are very nearly equal to $+1$ in the whole energy range measured, from 1.7 to 5 GeV. Note that Σ can take values between -1 and $+1$. Figure 6 shows P_σ at 9.3 GeV as a function of $|t|$ (^{19}). It is seen to be compatible with 1 in the whole measured $|t|$ range, from 0 up to 0.8 GeV².

As the leading un-natural J^P exchange contribution to ρ^0 photoproduction we may expect pion exchange. From SU_3 symmetry and the quark model one has $\Gamma_{\rho\pi\gamma} = (1/9)\Gamma_{\omega\pi\gamma} = 0.13$ MeV. Using this for the $\rho\pi\gamma$ coupling one

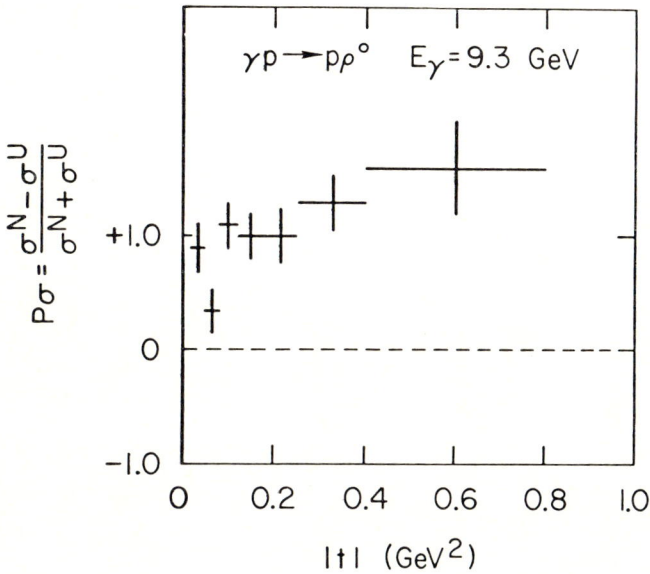

Fig. 6. – Parity asymmetry P_σ in the reaction $\gamma p \to \rho^0 p$ at $E_\gamma = 9.3$ GeV as a function of t (^{19}).

finds the pion exchange contribution to ρ^0 photoproduction as given in the bottom line of Table I. It is seen to be just compatible, within the experimental errors, with the un-natural t-channel exchange contributions found in the SLAC-Berkeley-Tufts experiments ($^{17, 19}$).

TABLE I. – *Un-natural exchange contribution* (^{17,19}), *and expected pion exchange contribution* (^{32}), *to* $\sigma(\gamma p \to \rho^0 p)$.

E_γ (GeV)	2.8	4.7	9.3
$\|t\|$ range (GeV²)	< 1	< 1	$0.05 < \|t\| < \|t\|_{max}$
$\sigma^U/(\sigma^N + \sigma^U)$	$(3.1 \pm 3.1)\%$	$(-1.1 \pm 2.8)\%$	$(-0.5 \pm 4.5)\%$
$\sigma_\pi/(\sigma^N + \sigma^U)$	2%	0.8%	0.2%

An interesting question is whether p-wave $\pi^+\pi^-$-systems produced by natural exchange and with helicity conservation, are also seen outside the ρ^0 mass region. Figure 7 shows $\varrho^{(0)}_{00}$, $\varrho^{(1)}_{1-1}$ and P_σ as a function of the $\pi^+\pi^-$ mass, determined from the data under the assumption that the $\pi^+\pi^-$ system is in

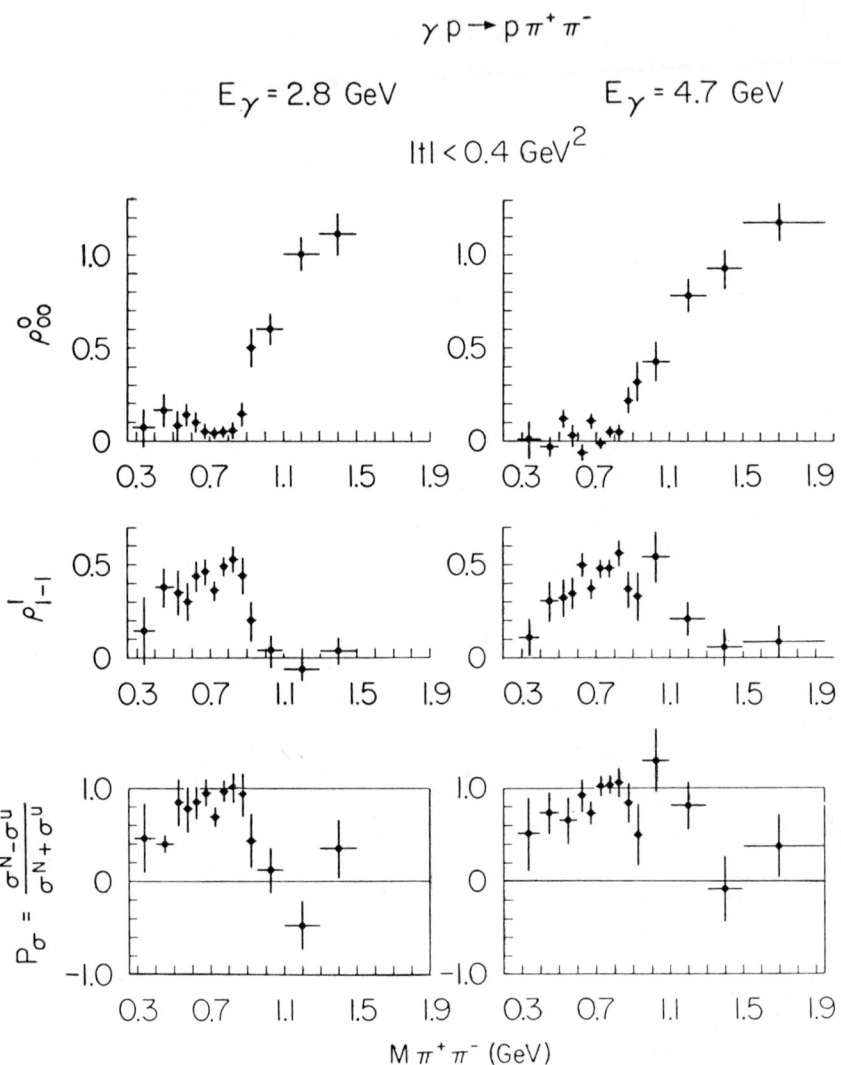

Fig. 7. – The density matrix elements $\varrho^{(0)}_{00}$ and $\varrho^{(1)}_{1,-1}$ and the parity asymmetry P_σ in the reaction $\gamma p \to \pi^+\pi^- p$ at 2.8 and 4.7 GeV for $|t| < 0.4$ GeV^2, as a function of $M_{\pi^+\pi^-}$ ([17]).

a pure p-wave state ([17]). In the ρ^0 region,

$\varrho_{00}^{(0)}$ = degree of longitudinal polarization of the $\pi^+\pi^-$ system, $= 0$;

$\varrho_{1-1}^{(1)}$ = correlation term between $\lambda_\varrho = \pm 1$ states for linearly polarized photons (necessary to give linearly polarized ϱ's), $= \frac{1}{2}$;

P_σ = parity asymmetry $= 1$;

but outside of the ρ^0 mass region these quantities change drastically. This is clear evidence for a background behaving quite different from the ρ^0. It is not unexpected of course, since (see Fig. 2) part of the higher-mass $\pi^+\pi^-$ states (however not all) are decay products of $\Delta(1236)$.

C) Does natural exchange imply helicity conservation? Now that we have seen (*e.g.* in Figs. 6 and 7) that natural J^P exchange dominates ρ^0 production, we must answer the recent remark ([33,34]) that this *implies* helicity conservation, at least at $0°$ (*). In reply we point out that there is still something surprising and unique about our results in the s-channel helicity

---

(*) A simplification of the idea of Houtebeyrie *et al.* ([33]) and of Choudhury and Rajaraman ([34]) is as follows:

If the reaction proceeds entirely by a single exchange X (see Sketch) then the T-matrix element factorizes

$$T = T^{\text{Upper}} T^{\text{Lower}}. \qquad (i)$$

Consider ρ^0 production at $0°$, and consider a set of helicities which flip at each vertex but of course conserve overall J_z. The exchange particle X then has a helicity λ_x, but in its rest frame (the t-channel) we describe λ_x by a *spin* σ_x. We now invoke parity at the upper vertex only: the helicities of the λ of the ρ^0 change sign, but σ_x does not, and T^{Upper} can change only by a sign $\eta = \pm 1$ (related to the parity of X), *i.e.* $T^{\text{Upper}} \to \eta T^{\text{Upper}}$. Now we have an overall amplitude $T' = \eta T^{\text{Upper}} T^{\text{Lower}}$ which does not conserve J_z and hence must vanish. Hence the original helicity flip amplitude (*i*) must vanish too.

This argument is generally true in the t-channel, but fails for $\theta \neq 0°$ in the s-channel because of the crossing matrix which relates the s- and t-channel helicity amplitudes.

frame, where helicity conservation holds for all our energies up to $|t| \sim 0.8$ GeV^2 (Figs. 7 and 4). By contrast, for the GJ and Adair frames, Fig. 4 shows that simple spin flip is already apparent at ~ 0.1 GeV^2.

D) *Rho mass shape and the interference model.* When we introduced Fig. 2, we already mentioned that at small t, the spectrum is skewed towards low $m_{\pi\pi}$. Figure 7.1 shows the SBT ρ^0 peaks at 2.8⟨4.7⟩ GeV ([17]). The — — — curve is a p-wave Breit-Wigner with $m_\varrho = 767$, $\Gamma_\varrho = 145$⟨770, 155⟩. Clearly, the data are again highly skewed. This skewing was noted by Ross and Stodolsky ([54]) in 1966, when they suggested that some kinematical effect near $t = 0$ multiplies the Breit-Wigner by $m_{\pi\pi}^{-4}$. With good statistics finally available, SBT tested this by allowing the exponent « 4 » to vary with t, i.e. $m_{\pi\pi}^{-n(t)}$. Good fits to the mass distributions were obtained, but the exponent $n = $ « 4 » was found to vary with t from $n = 5$ near $t = 0$ to $n = 0$ for

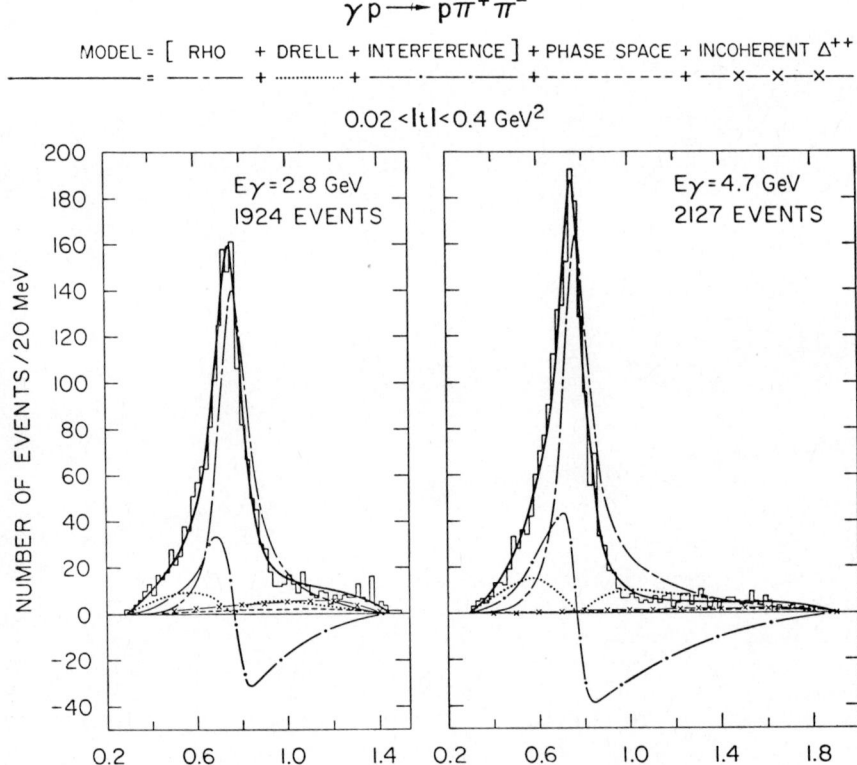

Fig. 7.1. – Contribution of various terms to the interference model fit. This is Fig. 30 of the SBT *Phys. Rev.* paper. ref. ([17]).

$|t| > 0.5$ GeV^2 i.e., the mass shift disappears above $|t| > 0.5$ GeV^2, in agreement with what we have seen qualitatively from the Chew-Low plot of Fig. 2. The conclusion is that the Ross-Stodolsky factor does not fit the data at small or large t values; it gives, however, a reasonable approximation to the mass spectrum averaged over all t. So another explanation is needed.

The SBT collaboration has made a detailed comparison of their data with another model ([47,48]) (illustrated in Fig. 7.2) which describes the ρ^0 mass shift as due to the interference of ρ^0 production (diagram a) with the production of pion pairs through a « Drell » mechanism ([46]) (diagrams b, c). Details are presented in the SBT *Phys. Rev.*, paper ([17]), Appendix B, but can be sketched as follows:

Model for $\gamma p \longrightarrow \rho^0 p$

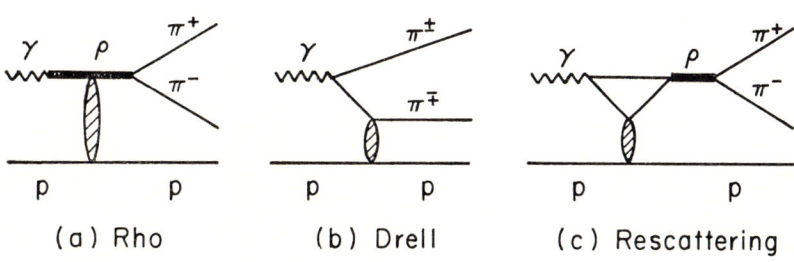

(a) Rho   (b) Drell   (c) Rescattering

Competing Explanations for $\pi p \to A_1 p$ or $Kp \to Qp$

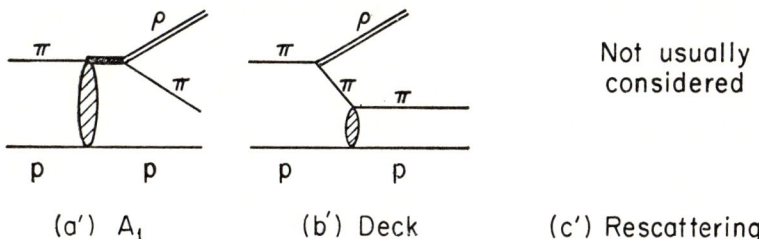

Not usually considered

(a') A_1 (b') Deck   (c') Rescattering

XBL 7111-4860

Fig. 7.2. – Diagrams for the production of $\pi\pi$ pairs in the reaction $\gamma p \to p\pi^+\pi^-$. Analogous diagrams below are used in the Deck or Multi-Regge description of diffractive resonance production by π and K beams.

The ρ^0 amplitude (diagram (a) of Fig. 7.2) is written

$$A_\varrho \propto i \exp\left[A \frac{t}{2}\right] BW(m_{\pi\pi}) \boldsymbol{\varepsilon}_\gamma \cdot \boldsymbol{p}_\pi$$

where BW is a *p*-wave Breit-Wigner amplitude, and where $\boldsymbol{\varepsilon}_\gamma \cdot \boldsymbol{p}_\pi$ expresses helicity conservation in the γ-ρ transition as described by eq. (1). Also, at the nucleon vertex helicity conservation is assumed.

The Drell amplitude of diagram (b) is

$$A_D = A(\pi^+) + A(\pi^-),$$

$$A_{\pi\pm} = \frac{\pm (\boldsymbol{\varepsilon}_\gamma \cdot \boldsymbol{p}_\pm) T(\pi^\pm p \to \pi^\pm p) \text{ Form Factor } (t)}{m_\pi^2 - t}$$

where T is the πp scattering amplitude.

What about rescattering (diagram c)? It has recently been pointed out that to avoid ρ^0 « double counting » one should add a rescattering term, and that this is equivalent ([49,51]) to multiplying the non-flip part of T by

$$\exp[i\delta_{\pi\pi}] \cos\delta_{\pi\pi} = \frac{m_\rho^2 - m_{\pi\pi}^2}{m_\rho^2 - m_{\pi\pi}^2 - im_\rho \Gamma_\rho}$$

Note the extreme difference between $\exp[i\delta]\cos\delta$ (which $\to 0$ at the ρ mass) and the familiar final-state factor $\exp[i\delta]\sin\delta$ which is maximum at the ρ.

Finally, we fit the ρ^0 portion of the data to

$$|A|^2 = |A_\rho + YA_D|^2$$

where Y is an adjustable parameter. It turns out that about 20% of the ρ^0 cross-section must be attributed to $Y^2|A_D|^2$. The individual terms $|A_\rho|^2$, $Y^2|A_D|^2$, and the interference term $2Y \operatorname{Re} A_\rho A_D$ are drawn in Fig. 7.1.

Since this model was invented to describe the skewed mass spectrum, it is gratifying, but not really surprising, that it succeeds. What surprises us is that as a by-product it also describes the angular distribution, not only for *s* and *p* waves, but also the higher moments up to Y_4 and Y_6 (see Fig. 7.3).

The interference model may not be the only model that can describe the data, and in fact Kramer ([52]) has a model which uses only diagram (b) and a final state enhancement $\exp[i\delta]\sin\delta$, and fits reasonably well. Other models are discussed by Wolf ([5]). The point of the discussion above is more to emphasize that *some* reasonable interference model is needed.

In Fig. 7.2 we pointed out the similarity between the diagrams that enter in the interference model, and those used in discussions of bumps like the $A_1(\to \rho\pi)$, A_3, Q, L([55]) which always appear about 200 MeV above threshold in diffractive reactions like $\pi p \to A_1 p$. In hadron physics, the Drell diagram is

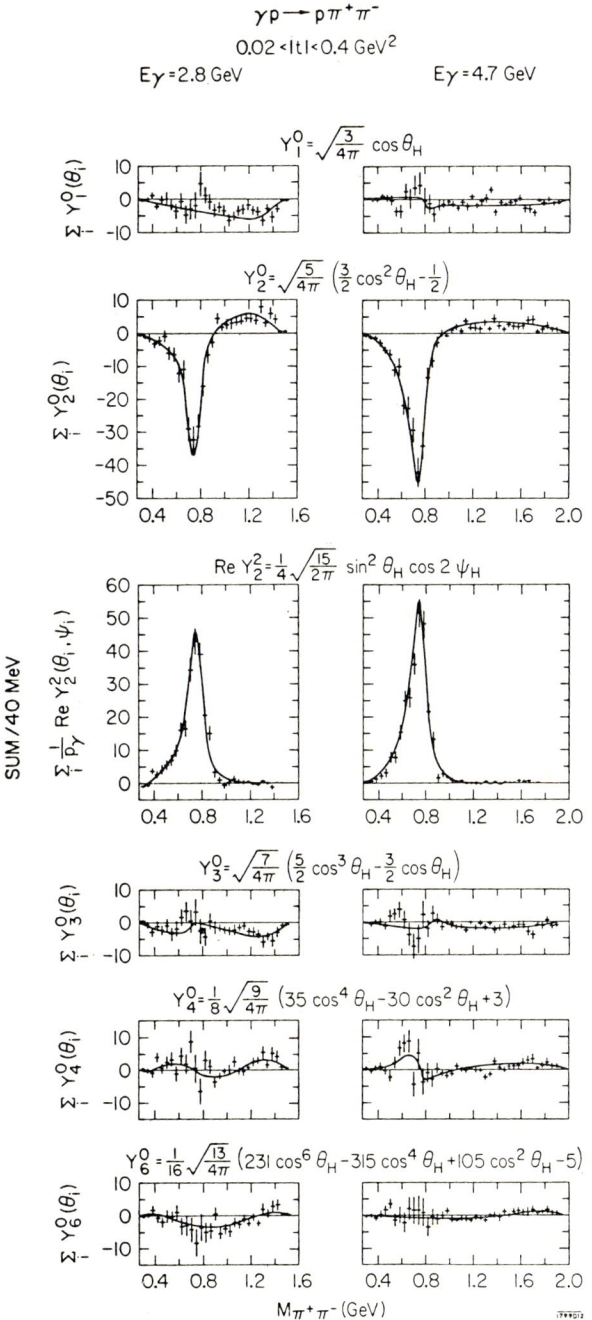

Fig. 7.3. – Reaction $\gamma p \to p\pi^+\pi^-$. The dipion moments $Y^0(\theta)$, $Y_2^0(\theta)$, Re $Y_2^2(\theta, \Psi)$, $Y_3^0(\theta)$, $Y_4^0(\theta)$, $Y_6^0(\theta)$ in the helicity frame as a function of $M_{\pi^+\pi^-}$ for $0.02 < |t| < 0.4$ GeV^2. The curves are obtained from the interference model (Sect. IV-C2). This is Fig. 14 of the SBT Phys. Rev., paper, ref. ([17]).

called the Deck ([112]) or double-Regge diagram and there is still a debate as to whether there « is » an A_1 meson (diagram a)) or the bump can be explained by « Deck effect ». The relevance of our new insight into photoproduction is that we now know that even the healthy ρ, 600 MeV above $\pi\pi$ threshold, and copiously produced, is greatly distorted by Deck = Drell diagrams. By contrast, the A_1 (assuming it exists) seems to be weakly produced, so that we expect it to be seen most clearly when it interferes with a Deck amplitude. So the properties of the A_1 will be dominantly influenced by the Deck mechanism. So we have learned that instead of a debate about « A_1 » vs. « Deck », there is a need for a thorough model with « A_1 » plus $Y \times$ « Deck ». Similarly for A_3, Q, and L. Of course the value of Y may turn out consistent with ∞ (pure Deck), but photoproduction says we will need some careful models before we can tell.

To summarize Sect. 3 we may state that the polarization properties found in the reaction $\gamma p \to \rho^0 p$ are compatible with s-channel helicity conservation at the bosonic vertex, and with natural J^P t-channel exchange. The contribution to the cross-section of un-natural exchange and of helicity flip in the photon-ρ^0 transition is quite small up to $|t| \sim 0.8$ GeV² at 9 GeV. A large nucleon helicity flip contribution cannot yet be excluded. As the most important t-channel exchanges we may expect exchange of P, P', and A_2. An interference model is needed to explain the highly skewed ρ mass spectrum.

4. Polarization properties of the reaction $\gamma p \to \omega p$.

This reaction has been studied with linearly polarized photons also by the SLAC-Berkeley-Tufts Collaboration ([18,19]). They detect the decay $\omega \to \pi^+\pi^-\pi^0$ in the bubble chamber. The formalism is the same as for $\gamma p \to \rho^0 p$, with one difference. In eq. (2) we showed that $\boldsymbol{\varepsilon}_\rho$ could be measured by $\boldsymbol{p}_\pi$. For ω decay, however, with an extra 0⁻ particle in the final state, the equivalent parity-conserving matrix element needs a pseudo-scalar operator, thus

$$T_\omega = \langle 3\pi | \boldsymbol{\varepsilon}_\omega \cdot \boldsymbol{n} | \omega \rangle \tag{12}$$

where $\boldsymbol{n}$ is the normal to the ω decay plane: $\boldsymbol{n} = \boldsymbol{p}_1 \times \boldsymbol{p}_2 = \boldsymbol{p}_2 \times \boldsymbol{p}_3 = \boldsymbol{p}_3 \times \boldsymbol{p}_1$. Hence we measure $\boldsymbol{\varepsilon}_\omega$ by the decay normal $\boldsymbol{n}$.

Figure 8 shows the decay angular distributions of the ω in the helicity system, and the parity asymmetry P_σ, at 2.8, 4.7 and 9.3 GeV ([18,19]). At all three energies, $W(\cos\vartheta)$ does not quite agree with the form $\sin^2\vartheta$

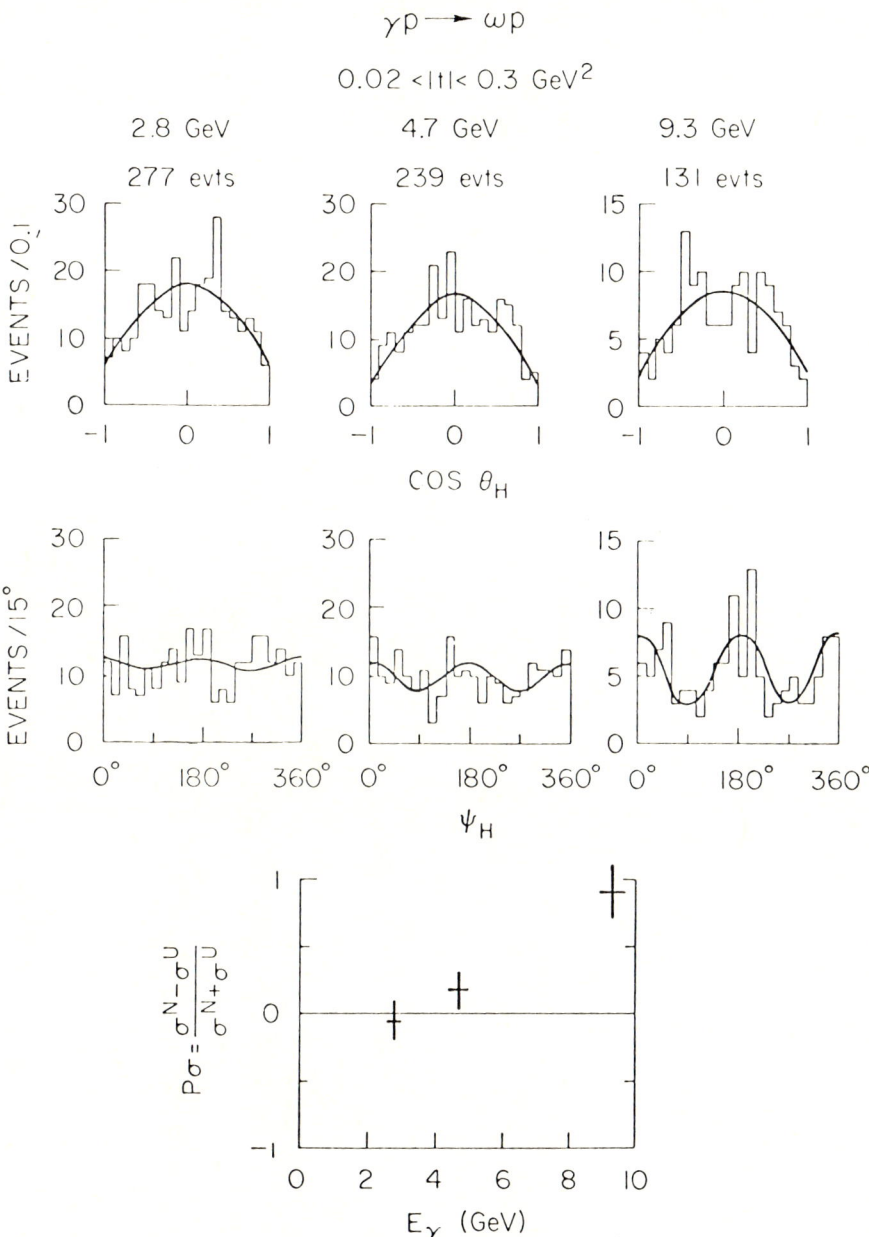

Fig. 8. – Helicity system decay angular distributions, and parity asymmetry P_σ, for ω events (0.74 GeV $< M_{\pi^+\pi^-\pi^0} <$ 0.84 GeV, without background subtraction) from the reaction $\gamma p \to \pi^+\pi^-\pi^0 p$ at 2.8, 4.7 and 9.3 GeV ([17,19]). The curves give the decay distributions resulting from the fitted helicity density matrix.

expected for *s*-channel helicity conservation. P_σ seems to be strongly energy-dependent, rising from 0 at 3 GeV to ≈ 1 at 9 GeV. A separation into natural and un-natural *t*-channel J^P exchange parts of the total ω photoproduction cross-section is shown in Fig. 9. The natural exchange part (open circles), is seen to be only weakly energy-dependent, the energy-dependence being

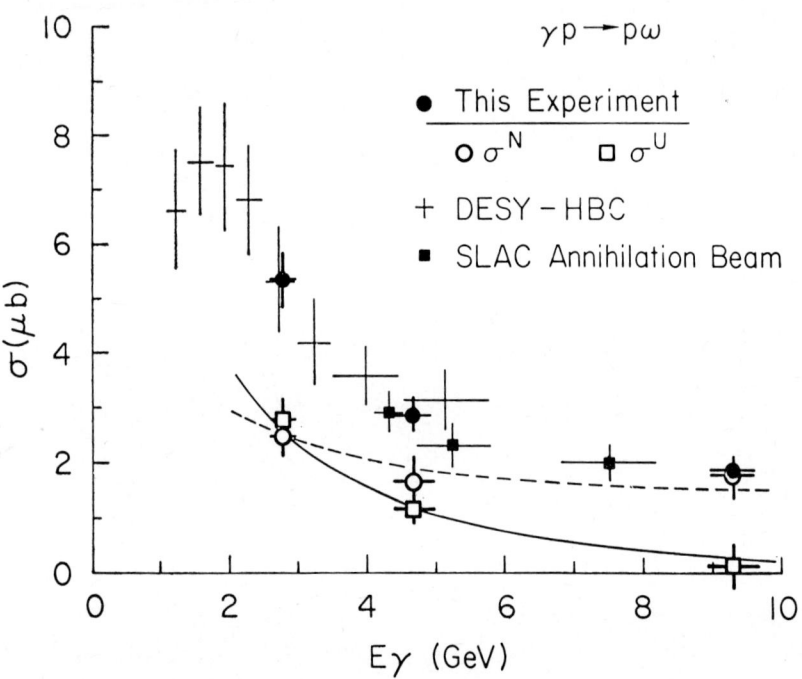

Fig. 9. – Total cross-sections for the reaction $\gamma p \to \omega p$ as a function of photon energy [19]. The points labeled « This Experiment », « DESY-HBC » and « SLAC Annihilation Beam » are from ref. [19], ref. [25] and ref. [63], respectively. Also shown are the natural and un-natural exchange parts, σ^N and σ^U, found from the polarized beam experiments [18,19]. The curves show the pion exchange (full) and diffractive (dashed) parts [19].

consistent with that for ρ^0 photoproduction (dashed curve). This suggests diffraction to be the dominant mechanism. At 9 GeV, $\sigma^N \approx 2 \mu b$. On the other hand the un-natural exchange cross-section drops like E_γ^{-2}. In fact it is quantitatively consistent with pion exchange with Benecke-Dürr form

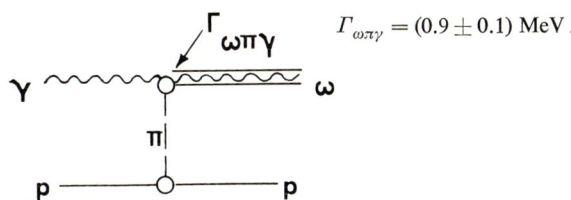

$\Gamma_{\omega\pi\gamma} = (0.9 \pm 0.1)$ MeV.

factors ([35,36]) (full curve in Fig. 9).

5. Polarization properties of the reaction $\gamma p \to \varphi p$.

This reaction has been measured by several groups, all of which detected the $\phi \to K^+K^-$ decay. The ϕ decay angular distribution $W(\cos\vartheta)$ in the helicity system has been looked at by the DESY-MIT group ([37]) (using however a nucleus as target), and the ABBHHM bubble chamber collaboration ([25]), both finding it consistent with $\sin^2\vartheta$ as expected for s-channel helicity conservation. These experiments suffered, however, either from a restricted ϑ-range available, or from small statistical accuracy.

The only published results with linearly polarized photons are from the Cornell group ([20]). They detected ϕ's produced near the forward direction at an average photon energy of 5.7 GeV. For the asymmetry ratio (defined in Sect. 3) they found

$$\Sigma = \begin{cases} 0.94 \pm 0.06 & \text{(on a } C \text{ nucleus target)} . \\ 0.53 \pm 0.15 & \text{(on a } H \text{ target)} \end{cases}$$

The large deviation of Σ on the H target from the expected value of 1 would mean a sizable nondiffractive (un-natural exchange) component, $d\sigma_\perp/d\sigma_\parallel = 0.30 \pm 0.12$. The Cornell group is presently looking into the question of « inelastic » ϕ production perhaps contaminating their measurements ([38]). (For example, the ABBHHM group has found a cross-section $\sigma(\gamma p \to \pi^+\pi^-\phi p) = (0.6 \pm 0.2)\,\mu b$ at $E_\gamma \sim 5$ GeV ([40])). Should the small measured value of Σ be confirmed it would seem rather a puzzle, since the reaction $\gamma p \to \phi p$ is thought, motivated mainly by the quark picture, to be a particularly pure example of a reaction proceeding by P exchange ([41,42]). Candidates for un-natural J_P exchange are π and η. However, with the recent Orsay values $\Gamma_{\varphi\pi\gamma} = (0.0076\pm0.0032)$ MeV and $\Gamma_{\varphi\eta\gamma} = (0.077\pm0.023)$ MeV ([39]), and taking account of the interference between the two exchanges, one computes a rather small contribution of un-natural exchange such that the resulting asymmetry Σ would still be $\geqslant 0.92$ at 5.7 GeV and small θ^* ([32]).

6. Cross-sections of the reactions $\gamma p \to V^0 p$.

A) *Difficulties and uncertainties.* – In the determination of cross-sections for ρ^0, ω and ϕ photoproduction one meets several difficulties. Part of them are of a purely instrumental nature. Thus, bubble and streamer chamber experiments usually miss events with $|t| \leqslant 0.02$ GeV^2, and some losses can occur up to $|t| = 0.05$ GeV^2. In most counter and spark chamber experiments only the decay products of the vector mesons are detected; since the photon beams are not monochromatic one has the problem of separating off the « inelastic background » (*) from reactions like ([43])

$$\gamma p \to V^0 p + n\pi \qquad (n \geqslant 1).$$

Moreover, in some of these experiments one has limited decay angular acceptance, which makes it necessary to *assume*, say, helicity conservation at small t for ρ^0 and ϕ in order to deduce cross-sections summed over all decay directions ([44]). Both difficulties were absent in the SLAC missing mass-type experiment where only the recoil proton is measured ([45]); however, here the mass resolution was not sufficient to separate ω from ρ^0.

In addition, the experimenters also face problems of a more fundamental nature when they try to determine V meson production cross-sections. We list only a few of them.

i) *Background subtraction and interpretation.* In our discussion of the Drell interference and Fig. 7.1 we saw that although there is a « clean » ρ peak,

---

(*) Inelastic background contributions to ρ^0 and φ photoproduction have been recently measured for specific kinematic conditions by the Cornell group, who have added a p recoil hodoscope to their forward pair spectrometer ([38]). They found these contributions to be of the order of $(5\div25)\%$ for $E_\gamma = 8.5$ GeV and $|t| < 0.5$ GeV^2.

there is actually an interfering background, and we are not sure if our model handles it correctly ([51-53]). So even at the peak of the ρ there is some uncertainty as to what to call the cross-section.

ii) *Problems with the shape of a wide resonance.* Even if we believe a model for the background, there is an uncertainty when we integrate over M to get a ρ cross-section:

$$\sigma_\varrho = \int dM_{\pi\pi} \frac{d\sigma}{dM_{\pi\pi}}.$$

The present uncertainty of ± 20 MeV on the width of the ρ ([55]) alone can cause a cross-section error of ± 15%.

iii) *Extrapolation of* $d\sigma/dt$ *to* $t = 0$. (This is mainly a problem for bubble and streamer chamber experiments, while in spark chamber experiments on H_2 targets at $E_\gamma \geq 7$ GeV one was essentially able to *measure* the $t = 0$ differential ϱ^0 cross-sections.) For elastic scattering, $d\sigma/dt$ behaves typically like an exponential at small $|t|$. A similar t dependence may be expected for diffractive production of a *narrow* resonance, except that $|t|_{\text{MIN}} \neq 0$. But for a wide resonance like the ρ, $|t|_{\text{MIN}}$ depends on the mass, resulting in a more complicated t dependence of the cross-section:

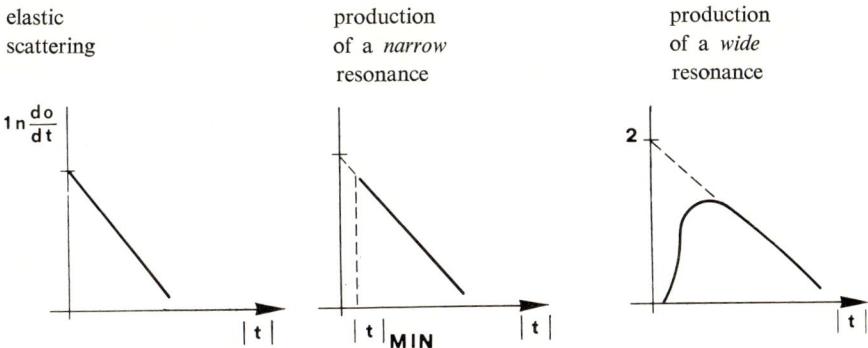

The extrapolation then becomes ambiguous. In some experiments one has effectively corrected the measured $d\sigma/dt$ values, at fixed photon energy, to zero width by a factor

$$\frac{d\sigma_{\Gamma \to 0}}{d\sigma_{\text{exp}}} = \frac{\int dM_{\pi\pi}^2 \delta(M_{\pi\pi}^2 - m_\varrho^2) d\sigma(M_{\pi\pi}^2)}{\int dM_{\pi\pi}^2 BW(M_{\pi\pi}^2) d\sigma(M_{\pi\pi}^2)}$$

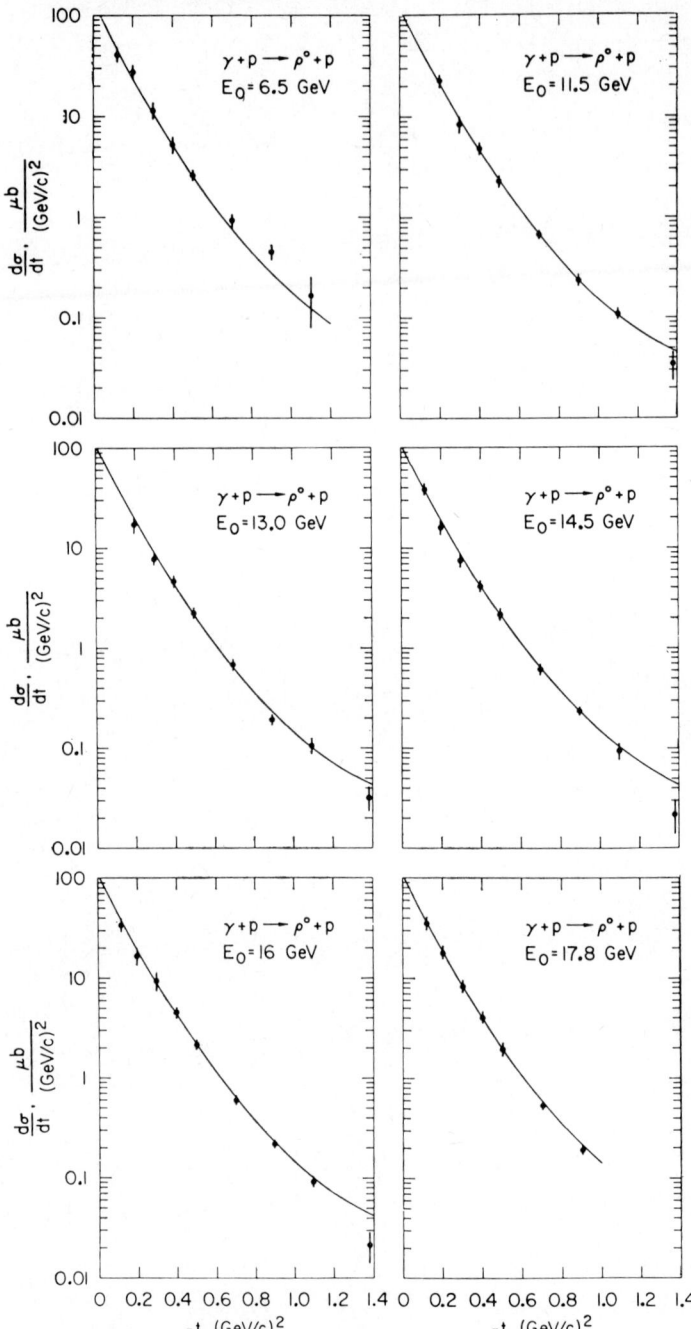

Fig. 10. – Differential cross-section for the reaction $\gamma p \to \rho^0 p$ for photon energies between 6.5 and 17.8 GeV, from ref. ([45]). The curves are from a fit with the vector dominance and quark model relation (see text), with one adjustable parameter $\gamma_\varrho^2/4\pi$.

(where $BW(M_{\pi\pi}^2) = \sin^2 \delta(M_{\pi\pi})/(\pi m_\varrho \Gamma(M_{\pi\pi}))$ is the Breit-Wigner function and $\delta(M_{\pi\pi})$ the *p*-wave phase shift), and then extrapolated the values so corrected. Alternatively, one may determine $d\sigma/d\Omega^*$ as a function of the cm-angle θ^*, convert this into $d\sigma/dt$ using a central ϱ mass, and extrapolate. In addition to such ambiguities there is the question of whether to include a t^2 term in the extrapolation of $\ln d\sigma/dt$. Inclusion of a quadratic term tends to give larger $d\sigma/dt|_{t=0}$ for ϱ^0 photoproduction, but this term is not really warranted by the data.

From all these difficulties it follows that the determination of ϱ^0 photoproduction cross-sections is model-dependent, with uncertainties of $\pm 15\%$ to be expected at finite t, and perhaps even larger uncertainties at $|t| \to 0$.

B) Results. After these preliminaries we show in Fig. 10 the results of the differential cross-section measurements for the reaction $\gamma p \to \varrho^0 p$, obtained in the SLAC missing mass experiment at $E_\gamma = (5.5 \div 18)$ GeV ([15]). The curves are calculated from the vector-dominance and additive quark-model relation ([56])

$$T_{\gamma p \to \varrho^0 p}(s,t) = \frac{e}{2\gamma_\varrho} T_{\varrho^0 p \to \varrho^0 p} = \frac{e}{2\gamma_\varrho} \frac{1}{2}[T_{\pi^+ p \to \pi^+ p} + T_{\pi^- p \to \pi^- p}], \qquad (13)$$

assuming the amplitudes T to have equal phase, taking $d\sigma/dt \propto |T|^2$, and adjusting the single parameter γ_ϱ. The authors obtain $\gamma_\varrho^2/4\pi = 0.61$ as an average over the whole energy range. The success of this fit shows that the s and t dependence of the ϱ^0 photoproduction cross-section agrees well with that of elastic pion-nucleon scattering ([57]).

The extrapolated forward differential ϱ^0 production cross-section from this and from several other experiments ([17,19,25,58-62]) are compiled in Fig. 11. From what has been said it is clear that one cannot expect consistency among all these values. As a general tendency we note a decrease of the forward cross-section with increasing energy up to $E_\gamma \sim 6$ GeV. For $E_\gamma \leqslant 5$ GeV we have

$$\left.\frac{d\sigma}{dt}\right|_{t=0} \approx (80 \div 135) \, \mu\text{b GeV}^{-2}.$$

Within the present errors no indication for *s*-channel resonance structure at the lower energies is apparent. One has probably to look in the backward direction in order to be more sensitive to resonant amplitudes.

From fits of the form

$$\frac{d\sigma}{dt} = \frac{d\sigma}{dt}\bigg|_{t=0} \exp(A_\varrho t) \qquad (15)$$

to the differential ϱ^0 production cross-sections, one obtains slopes in the range of

$$A_\varrho = (6\text{—}9) \text{ GeV}^{-2}$$

at $E_\gamma \leqslant 4$ GeV. The integrated total ϱ^0 production cross-section behaves as (*)

$$\sigma_\varrho \cong \frac{e^2}{4\gamma_\varrho^2} \frac{1}{2}(\sigma^{el}_{\pi^+p} + \sigma^{el}_{\pi^-p}) \sim E_\gamma^{-0.4} \qquad (E_\gamma \geqslant 3 \text{ GeV}) \qquad (16)$$

(with $\gamma_\varrho^2/4\pi \sim 0.7$), *i.e.* it is weakly energy-dependent.

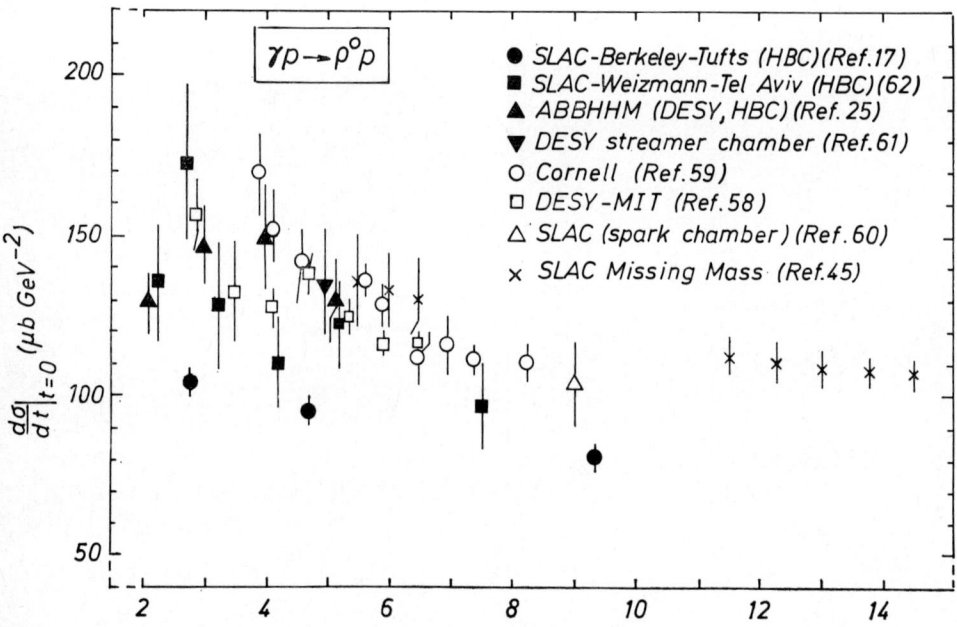

Fig. 11. – Compilation of recent data on $d\sigma/dt|_{t=0}$ for the reaction $\gamma p \to \varrho^0 p$, as a function of photon energy.

(*) We leave the reader to get from eq. (13) to eq. (16) with the warning that one cannot just square (13), since that would introduce a term $2 \operatorname{Re} T^*_{\pi^+p \to \pi^+p} \cdot T_{\pi^-p \to \pi^-p}$.

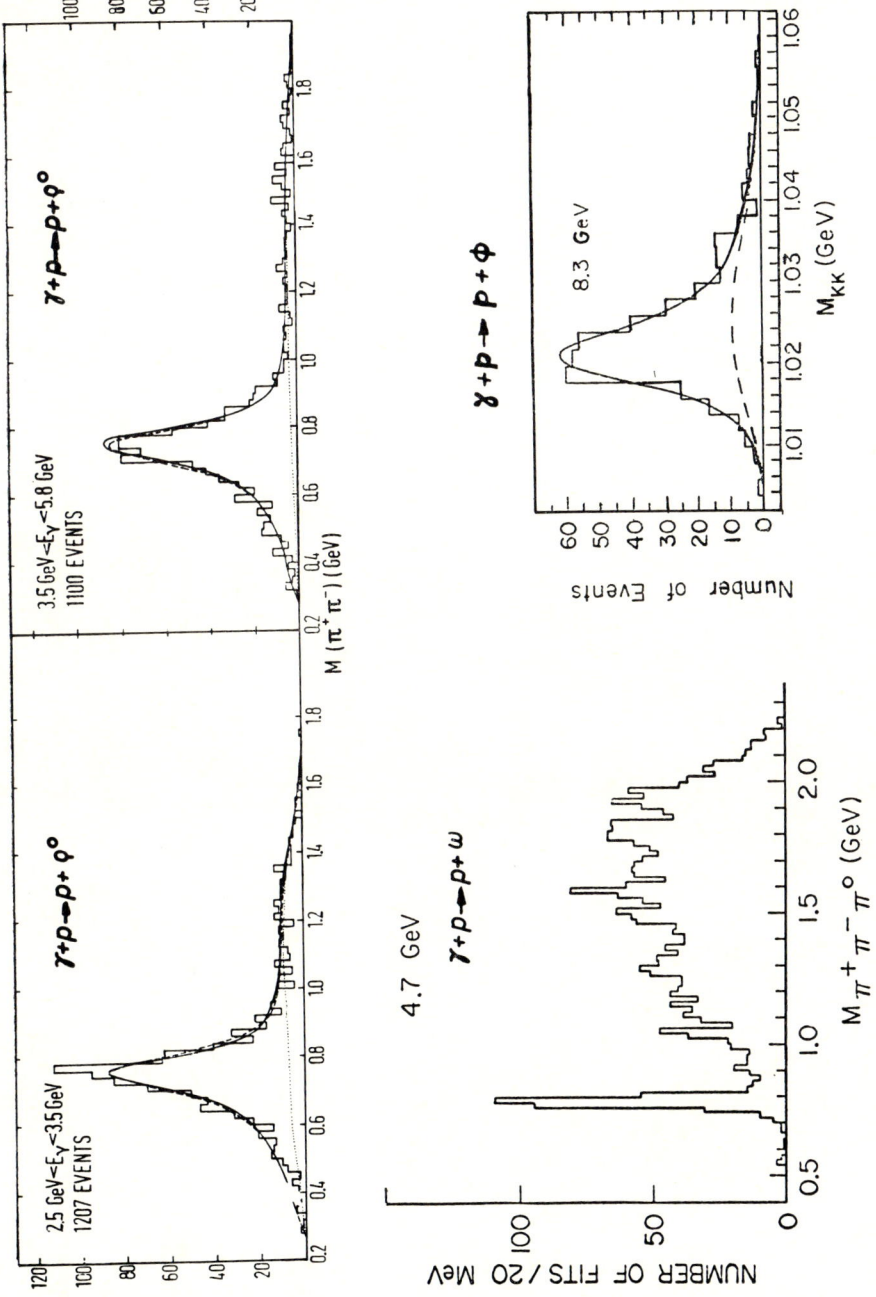

Fig. 12. – Typical appearance of ρ^0, ω and φ peaks (in the mass spectra of $M_{\pi^+\pi^-}$, $M_{\pi^+\pi^-\pi^0}$ and $M_{K^+K^-}$, respectively) in high-energy photoproduction. The data are from refs. [18,25,65].

We thus see that ρ^0 photoproduction behaves much like hadronic diffraction scattering, as expected from the vector-dominance model. From the weak E_γ dependence we infer that **P** exchange is the dominant t-channel contribution.

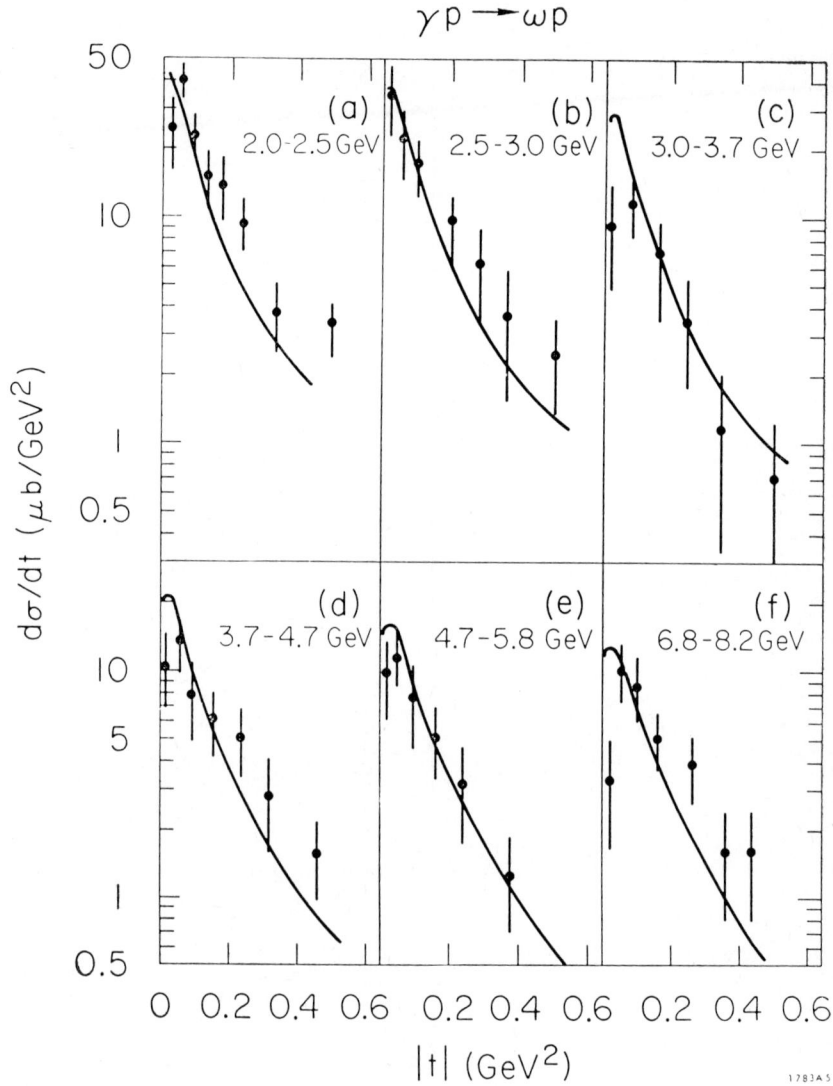

Fig. 13. – Differential cross-section for the reaction $\gamma p \to \omega p$ in various photon energy intervals from 2 to 8.2 GeV ([63]). The curves are from a fitted model, assuming diffraction and pion exchange (see text).

The determination of ω photoproduction cross-sections does not suffer from the large systematic uncertainties described, due to the smaller width of the ω. E.g. from Fig. 12 which shows typical ρ^0, ω and ϕ mass peaks from photoproduction experiments, it is evident that background subtraction under the ω is not a problem. On the other hand, the statistical errors are relatively large since one has to rely on bubble and streamer chamber experiments, counter/spark chamber experiments having problems with background from missing pions.

A compilation of differential ω production cross-sections from various experiments in the (2÷8) GeV energy range, from a recent SLAC-Rehovoth paper ([63]), is shown in Fig. 13. These cross-sections are seen to decrease much more rapidly with increasing energy than the ρ^0 production differential cross-sections (Fig. 10). The curves in Fig. 13 are from a model ([63]) in which the cross-section is expressed as a sum of a diffractive term (whose behaviour is assumed identical with that of the ρ^0 production cross-sections of the same group ([62])) and a pion exchange term with absorptive corrections ([64]). The amount of the diffractive contribution is fitted to the data, mainly exploiting the different energy dependence of diffraction and pion exchange. The diffractive part comes out to be $\sigma_{\omega,\mathrm{diff}} \triangleq (1.5 \pm 0.3)$ μb, not inconsistent with the natural exchange contribution as determined in the polarized beam experiment of the SLAC-Berkeley-Tufts Collaboration ([18]) (see Fig. 9 and associated discussion). The SBT Collaboration has also separated the natural and unnatural exchange contributions in the differential ω production cross-section ([18,19]). For the natural J^P part they find

$$\left.\frac{d\sigma^N}{dt}\right|_{t=0} = \begin{cases} (12.4 \pm 4.2)\,\mu\mathrm{b\,GeV}^{-2} & \text{(at 2.8 GeV)} \\ (13.9 \pm 3.8) & \text{(at 4.7 GeV)} \\ (10.6 \pm 2.2) & \text{(at 9.3 GeV)} \end{cases}$$

and a slope of

$$A^N_\omega = (6-8)\ \mathrm{GeV}^{-2}.$$

Turning now to cross-sections for the reaction $\gamma p \to \phi p$, we show in Fig. 14 a compilation of $d\sigma/dt$ data at photon energies of (2.5—12) GeV ([25,37,45]), taken from a recent Cornell paper ([65]). The curve is a fit to the Cornell

(8 – 9) GeV data (*); it gives

$$\frac{d\sigma}{dt}\bigg|_{t=0} = (3.4 \pm 0.2) \, \mu b \, GeV^{-2}$$

and

$$A_\varphi = (4.7 \pm 0.2) \, GeV^{-2} \, .$$

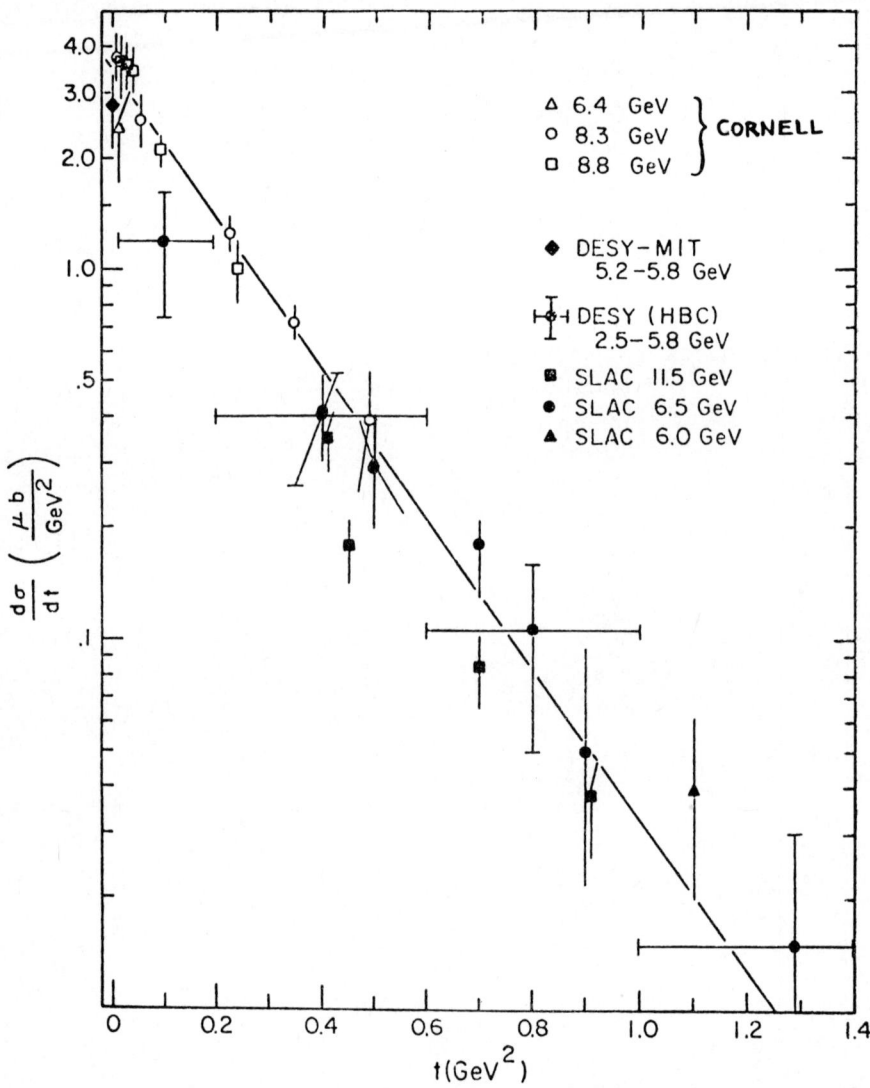

Fig. 14. – Differential cross-section for the reaction $\gamma p \to \varphi p$ for photon energies between 2.5 and 12 GeV (from ref. ([65])). The points labeled «CORNELL» are from ref. ([65]). «DESY-MIT» from ref. ([37]), «DESY-HBC» from ref. ([25]), and «SLAC» from ref. ([45]), The straight line represents a fit ([65]) to the Cornell data at 8.3 and 8.8 GeV.

There is certainly no drastic variation of the ϕ cross-section with E_γ; however, it appears from the SLAC 11.5 GeV data ([45]) in Fig. 14 that the differential cross-section may fall sligthly with E_γ at the higher energies. The SLAC group has tried a fit to their ϕ data similar to the one described before for their ρ^0 data, using

$$T_{\gamma p \to \Phi p}(s,t) = \frac{e}{2\gamma_\Phi} T_{\Phi p \to \Phi p} = \frac{e}{2\gamma_\Phi}[T_{K^+ p \to K^+ p} + T_{K^- p \to K^- p} - T_{\pi^- p \to \pi^- p}]$$

from vector dominance and the additive quark model ([45,56]). It turned out that although the t dependence agreed reasonably with the model prediction, it was not possible to fit the data at all energies with the *same* value of $\gamma_\Phi^2/4\pi$. The ϕ cross-sections decreased faster with increasing E_γ than the quark model prediction from K^+p, K^-p and π^-p cross-sections ([57]). This energy dependence is also indicated in the total cross-section for the reaction $\gamma p \to \phi p$ shown in Fig. 15 ([25,38,45,66]). (Note, however, that the SLAC experiment ([45]) only has data at $|t| > 0.3$ GeV^2 and therefore detects only about 1/4 of the ϕ's produced.)

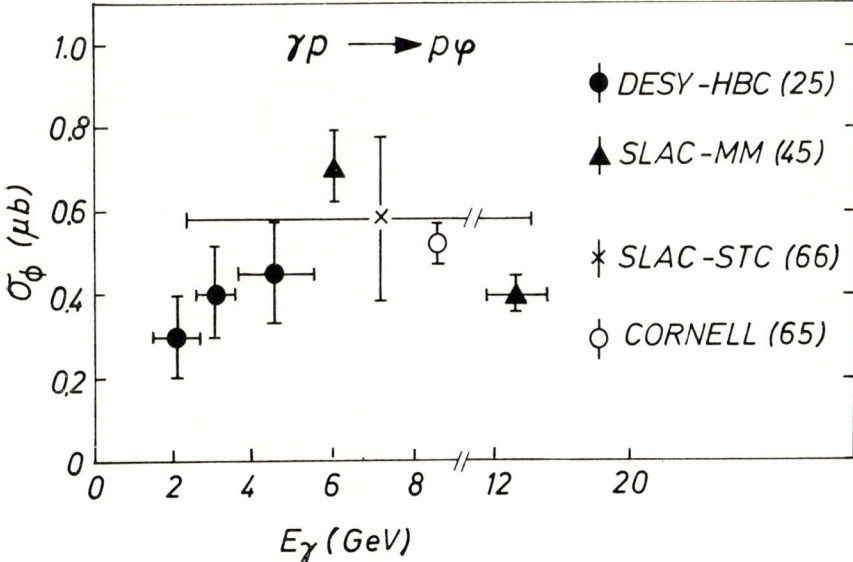

Fig. 15. – Total cross-section of the reaction $\gamma p \to \varphi p$ as a function of photon energy.

(*) These data ([65]) contain, like probably some of the other ϕ data, contributions from «inelastic» ϕ production reactions like $\gamma p \to \phi \pi \pi p$. After substraction of this background (see footnote on p. 908) the Cornell group ([38]) obtained the revised values $d\sigma/dt|_{t=0} = (2.85 \pm 0,2)$ μb GeV^{-2} and $A_\varphi = (5.4 \pm 0.3)$ GeV^{-2}.

7. Test of the vector dominance model.

With the data on ρ^0, ω and ϕ photoproduction discussed we can test the following relation ([67]):

$$\sigma_{tot}(\gamma p) = \sqrt{16\pi}\ \text{Im}\ [\text{diagram}]_{t=0} \qquad \text{(optical theorem)} \quad (17)$$

$$= \sqrt{16\pi} \sum_V \text{Im}\ [\text{diagram with } V^0_{trans}]_{t=0} \qquad \text{(vector dominance)} \quad (18)$$

$$= \sqrt{16\pi} \sum_V \frac{e}{2\gamma_V}\ \text{Im}\ [\text{diagram}]_{t=0} \qquad (19)$$

$$= \sqrt{16\pi} \sum_V \sqrt{\frac{e^2}{4\gamma_V^2} \frac{d\sigma^{Im,\ trans}}{dt}(\gamma p \to V^0 p)}\bigg|_{t=0} \qquad (20)$$

As an estimate of the imaginary parts of the amplitudes for production of transversely polarized vector mesons (with no spin flip on either vertex) we use the square roots of $d\sigma^N/dt$ (note that e.g. the pion exchange amplitude vanishes at $t=0$). We take γ_V from the Orsay storage ring experiment ([68]) on $e^+e^- \to \rho, \omega, \phi$:

$$\gamma_\varrho^2/4\pi = 0.64 \pm 0.06, \quad \gamma_\omega^2/4\pi = 4.8 \pm 0.5, \quad \gamma_\Phi^2/4\pi = 2.75 \pm 0.22$$

(Note that the value for $\gamma_\varrho^2/4\pi$ agrees with the one obtained by Anderson et al. ([45]) from the vector dominance and quark model relation of Sect. 6.) Using photoproduction data in the $E_\gamma = (8 \div 9)$ GeV energy region (see

Sect. 6) we then have the following contributions to the vector-dominance sum:

Vector meson	$(d\sigma/dt)$ Im, trans$|_{t=0}$	Contribution to $\sigma_{tot}(\gamma p)$
ρ^0	$(80 \div 115)$ μb GeV^{-2}	$(67 \div 80)$ μb
ω	11 μb GeV^{-2}	9 μb
φ	3 μb GeV^{-2}	7 μb
		sum $(83 \div 96)$ μb

The total photon-proton cross-section ([69]) at this energy is 120 μb, so that a considerable part of the cross-section remains unaccounted for. If we insist on saturating $\sigma_{tot}(\gamma p)$ with the ρ, ω and φ contributions, then we have to decrease the values of γ_V (which here apply to the photon mass shell, $k^2 = 0$) relative to the Orsay values (which are for $k^2 = m_V^2$). For the ρ coupling this leads to

$$\frac{\gamma_\rho^2}{4\pi} = 0.26 \div 0.38.$$

The two values for $\gamma_\rho^2/4\pi$ would agree better if the value of $d\sigma/dt|_{t=0}$ for ρ^0 photoproduction was larger (e.g., as obtained by quadratic extrapolation to $t=0$). Our neglect of the real parts of the $\gamma p \rightarrow V^0 p$ amplitudes (see Sect. 10) is not responsible for the discrepancy; for example a real part of the natural-exchange ρ^0 forward production amplitude of 20% would only reduce the value of $\gamma_\rho^2/4\pi$ by 4%.

A similar result is obtained if one compares the square root of the *differential* elastic (Compton) scattering cross-section $d\sigma/dt(\gamma p \rightarrow \gamma p)$, with an analogous sum over $[d\sigma/dt(\gamma p \rightarrow V^0 p)]^{\frac{1}{2}}$ at finite t, assuming the phases are all equal. The slopes of $d\sigma/dt$ are compatible within their relatively large errors, but the same discrepancy in the magnitude occurs as we found for the $t=0$ amplitude.

We mention some of the obvious possible reasons for the discrepancy:

i) The coupling constants γ_V may depend on k^2.

ii) The amplitude for the reaction $\gamma p \rightarrow V^0 p$ may depend strongly on the mass of the vector meson produced.

iii) There may exist additional hadronic vector states (so that on the right hand side of the vector-dominance relation, the sum runs over more states than just the ρ^0, ω and ϕ). See Sect. 11.

iv) There may be an additional «direct» interaction of the photon with the hadrons, outside the framework of the vector-dominance assumption.

As we will discuss in Sect. 8 and 9, vector dominance seems to correctly relate ρ^0 photoproduction with ρ^0 elastic scattering by nucleons, with a coupling constant in agreement with the Orsay value of $\gamma_\varrho^2/4\pi = 0.64$. This suggests that i) and ii) are not the principal reasons for its failure in the present case. On the other hand, we note that the vector dominance relation between single pion photoproduction and vector meson production by pions ([2]) tends to give similarly small values of $\gamma_\varrho^2/4\pi$ as we have obtained here from $\sigma_{tot}(\gamma p)$ and vector meson photoproduction.

8. Vector meson photoproduction on the deuteron.

We now consider the reaction

$$\gamma d \to V^0 d$$

i.e. no break-up of the d. (Such reactions are also called «coherent».) We have $I = 0$ in the t-channel. There are only a few experiments on coherent V^0 production in which the presence of the d in the final state was actually detected.

One of these experiments is the missing-mass experiment done at SLAC, in which only the d was measured ([70]). The results for $d\sigma/dt$ from this experiment are shown in Fig. 16. They cover a $|t|$ range of $(0.15 \div 1.4)$ GeV^2 at 6, 12 and 18 GeV incident photon energy. At $|t| < 0.4$ GeV^2 one finds a very steep slope, corresponding to the d size. Then, a break appears, followed by a much smaller slope. This shows beautifully the regions of single and double scattering in the deuteron ([71]). The diagrams for single and double scattering are the following:

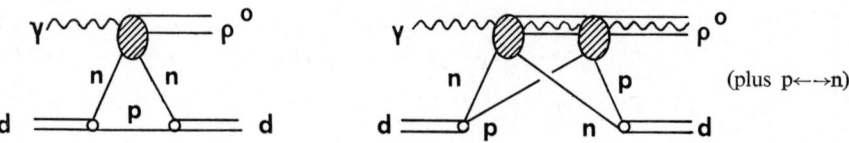

Double scattering dominates at larger $|t|$, while the single scattering cross-section falls with $|t|$ essentially like the square $F^2(|t|/4)$ of the d form factor.

If we consider for a moment the double-scattering term, we see that as the intermediate propagating particle the ρ^0 dominates, while ω and ϕ are strongly suppressed. This is due to the fact that we must have $I = 1$ exchange

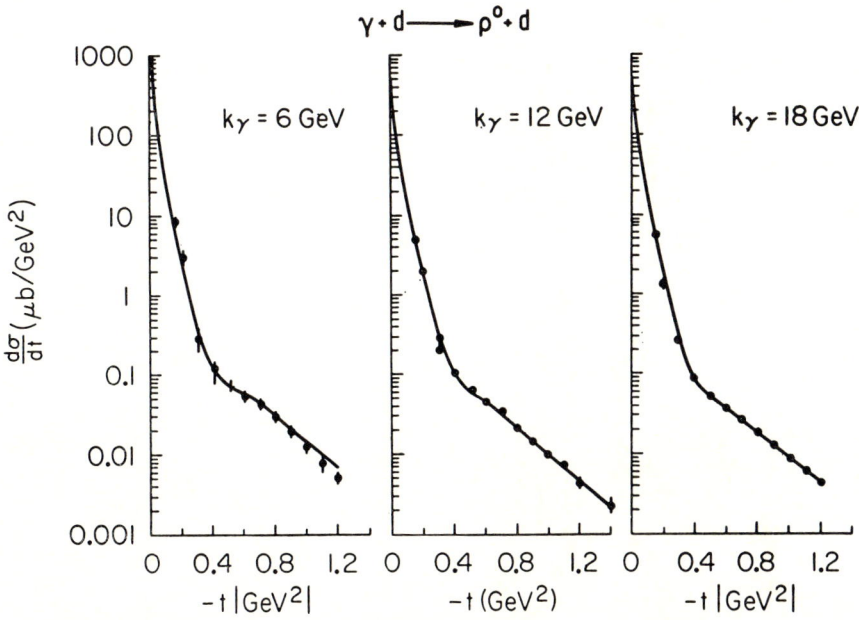

Fig. 16. – Differential cross-sections for coherent ρ^0 photoproduction from deuterons (ref ([70]); figure taken from ref. ([4])). The curves are obtained from fits, using Glauber theory, to the double-scattering region (see text).

in *both* scatterings if we are to have it in one scattering, because only isovector photons can contribute to the overall process. Therefore, double scattering is determined by a product of amplitudes for $\gamma \mathcal{N} \to \rho^0 \mathcal{N}$ and for $\rho^0 \mathcal{N} \to \rho^0 \mathcal{N}$ elastic scattering, and thus provides the chance to observe $\rho^0 \mathcal{N}$ scattering in a rather « clean » and direct way. Also, the real parts of these amplitudes enter only quadratically, so that the results are not sensitive to uncertainties in the real parts (in contrast to the situation with complex nuclei, see Sect. 9).

The curves in Fig. 16 are from a fit *to the double scattering region* $(|t| = (0.7 \div 1.4) \text{ GeV}^2)$, with $d\sigma/dt$ for $\gamma \mathcal{N} \to \rho^0 \mathcal{N}$ taken from the proton data of the same group ([45]). By the fit one can then determine some of the parameters of $\rho^0 \mathcal{N}$ elastic scattering; in particular,

$$\sigma_{\rho^0 N} = (28 \pm 2) \text{ mb} \quad \text{(slightly decreasing between 6 and 18 GeV)}$$

$$\rho^0 \mathcal{N} \text{ slope} \approx \pi^- \text{p slope}$$

is found. The $\rho^0 \mathcal{N}$ cross-section « measured » in this way is reasonably consistent with the additive quark model ([56]) value of about 25 mb (also slightly decreasing between 6 and 18 GeV); the values deduced from ρ^0 photoproduction on complex nuclei (see Sect. 9) also agree within errors with this value. With the results from this experiment one can test the vector dominance model in a finite t region, using the relation

$$\frac{d\sigma}{dt}(\gamma \mathcal{N} \to \rho^0 \mathcal{N}) = \left(\frac{e}{2\gamma_\varrho}\right)^2 \frac{d\sigma}{dt}(\rho^0 \mathcal{N} \to \rho^0 \mathcal{N}).$$

The authors obtain

$$\frac{\gamma_\varrho^2}{4\pi} = 0.68 \pm 0.13,$$

similar to the Orsay value and to the values deduced from complex nucleus experiments (Sect. 9). The fit of Fig. 16 also agrees with the data in the single scattering region at small $|t|$, which shows that the assumption of $d\sigma/dt$ ($\gamma n \to \rho^0 n$) to be equal to $d\sigma/dt(\gamma p \to \rho^0 p)$ does not lead to contradictions.

At smaller $|t|$ than reached by the SLAC experiment, data have been supplied from the DESY and the SLAC 40" bubble chambers ([72,73]). Figure 17 shows results ([72]) for $d\sigma/dt$ in $|t| = (0.04 \div 0.2)$ GeV^2 at $E_\gamma = (1.8 \div 5.3)$ GeV. ($|t| = 0.04$ is the smallest $|t|$ value at which the d can be safely identified in the bubble chamber.) $d\sigma/dt$ has a slope of about $A \approx 25$ GeV^{-2} in this t region. Here we are definitely in the domain dominated by single scattering. The curves are absolute predictions from the single plus the *small* double scattering diagrams, using $\sigma_{\varrho^0 N} = \frac{1}{2}(\sigma_{\pi^+ p} + \sigma_{\pi^- p})$ from the quark model for the calculation of the latter (but the result is not sensitive to $\sigma_{\varrho^0 N}$ at these small $|t|$). The essential assumption made in the calculation is that ρ^0 production on single nucleons proceeds entirely by $I = 0$ exchange, so that the p and n amplitudes are identical. Of course, here in single scattering, one can have only $I = 0$ exchange anyway. But one *calculates* it under the assumption that the $I = 0$ exchange part of $\gamma \mathcal{N} \to \rho^0 \mathcal{N}$ is identical with the measured $\gamma p \to \rho^0 p$ cross-section. From the nice agreement seen in Fig. 17

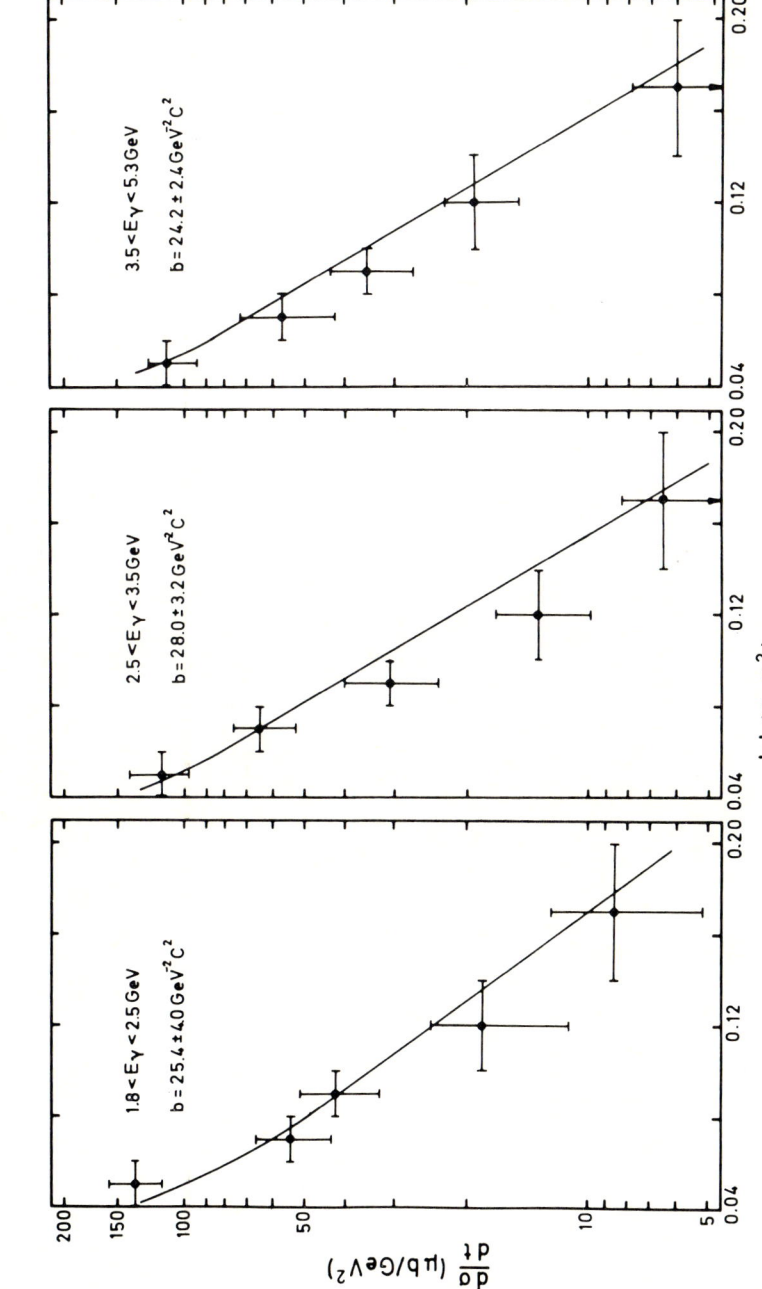

Fig. 17. – Differential cross-sections for coherent ρ^0 photoproduction from deuterons at small $|t|$ [72]. The curves are predictions, calculated from Glauber theory under the assumption that ρ^0 production on single nucleons is pure isoscalar exchange.

it follows that the $I=1$ exchange contributions to ρ^0 photoproduction on single nucleons cannot be very large. We mention in passing that the data on $\gamma d \to \rho^0 d$ for $|t|<0.2$ GeV^2 are found to be compatible with helicity conservation ([72,73]).

A somewhat more sensitive but experimentally difficult test on $I=1$ exchange is provided by a measurement of the reaction

$$\gamma n \to \rho^- p.$$

Possible exchanges are π, ρ and A2:

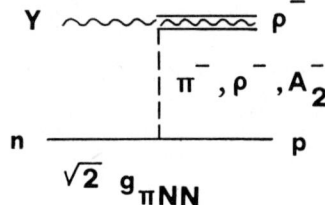

Figure 18 shows the data from the ABBHHM bubble chamber experiment at DESY ([74]). The large errors shown are due to the difficulties stemming from the d target and the presence of a π^0 in the final state, from ρ^- decay. Nevertheless this gives evidence that for 3.5 GeV $< E_\gamma <$ 5.3 GeV we have $\sigma_{\rho^-} \lesssim 1.5\ \mu$b.

Comparing this with the $I=1$ exchange diagram for ρ^0 production (note the Clebsch-Gordan factor of $\sqrt{2}$ vs. 1 at the nucleon vertex) this

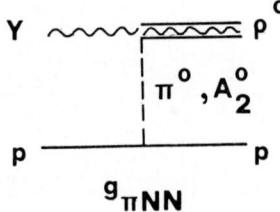

suggests (*) that

$$\frac{\sigma_{I=1} \text{exchange}}{\sigma_{I=0} \text{exchange}} < 0.05 \quad \text{for } \gamma \mathcal{N} \to \rho^0 \mathcal{N}$$

(which still allows 20% $I=1$ contribution in amplitude).

(*) This is not rigorous since although π and A2 exchanges do not interfere at high energies, the A2 and ϱ exchanges *could* interfere destructively in ϱ^- production.

It appears remarkable that also in the low-energy (s-channel resonance) region, σ_{ϱ^-} is much smaller than σ_{ϱ^0}, as is apparent from Fig. 18.

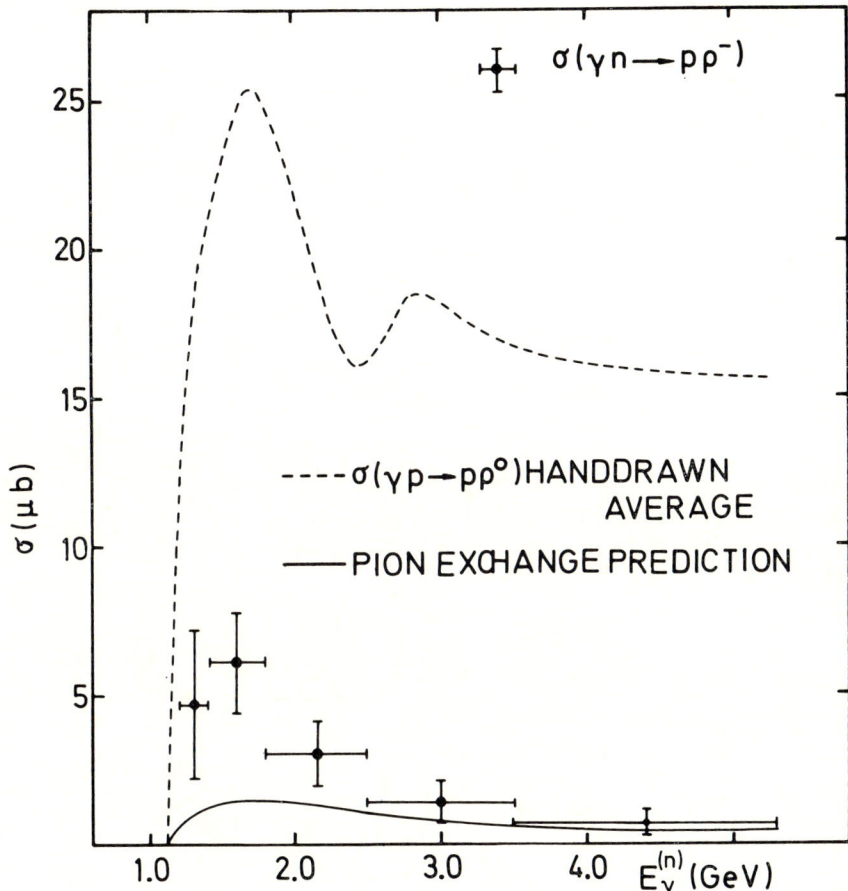

Fig. 18. – Total cross-section for the reaction $\gamma n \to \varrho^- p$, with the restriction $|t| < 1.1$ GeV^2, as a function of photon energy ([74]). No corrections for d effects are included. The solid curve shows the pion exchange prediction with $\Gamma_{\varrho\pi\gamma} = 0.13$ MeV. The dashed curve shows the qualitative behaviour of $\sigma(\gamma p \to \varrho^0 p)$.

First data on coherent ω photoproduction, $\gamma d \to \omega d$, have been recently shown by the Weizmann group ([73]). Within rather large statistical uncertainties they find their data on the ratio of the ϱ^0 to ω coherent forward production cross-sections at $E_\gamma = 4.3$ GeV to be consistent with the value 9, expected from vector-dominance plus unbroken $SU(3)$ plus the additive quark model.

In addition to the experiments mentioned, spark chamber measurements of the reactions

$$\gamma d \to V^0 \genfrac{}{}{0pt}{}{d}{pn}$$

(*i.e.* summing over d breakup and non-breakup reactions) have been made for the ρ^0 at Cornell ([59,75]) and at SLAC ([60]), for the ω by the Rochester group at Cornell ([76]), and for the ϕ at Cornell ([65]). In these experiments the t distributions were measured at energies in the (5÷16) GeV range, detecting only the decay products of the vector mesons. From their different slopes (roughly $d\sigma/dt \propto (d\sigma/dt)_{\text{single nucleon}} \times F^2(|t|/4)$ for the non-breakup («coherent») part, and much flatter for the breakup reaction, according to Glauber theory ([71])) one can separate the differential cross-section into « coherent » and « incoherent » (breakup) parts. For $|t| \to |t|_{\min}$ the incoherent part becomes relatively small. There may be inelastic coherent background (reactions like $\gamma d \to \pi^0 V^0 d$) but estimates show this to be small at small $|t|$, due to the larger $|t|_{\text{MIN}}$. From Glauber theory ([71]), taking account of double scattering effects, one predicts values of

$$\left. \frac{d\sigma/dt\,(\gamma d \to V^0 d)}{d\sigma/dt\,(\gamma p \to V^0 p)} \right|_{t=0} \simeq 3.6 \div 3.9$$

(depending on the type of vector meson and the energy) *if* one assumes that $\gamma p \to V^0 p$ is pure $I = 0$ exchange. This prediction is generally found to agree with the extrapolated ρ^0 and ϕ data for energies above 6.5 GeV, within the experimental uncertainties on the ratio of about ± 0.2. Between 4 and 6 GeV for ρ^0 mesons, however, the Cornell d/p ratios are significantly smaller than the prediction with pure $I = 0$ exchange, indicating an $I = 1$ exchange amplitude of size $\sim 15\%$ of the magnitude of the total amplitude for ρ^0 production on the nucleon ([75]).

It is interesting to check the vector-dominance relation of Sect. 7 with the extrapolated coherent d cross-sections, since isovector exchange amplitudes are absent here. In the reactions on single nucleons these amplitudes might be suspected to cause trouble for the vector-dominance comparison by contributing real parts and/or longitudinal polarization of the vector mesons. With the Orsay coupling constants (see Sect. 7) and photoproduction data in the (6÷8) GeV energy region, we have (assuming zero real parts and zero helicity flip in the forward direction):

Vector meson	$(d\sigma/dt)\|_{t=0}(\gamma d \to V^0 d)$	Contribution to $\sigma_{tot}(\gamma d)$
ρ^0	390 μb GeV^{-2}	148 μb
ω	~36 μb GeV^{-2} (*)	~17 μb
φ	10 μb GeV^{-2}	12 μb
		sum 177 μb

This is to be compared with the measured total cross-section $\sigma_{tot}(\gamma d) \simeq$ $\simeq 230$ μb ([69,77]) (*). Saturating $\sigma_{tot}(\gamma d)$ with the ρ, ω and φ vector-dominance contributions would require a value of

$$\frac{\gamma_\rho^2}{4\pi} = 0.35 \pm 0.06.$$

We thus find a similar difficulty with the vector-dominance model as in γp reactions (Sect. 7).

9. The reaction $\gamma A \to V^0 A$ on complex nuclei.

In the experiments to be discussed now, one uses the nucleus as a reabsorbing and refracting target of variable thickness for the vector mesons. One can relate the differential cross-section $d\sigma_{coh}/dt$ for the coherent reaction

$$\gamma A \to V^0 A$$

to the spin- and isospin-independent part $d\sigma_0/dt(\gamma N \to V^0 N)$ of the photoproduction differential cross-section on a single nucleon at $t = 0$, using an impact parameter approach, and taking account of reabsorption of the V^0,

---

(*) This value is estimated by extrapolating the closure fit to the Rochester data ([76]) towards $t = 0$. It agrees with the coherent forward cross-section quoted in ref. ([73]).

hence σ_{VN} enters:([78,79])

$$\frac{d\sigma_{coh}}{dt} = \frac{d\sigma_0}{dt}(\gamma\mathcal{N} \to V^0\mathcal{N})\bigg|_{t=0} \cdot \bigg| \int_0^\infty 2\pi b\, db \int_{-\infty}^{\infty} dz J_0(b\sqrt{-t_\perp})\varrho(b,z) \exp(iz\sqrt{-t_\parallel}) \cdot$$

$$\cdot \exp\left[-\frac{\sigma_{VN}}{2}(1-i\alpha_{VN})\int_z^\infty dz'\varrho(b,z')\right]\bigg|^2$$

Here $\sqrt{-t_\parallel}$ and $\sqrt{-t_\perp}$ are the longitudinal and transverse four-momentum transfers, $\varrho(b, z)$ is the nuclear density distribution (normalized to A), α_{VN} the ratio of real to imaginary parts of the forward $V^0\mathcal{N}$ elastic scattering amplitude, and σ_{VN} the total vector-meson nucleon cross-section. The factor $\exp[iz\sqrt{-t_\parallel}]$ results from the lengthening of the wavelength of the emerging vector meson relative to the incident photon, caused by the photon-vector meson mass difference.

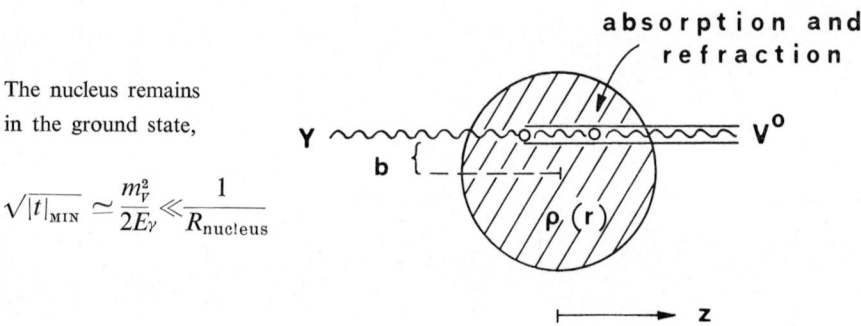

The nucleus remains in the ground state,

$$\sqrt{|t|}_{MIN} \simeq \frac{m_V^2}{2E_\gamma} \ll \frac{1}{R_{nucleus}}$$

Corrections for nucleon-nucleon correlations (which can have a 10% effect on the effective σ_{VN}) have in some cases also been taken into account ([80]).

As input for the analysis of the nuclear data with this model one uses the measured t and A dependence of the cross-section for $\gamma A \to V^0 A$ and the value of the ratio α_{VN} of real to imaginary parts. Further, one has to adopt some model for the density distribution $\varrho(r)$. One then obtains as output the values of σ_{VN} (where $\mathcal{N}$ stands for the average of the protons and neutrons in the nucleus) and of $d\sigma_0/dt(\gamma\mathcal{N} \to V^0\mathcal{N})|_{t=0}$. In addition, from the diffraction slope of $(d\sigma_{coh}/dt)(\gamma A \to V^0 A)$ one can determine nuclear radii.

With these quantities one may test the vector dominance model and determine the photon-vector meson coupling constants, using the relation

$$\frac{d\sigma_0}{dt}(\gamma\mathcal{N} \to V^0\mathcal{N})\bigg|_{t=0} = \underbrace{\frac{e^2}{4\gamma_V^2} \frac{\sigma_{VN}^2}{16\pi}(1 + \alpha_{VN}^2)}_{= (\mathrm{Im}\, T_{VN})^2}$$

This simple relation holds only if contributions of intermediate vector-meson states $V^{0'} \neq V^0$ can be neglected.

A major uncertainty in the analysis of the photoproduction data on complex nuclei (but not on the deuteron, see Sect. 8) is caused by the fact that the real parts of the $V^0\mathcal{N}$ scattering amplitudes have a strong influence on the resulting nuclear photoproduction amplitudes ([81]). Unfortunately, direct measurement of the real parts is difficult and uncertainties are still large (see Sect. 10). Therefore, values estimated from vector dominance and total $\gamma\mathcal{N}$ cross-sections using dispersion relations ([82]), or from the real parts of $\pi\mathcal{N}$ and $K\mathcal{N}$ scattering with the additive quark model ([56,83]), have also been used in the analysis of the data. It may be comforting that the procedure seems at least to be consistent, in that the imaginary parts (*i.e.* the total nucleon cross-sections) which one then obtains, agree with the prediction from $\pi\mathcal{N}$ and $K\mathcal{N}$ scattering with the quark model (see below). The results on $\sigma_{\varrho^0 N}$ are also consistent with the values from double scattering in the deuteron (Sect. 8), which are much less sensitive to the real parts.

As an example of the measurements that have been performed, Fig. 19 shows values of $d\sigma/d\Omega\,dM_{\pi\pi}$ for ϱ^0 photoproduction on various nuclei, as obtained by the DESY-MIT-Group in a two-arm counter experiment at $\langle E_\gamma \rangle = 6.2$ GeV ([84]). About 10^6 events were collected in this experiment. The range of the square of the transverse four-momentum transfer is $0.001 \text{ GeV}^2 < |t| < 0.01 \text{ GeV}^2$. From these measured differential cross-sections one has to subtract the « incoherent » background (with excitation or breakup of the nucleus, which is non-negligible on light nuclei) ([85]). One also has, similar as with proton photoproduction data, to separate the ϱ^0 production from the non-ϱ^0 background, using suitable models for the latter (*e.g.* phase space, or Drell process) to fit the $M_{\pi^+\pi^-}$ distribution. The uncertainties on the final results of the experiment mainly stem from this background subtraction.

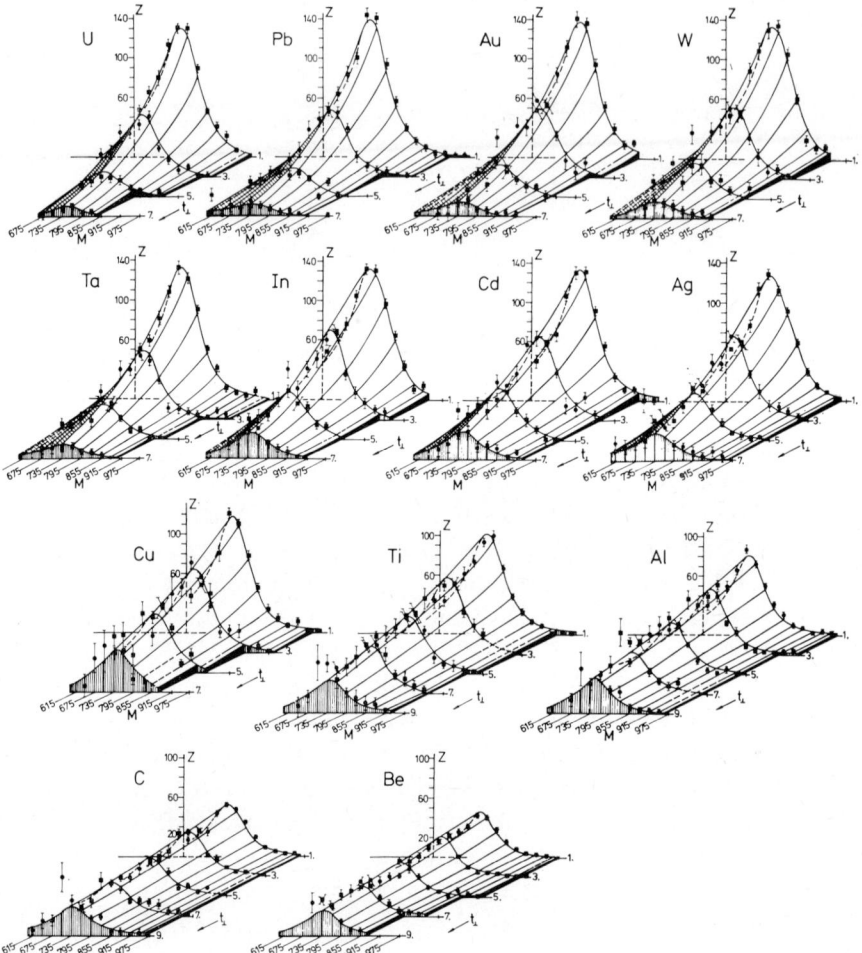

Fig. 19. – Differential cross-sections $Z = d\sigma/d\Omega\, dM_{\pi\pi}$ (μb/ster/MeV/nucleon) as a function of $M_{\pi\pi}$(MeV) and t (units -0.001 GeV^2), for the reaction $\gamma A \to \pi^+\pi^- \ldots$ at $E_\gamma = 6.2$ GeV and with various different A ([84]). The curves are fits with a superposition of coherent and incoherent ρ^0 production, and non-ρ background.

Measurements of ρ^0 photoproduction have also been done by the Cornell ([59,86]), Rochester ([87]) and SLAC ([88]) groups in the energy range from 5 to 16 GeV. The Cornell group used a two-arm spectrometer with spark chambers, while the Rochester and SLAC groups used large spark chamber systems. The angular acceptance in the SLAC experiment allowed to verify that the ρ^0's are indeed transversally polarized. The results from these various experiments are consistent among each other. The value obtained of

$$\frac{d\sigma_0}{dt}(\gamma\mathcal{N} \to \rho^0\mathcal{N})\bigg|_{t=0} = 118 \;\mu\text{b GeV}^{-2}$$

is compatible with the ρ^0 forward cross-section on single protons (Sect. 6). The results on $\sigma_{\rho N}$ and $\gamma_\rho^2/4\pi$ from the various experiments are compiled in Fig. 20. Average values obtained are

$$\frac{\gamma_\rho^2}{4\pi} \sim 0.65, \qquad \sigma_{\rho N} \approx 27 \text{ mb} \qquad (\text{at } E_\gamma = (5 \div 16) \text{ GeV})$$

(photon mass shell)

in agreement with the Orsay value ([68]) of $\gamma_\rho^2/4\pi = 0.64 \pm 0.06$ on the ρ mass

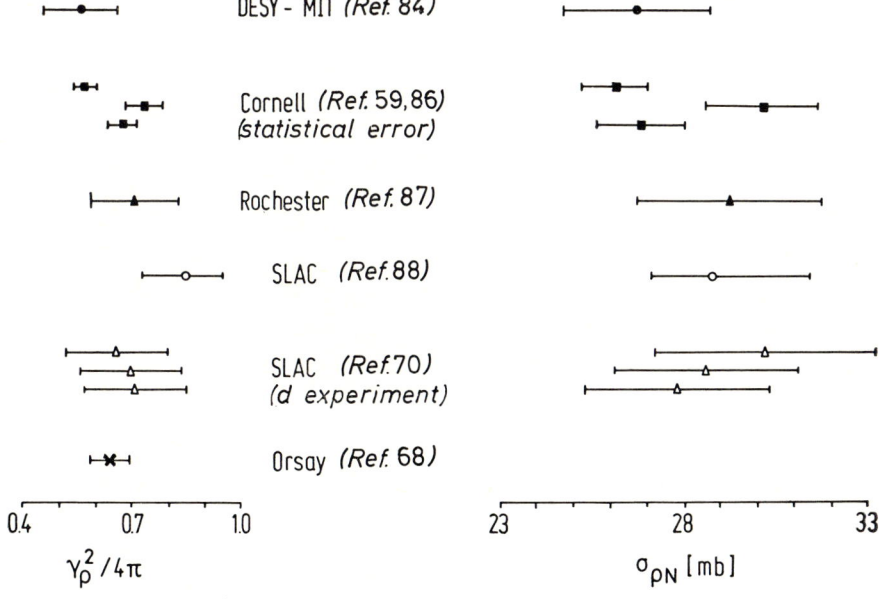

Fig. 20. – Values of $\gamma_\rho^2/4\pi$ and $\sigma_{\rho N}$ as obtained from recent ρ^0 photoproduction experiments on complex nuclei (Figure adapted from ref. ([4])). Included are the results of the SLAC experiment on ρ^0 scattering in the deuteron ([70]), and the ρ mass-shell measurement of $\gamma_\rho^2/4\pi$ from Orsay ([68]).

shell. The value for $\sigma_{\rho N}$ is in good agreement with the additive quark model prediction

$$\sigma_{\rho^0 p} = \sigma_{\omega p} = \frac{1}{2}(\sigma_{\pi^+ p} + \sigma_{\pi^- p}) = \begin{cases} 28 \text{ mb at } 5 \text{ GeV} \\ 25 \text{ mb at } 14 \text{ GeV}. \end{cases}$$

The values for both $\gamma_\varrho^2/4\pi$ and for $\sigma_{\varrho^0 p}$ are also compatible with the results from the SLAC experiment on double-scattering in the deuteron ([70]).

Results from ω photoproduction on complex nuclei are shown in Table II. The Rochester group ([89]) has detected the $\pi^+\pi^-\pi^0$ decay, while the Bonn-Pisa group ([90]) measured the $\pi^0\gamma$ decay of the ω. Problems with large width, as for the ϱ, are absent here, but there is higher incoherent background, due to the pion exchange contribution to ω production on nucleons. The values obtained for $(d\sigma_0/dt)(\gamma N \to \omega N)|_{t=0}$ agree, within the rather wide errors, with

TABLE II. – Results from the reaction $\gamma A \to \omega A$.

Group	E_γ (GeV)	$d\sigma_0/dt(\gamma N \to \omega N)|_{t=0}$ [μb GeV^{-2}]	$\sigma_{\omega N}$ (mb)	$\gamma_\omega^2/4\pi$
Rochester (Cornell) ([89])	6.8	11.4 ± 1.9	25.3 ± 7.8	$7.6^{+1.8}_{-1.1}$
Bonn-Pisa (DESY) ([90])	5.7	15.1 ± 3.1	$30.0^{+7.0}_{-6.0}$	5.8 ± 1.3
(Orsay $e^+e^- \to \omega$) ([68])				(4.8 ± 0.5)

the natural J^P-exchange contribution in the reaction $\gamma p \to \omega p$ (see Sect. 6). This is consistent with the A_2 exchange contribution to ω photoproduction on protons being rather small. The $\sigma_{\omega N}$ values obtained are seen to be compatible with the quark model prediction of ~ 28 mb.

Experiments on ϕ photoproduction on complex nuclei ([6,37,65]) are quite difficult since the ϕ is measured via its decay into K^+K^-, the angle between the kaon's momenta being very small, and the kaons decay so rapidly that only a small fraction of them are detected and the decay products may cause background. The results are summarized in Table III. The forward differential cross-section $(d\sigma_0/dt)(\gamma N \to \phi N)|_{t=0}$ is consistent with the forward

TABLE III. – Results from the reaction $\gamma A \to \varphi A$.

Group	E_γ (GeV)	$d\sigma_0/dt(\gamma N \to \varphi N)|_{t=0}$ (μb GeV^{-2})	$\sigma_{\Phi N}$ (mb)	$\gamma_\omega^2/4\pi$
Cornell ([65])	6.4, 8.3	4.3	12	5.8 ± 2.4
DESY-MIT ([6,37])	5.2	3.2 ± 0.3	11.3 ± 3	3.8 ± 1.4
(Orsay $e^+e^- \to \varphi$) ([68])				(2.75 ± 0.22)

differential cross-section for ϕ production on protons (Sect. 6). A striking result is the smallness of the values for $\sigma_{\Phi N}$ obtained, compared with $\sigma_{\varrho^0 N}$, $\sigma_{\omega N}$ and any other known total hadronic cross-section. An explanation of this remarkable fact is given by the simple additive quark model ([56]). The ϕ, as a nearly pure $(\lambda\bar{\lambda})$ state, interacts with the nucleon in this model only through strange-nonstrange quark-quark scattering, which is assumed to have a smaller cross-section than the scattering between nonstrange quarks. The simple prediction from this model,

$$\sigma_{\Phi p} = \sigma_{K^+ p} + \sigma_{K^- n} - \sigma_{\pi^+ p} = 13 \text{ mb at } 5 \text{ GeV},$$

is in perfect agreement with the measured values of $\sigma_{\Phi N}$ given in Table III.

Summarizing the results on the photon-vector meson coupling constants $\gamma_V^2/4\pi$, their values (at $k^2 = 0$) as obtained from V^0 photoproduction on nuclei agree with the Orsay value ([68]) (at $k^2 = m_V^2$) in the case of the ρ, and are perhaps somewhat larger than the Orsay values for ω and ϕ. The ratio

$$\frac{1}{\gamma_\varrho^2} : \frac{1}{\gamma_\omega^2} : \frac{1}{\gamma_\Phi^2} = 9 : (0.9 \pm 0.3) : (1.5 \pm 0.5) \quad \text{from } \gamma A \to V^0 A$$

is still compatible with the expected ratio of 9:0.65:1.33 ([91]). Thus, within the relatively big errors (caused to large extent by the uncertainty in the real parts), vector-dominance seems to do reasonably well in relating V^0 photoproduction with V^0 elastic scattering. This could be a hint that the failure of the vector-dominance model in relating γN scattering with the sum of the vector-meson photoproduction amplitudes (see Sect. 7) is *not* primarily due to a k^2 dependence of the coupling constants γ_V.

10. The phase of the ρ, ω and φ forward elastic scattering.

From the polarization and energy dependence of the reaction $\gamma p \to \rho^0 p$ we were led to the conclusion that **P** is the dominant exchange. If this is correct then the ratio of the real to the imaginary part of the spin-independent forward amplitude of this reaction will be small at high energy. From the vector-dominance picture we then expect the corresponding ratio for elastic $\rho^0 p$ scattering to be similarly small.

The phase of the vector-meson photoproduction amplitude near the forward direction can be measured by observing its interference with the purely real Bethe-Heitler wide-angle lepton pair production amplitude, which can be calculated in quantum-electrodynamics. In order to have identical final

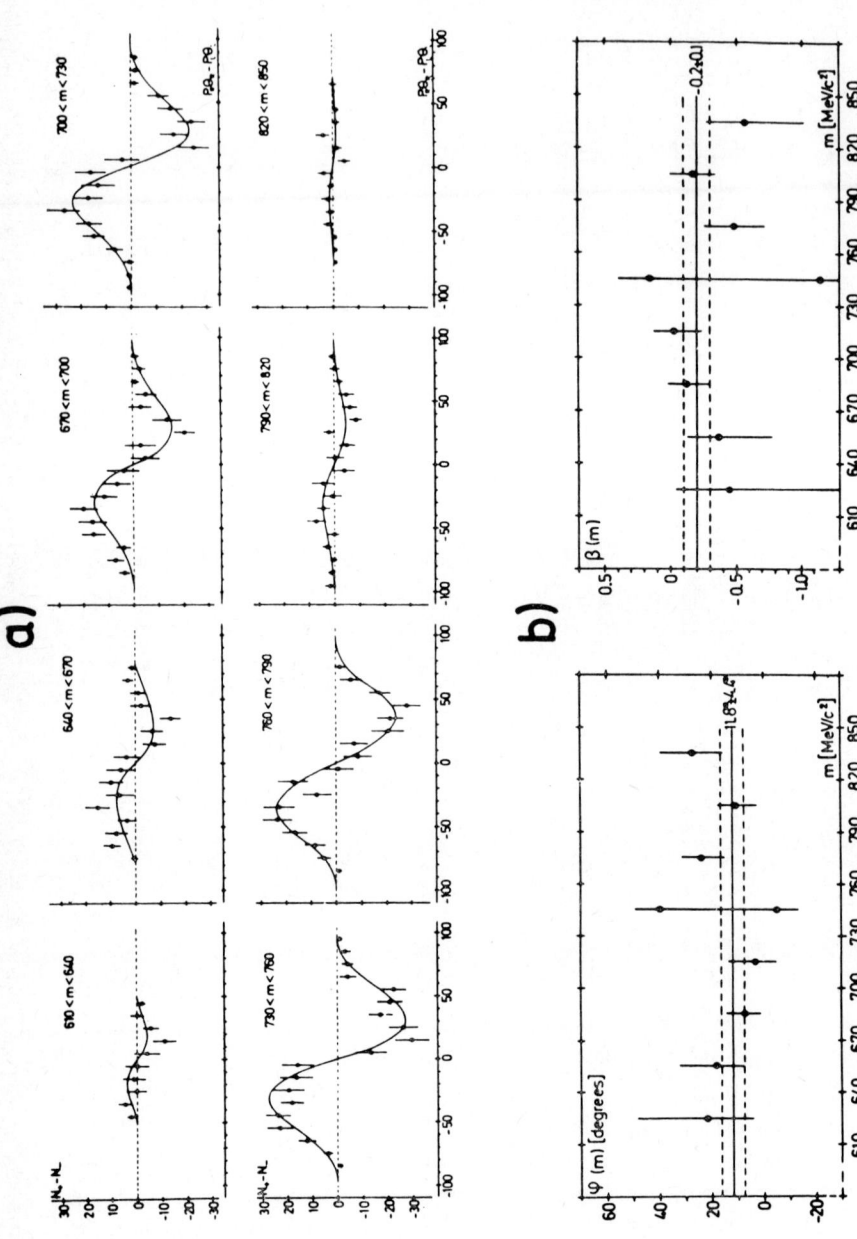

Fig. 21. – Reaction $\gamma\text{Be} \to e^+e^-\text{Be}$ at $(4 \div 6)$ GeV ([92]). a) Measured difference $N_+ - N_-$ of event numbers in the two arms of the spectrometer, as a function of the asymmetry $\delta = p_{e^+}\theta_{e^+} - p_{e^-}\theta_{e^-}$, in various regions of the $\pi^+\pi^-$ mass. The curves are from fits with $\alpha_{\varrho N} = -0.2 \pm 0.1$. b) Fitted values of the deviation φ of the nuclear $(\pi^+\pi^-)$-photoproduction amplitude from $\pi/2$ (left part), and of the ratio $\beta = -\alpha_{\varrho N} = -$ (real/imaginary) parts of the photoproduction amplitude on single nucleons (right part), as a function of the $\pi^+\pi^-$ mass.

states one has to observe the e^+e^- or $\mu^+\mu^-$ decays of the vector mesons:

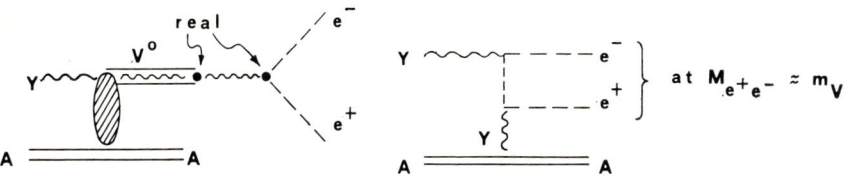

(phase = phase of $T_{\gamma A \to V^0 A}$ + phase of Breit-Wigner) (real Bethe-Heitler amplitude)

Since in the photoproduction amplitude the e^+e^- system couples to one photon, it has $C = -1$; whereas in the Bethe-Heitler graph the coupling is to two photons and thus $C = +1$. Consequently, the interference term in the cross-section is asymmetric under the interchange of e^+ and e^- (i.e. keeping the momenta fixed and interchanging the charges). One can therefore detect this interference term by varying e.g. $p_{\perp,e^+} - p_{\perp,e^-} \triangleq p_{e^+}\theta_{e^+} - p_{e^-}\theta_{e^-}$ (where $p_\perp$ is the transverse momentum), as shown in Fig. 21 from an experiment of the DESY-MIT group at $(4.6 \div 6.1)$ GeV on a Be target ([92]). For « symmetric pairs » $p_{\perp,e^+} = p_{\perp,e^-}$ and the interference term must vanish. One sees from Fig. 21 that the interference is large in the ρ^0 region of e^+e^- masses, where the ρ Breit-Wigner phase is $\approx \pi/2$. This immediately shows that $T_{\gamma A \to \rho^0 A}$ must be predominantly imaginary. The phase of the photoproduction amplitude on a single nucleon does not differ much from that of the nuclear amplitude, but detailed analysis has to take account of the phase change due to rescattering of the ρ^0 in the nucleus.

The result of the DESY-MIT experiment ([92]) for the ratio of real to imaginary parts of the ρ^0 photoproduction amplitude on single nucleons is

$$\alpha_{\rho N} = -0.2 \pm 0.1 \quad \text{at} \quad \langle E_\gamma \rangle = 5 \text{ GeV}$$

(see Fig. 21b). At a similar experiment at NINA ([93]) one C nucleus target gave

$$\alpha_{\rho N} = -0.28 \pm 0.12 \quad \text{at} \quad \langle E_\gamma \rangle = 4 \text{ GeV}.$$

The large error in these results is mainly due to the high sensitivity to the uncertainties in the value of the ρ^0 mass. In a third experiment, measuring electroproduction of $\rho^0 \to \mu^+\mu^-$ from C at CEA, the presence of a real part of the ρ photoproduction amplitude was also indicated ([94]). The results for $\alpha_{\rho N}$ agree with the prediction $\alpha_{\rho N} \triangleq -0.2$ at $E_\gamma = (4 \div 6)$ GeV of the simple additive quark model ([56,83]) via the relation to πN scattering amplitudes (as given in Sect. 6). They are also compatible with the values of $\alpha_{\gamma N}$ calculated from total photoproduction cross-section data using the forward dispersion relation ([82]).

The ϕ photoproduction phase has recently also been observed by the DESY-MIT group with the result ([95])

$$\alpha_{\Phi N} = -0.48^{+0.33}_{-0.45} \quad \text{at} \ \langle E_\gamma \rangle = 6.6 \text{ GeV}.$$

The additive quark model gives $\alpha_{\Phi N} = -0.3 \pm 0.45$ in the energy range of $E_\gamma = (7 \div 15)$ GeV ([83]).

The ω nuclear photoproduction phase has been measured relative to the ρ^0 production phase, by observing ρ/ω interference in the e^+e^- mass spectrum of the reaction $\gamma A \to e^+e^- A$. (The Bethe-Heitler interference terms may in this case be cancelled out by observing « symmetric pairs », i.e. keeping the experimental acceptance symmetric under interchange of e^+ and e^-.) Measured relative phases are

NINA ([92,96]): (118^{+13}_{-22}) deg (at $E_\gamma = 4$ GeV on C nucleus)

DESY-MIT ([97]): (41 ± 20) deg (at $E_\gamma = 5.1$ GeV on Be nucleus).

From these phase differences the effects of ϱ/ω mixing (which can amount to something like 20 deg) still have to be subtracted ([98]).

11. Photoproduction of heavy (vector) mesons ([99]); the ϱ' (1500).

Note added in proof, April 1972. This whole section is rendered somewhat obsolete by the recent discovery of the ϱ' at a mass of about 1500 MeV in e^+e^- storage-ring experiments and in photoproduction, not in the channel $\gamma p \to p\pi^+\pi^-$ or $p\bar{K}K$ where it was expected, but in $p\pi^+\pi^-\pi^+\pi^-$ with a cross-section $\sigma = (1.4 \pm 0.4)$ μb. Specifically, our SBT experiment has now established that ϱ' decays mainly into $\varrho\varepsilon$ (ε means the s-wave $I = 0$ $\pi\pi$ partial wave) with a width $\Gamma \sim 500$ MeV. Its branching fraction to 2π is $\leqslant 10\%$, to $\bar{K}K \leqslant 4\%$. The 2π bump seen at the same mass at DESY (Fig. 22 below) cannot be detected as a 4π bump in the DESY expt., so the connection between Fig. 22 and the newer ϱ' data must still be established.

See the following recent references:
1) Frascati experiments: G. BACCI et al.: *Phys. Lett.*, **38** B, 551 (1972); G. BARBARINO et al.: *Lett. Nuovo Cimento*, **3**, 689 (1972).
2) SLAC-Berkeley experiment with polarized photons into 82" bubble-chamber: G. SMADJA et al.: Lawrence Berkeley Laboratory Report LBL 991 and *Proceedings of the* 1972 *Philadelphia Conference on Meson Spectroscopy* (Am. Inst. of Phys. 1972). A *Phys. Lett.* will appear in 1972 under the name of BINGHAM et al.

Of the searches for photoproduction of vector mesons ([100-105]) heavier than the ϕ, the most intriguing result is still the one of Fig. 22. It shows, on a logarithmic scale, the $\pi^+\pi^-$ mass distribution in the reaction

$$\gamma C \rightarrow \pi^+\pi^- + \text{anything}$$

at $E_\gamma = (5.4 \div 6.8)$ GeV and $|t_\perp| \leqslant 0.01$ GeV, measured by the DESY-MIT group ([103]). The curve is the sum of the coherent and incoherent forward production cross-sections according to a closure calculation by Trefil ([85]),

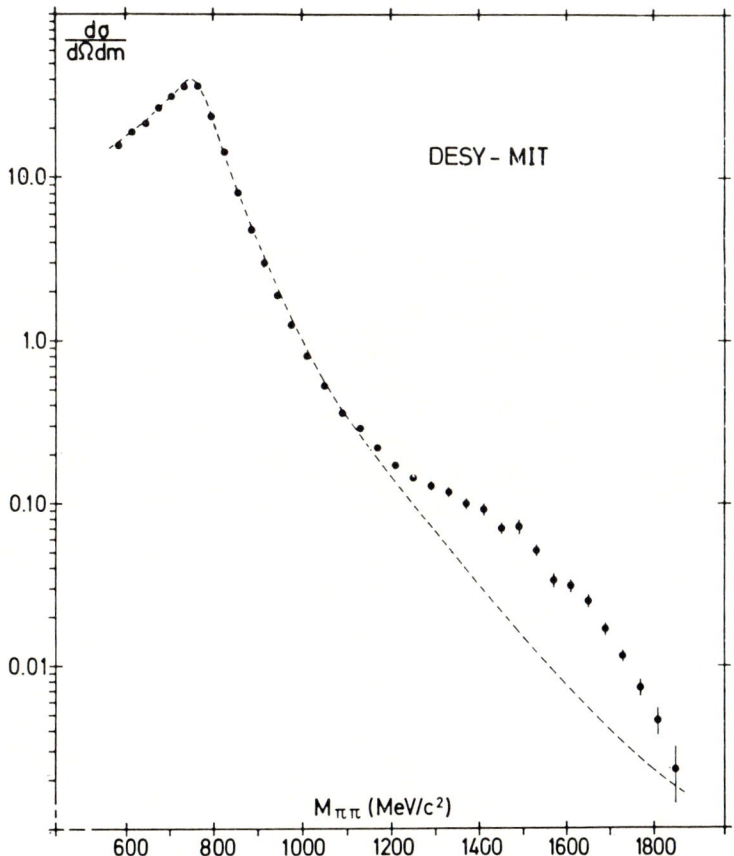

Fig. 22. – Dipion mass spectrum of the reaction $\gamma C \rightarrow \pi^+\pi^- + ...$ at $(5.4-6.8)$ GeV and $|t_\perp| \leqslant 0.01$ GeV^2 (ref. ([103])). The cross-sections are averaged over the spectrometer aperture. The errors are statistical only. The curve is approximated from a fit with a superposition of coherent and incoherent ρ production plus non-ρ polynomial background, fitted in the ρ mass region $((600 \div 900)$ MeV) and extrapolated towards higher dipion masses.

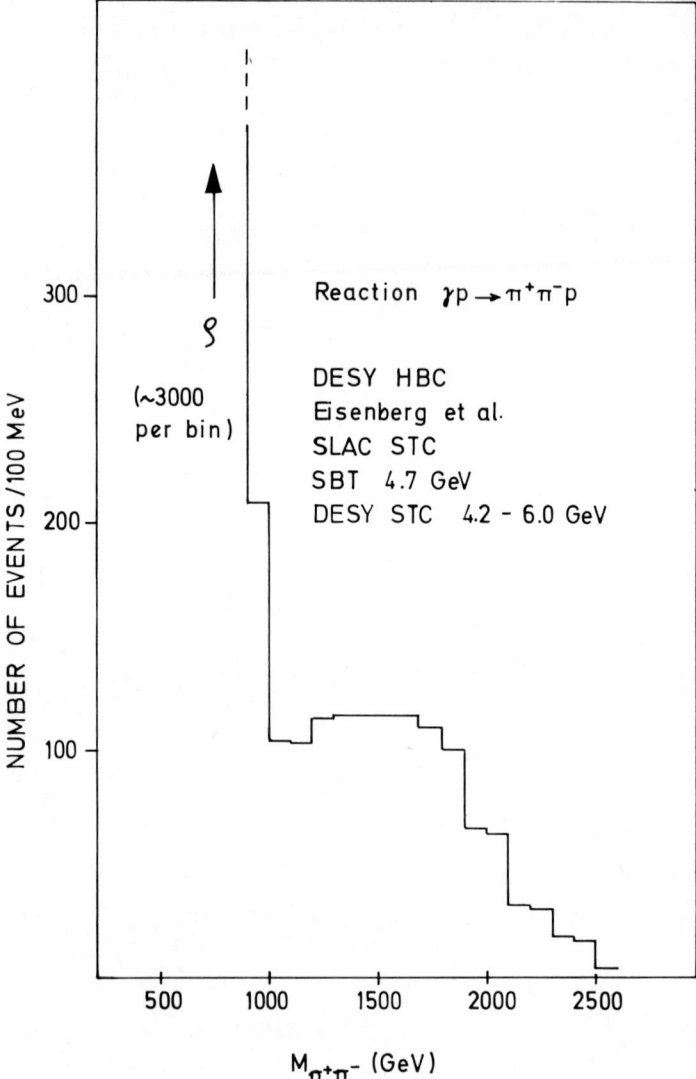

Fig. 23. – Dipion mass spectrum of the reaction $\gamma p \to \pi^+\pi^- p$, from a compilation of various bubble and streamer chamber experiments at energies above 4 GeV (refs. ([17,25,61,62,66])). (In considering the significance of structures in distributions compiled from different experiments, one should keep in mind that the phase space distributions of the various experiments differ, due to different beam momenta.)

multiplied with a Breit-Wigner function and a factor $M_{\pi\pi}^{-4}$ ([54]), plus a non-ϱ background term, polynomial in $\pi^+\pi^-$ mass. There appears a shoulder in the (1300÷1800) MeV region, for which no satisfactory explanation seems to have been found. A similar effect has been observed by the SLAC group at 16 GeV on a Be target ([102]). It cannot be a reflection from e.g. $\Delta(1236)$ production since only symmetrically decaying dipions were detected in the experiment, and these do not overlap with the $\Delta(1236)$ bands in the Dalitz plot (compare Fig. 2). There could of course be some background from reactions with additional undetected pions. The experiment has been repeated on a hydrogen target, with a similar result ([106]).

Figure 23 shows the $\pi^+\pi^-$ mass distribution from a compilation of various bubble and streamer chamber experiments (all of which had essentially complete decay angular acceptance for the $\pi^+\pi^-$ system) at energies above 4 GeV ([17,25,61,62,66]). The broad shoulder at the high-mass side of the ρ^0 may here be partly due to reflection from $\Delta^{++}(1236)$ decays.

Since decay into charged lepton pairs is allowed for any vector meson coupled to the photon, searches in the $\mu^+\mu^-$ mass spectrum have particular significance ([104,105]). In the mass region surveyed, $m_\phi < M_{\mu^+\mu^-} < 2100$ MeV, no vector-meson was found within a cross-section level of a few percent of σ_ρ.

An experiment in which the search was not restricted to vector-mesons, or mesons decaying into $\pi^+\pi^-$, was done at SLAC ([45]). Here the reaction

$$\gamma p \to p + \text{missing mass}$$

was measured in the energy range of (16÷17.8) GeV, detecting only the proton and using bremsstrahlung end-point substraction. Nothing was found in the (1÷2) GeV range of masses. The upper limit (at a 90% confidence level) of the cross-section for production of any meson with 1.3 GeV $< M <$ 2 GeV and $\Gamma \leq 200$ MeV from this experiment is 5% of the ρ^0 production cross-section. Note however that the ϕ cross-section, at 16 GeV, is already below this limit.

The SLAC group did observe, however, a bump in the missing-mass spectrum at about 1240 MeV, at a photon energy of $E_\gamma \approx 14$ GeV ([45]). This observation was confirmed in the bubble chamber experiment of the SBT collaboration ([29]) and in the DESY streamer chamber experiment ([61]), where the enhancement was found to occur in the pionic system of the reaction

$$\gamma p \to p\pi^+\pi^- + n\pi^0 \qquad (n \geq 2)$$

at E_γ between 3 and 6 GeV. Mass and width (1250 MeV and 100 MeV, respectively) of this effect suggest that it may be due to the B^0(1235), probably an axial vector-meson which decays into $\omega + \pi^0$. Indeed, a selection of $\pi^+\pi^-$

states in the kinematic region where the ω decay matrix element is largest, was found to enhance the effect. Since this effect, supposedly B meson production, has similar cross-sections from 3 to 14 GeV, it is interesting to speculate that it may be a diffractive process (P exchange).

The searches discussed so far did not extend much beyond 2 GeV in mass. The SLAC streamer chamber group has searched for vector-mesons of mass up to 3.5 GeV, decaying into four pions, in the reaction

$$\gamma p \to \pi^+\pi^-\pi^+\pi^- p$$

at $E_\gamma = (6-18)$ GeV ([107]). They have found an enhancement with mass $M_{4\pi} \triangleq 1600$ MeV and a width of several 100 MeV. Its interpretation is not yet clear.

There are several reasons to expect vector mesons heavier than the ϕ to exist. In the quark model the $^3D_1$ rotational level is a $J^{PC} = 1^{--}$ nonet, with masses expected to be somewhere in the $(1500 \div 2000)$ MeV region. The Veneziano model predicts a ρ' at 1250 MeV (degenerate with the f) and a ρ'' at 1650 MeV (degenerate with the g) ([108]). Coherent diffractive photoproduction was expected to be an effective « filter » for vector meson states. It has however been argued recently on the basis of a multiperipheral production mechanism and duality, that even with rather large couplings of these heavy mesons to the photon the resulting photoproduction cross-sections will still be small enough so that the ρ' could have remained undetected until now ([109]). For the quantity (production cross-section)×(branching fraction into $\pi^+\pi^-$), empirical upper limits at $E_\gamma = 9$ GeV of 0.5 μb for ρ' and 0.2 μb for ρ'' have been established, provided the width of these states does not exceed 200 MeV ([19]) (*).

It may be interesting to briefly list the experimental evidence on photoproduction of other mesons of the natural J^P series.

i) $J^{PC} = 0^{++}$ ($\gamma p \to \varepsilon p$): No indication has been seen. The main argument for small cross-section is the zero forward/backward asymmetry of the $\pi^+\pi^-$ decays in the ρ^0 mass region (in contrast e.g. to the reaction $\pi^- p \to \pi^+\pi^- n$) ([17,25]).

ii) $J^{PC} = 2^{++}$: Of the reaction $\gamma p \to fp$ at most slight indications have been seen. Only a limit of $\sigma \leqslant 0.4$ μb in the energy region of $(2.5 \div 5)$ GeV can be stated ([17,25]). The reaction $\gamma p \to A_2^+ n$ has been reported and seems

---

(*) In the reaction $\bar{p}p \to K_S^0 K_L^0$ evidence suggestive of a vector-meson with $M = 1968$ MeV and $\Gamma = 35$ MeV has recently been reported ([110]).

to occur with a cross-section of ~ 1 μb in the (4÷5) GeV energy region ([29,62,111]). No firm evidence for the reaction $\gamma p \to A_2^0 p$ has been found (in contrast to charged A_2 photoproduction, pion exchange does not contribute here), so only a limit of $\leqslant 1$ μb for $E_\gamma = (2.5 \div 6)$ GeV (at the 90% confidence level) can be quoted ([25,29,62]).

iii) $J^{PC} = 3^{--}$ ($\gamma p \to g p$): This reaction has not yet been observed.

Acknowledgement.

We would like to thank U. Becker, E. Lohrmann, H. Meyer, W. J. Podolsky, and G. Wolf for valuable discussions on the subjects covered in this talk.

REFERENCES

1) J. J. SAKURAI: *Ann. Phys.*, **11**, 1 (1960); M. GELL-MANN and F. ZACHARIASEN: *Phys. Rev.*, **124**, 953 (1961); M. GELL-MANN: *Phys. Rev.*, **125**, 1067 (1962); N. M. KROLL, T. D. LEE and B. ZUMINO: *Phys. Rev*, **157**, 1376 (1967).
2) J. J. SAKURAI: *Proceedings of the IVth International Symposium on Electron and Photon Interactions at High Energies*, Liverpool (1969), p. 91; D. SCHILDKNECHT: *Zeits Phys.*, **229**, 278 (1969). See also ref. (4,) (5,) and (8).
3) SLAC-BERKELEY-TUFTS COLLABORATION: *Phys. Rev. Lett.*, **24**, 960, 1467 (E) (1970).
4) K. LÜBELSMEYER: *Meson Photoproduction*, Rapporteur talk at the *XVth International Conference on High Energy Physics*, Kiev (1970); Bonn University preprint PIB 1-126 (1971).
5) G. WOLF: *Photoproduction II*, in *Proc. 1971 Cornell eγ Conference* and DESY-71/50; G. WOLF: *Photoproduction of Vector Mesons.* Invited talk presented at the *Symposium on Meson Photo- and Electro-Production at Low and Intermediate Energies*, University of Bonn (1970), DESY-70/64 (1970) and *Springer Tracts in Modern Physics*, vol. **59** (1971), to be published.
6) R. MARSHALL: *Photoproduction of Vector Mesons*, Talk presented at the *Daresbury Study Weekend on Vector Meson Production and Omega-Rho Interference* (1970), DESY-70/32 (1970).
7) U. MAOR: *Nucl. Phys.*, B **24**, 1 (1970).
8) D. W. G. S. LEITH: in *Hadronic Interactions of Electrons and Photons* (Ed. J. CUMMING and H. OSBORN), 1971, p. 195.
9) P. L. BRACCINI: *Vector Meson Photoproduction*, in *Proceedings of the Ve Rencontre de Moriond sur les Interactions Electromagnetiques*, p. II.94 (1970).
10) A. SILVERMAN: in *Proceedings of the IVth International Symposium on Electron and Photon Interactions at High Energies*, Liverpool (1969), p. 71.
11) E. LOHRMANN: in *Proceedings of the Lund International Conference on Elementary Particles*, Lund, (1969), p. 13.
12) H. ÜBERALL: *Phys. Rev.*, **103**, 1055 (1956); **107**, 223 (1957); G. BARBIELLINI et al., *Phys. Rev. Lett.*, **8**, 112 (1962).

13) G. DIAMBRINI-PALAZZI: *Rev. Mod. Phys.*, **40**, 611 (1968); U. TIMM: *Fortschr. Physik*, **17**, 765 (1969).
14) R. H. MILBURN: *Phys. Rev. Lett.*, **10**, 75 (1963).
15) F. R. ARUTYUNIAN and V. A. TUMANIAN: *Phys. Lett.*, **4**, 176 (1963).
16) C. K. SINCLAIR et al.: *IEEE Trans. on Nucl. Sci.*, **16**, 1065 (1969).
17) SLAC-BERKELEY-TUFTS COLLABORATION: *Phys. Rev. Lett.*, **24**, 955 (1970); **24**, 960, 1467 (E) (1970); SLAC-PUB-941 (1971), Submitted to *Phys. Rev.*; K. C. MOFFEIT: UCRL-19890 (1970), unpublished.
18) SLAC-BERKELEY-TUFTS COLLABORATION: *Phys. Rev. Lett.*, **24**, 1364 (1970); **26**, 155 (E) (1971); W. J. PODOLSKY: UCRL-20128 (1971), unpublished.
19) SLAC-BERKELEY-TUFTS COLLABORATION: *Results at 9.3 GeV*, Submitted to 1971 Cornell eγ Conference.
20) G. MCCLELLAN et al.: *Phys. Rev. Lett.*, **26**, 1597 (1971).
21) C. BERGER et al.: *Phys. Rev. Lett.*, **25**, 1366 (1970).
22) M. JACOB and G. C. WICK: *Ann. Phys.*, **7**, 404 (1959).
23) K. SCHILLING, P. SEYBOTH and G. WOLF: *Nucl. Phys.*, B **15**, 397 (1970).
24) C. ZEMACH: *Phys. Rev.*, **140**, B 97 (1965).
25) AACHEN-BERLIN-BONN-HAMBURG-HEIDELBERG-MUNICH COLLABORATION: *Phys. Rev.*, **175**, 1669 (1968).
26) R. K. ADAIR: *Phys. Rev.*, **100**, 1540 (1955); *Rev. Mod. Phys.*, **37**, 473 (1964); Y. EISENBERG et al.: *Phys. Lett.*, **22**, 223 (1966); G. KRAMER: DESY-67/32 (1967), unpublished.
27) K. GOTTFRIED and J. D. JACKSON: *Nuovo Cimento*, **33**, 309 (1964); J. D. JACKSON: *Nuovo Cimento* **34**, 1644 (1964).
28) AACHEN-BERLIN-BONN-CERN-CRACOW-HEIDELBERG-LONDON-VIENNA COLLABORATION: *Phys. Lett.*, **34** B, 160 (1971); G. ASCOLI et al.: *Phys. Rev. Lett.*, **26**, 929 (1971); F. GRARD et al.: *Lett. Nuovo Cimento*, **2**, 305 (1971).
29) W. J. PODOLSKY: UCRL-20128 (1971), unpublished.
30) L. CRIEGEE et al., *Phys. Rev. Lett.*, **25**, 1306 (1970).
31) G. DIAMBRINI-PALAZZI et al., *Phys. Rev. Lett.*, **25**, 478 (1970).
32) G. WOLF: private communication; see also ref. (5).
33) M. HOUTEBEYRIE et al.: *Phys. Lett.*, **36** B, 98 (1971).
34) S. RAI CHOUDHURY and R. RAJARAMAN: University of Delhi preprint (1971).
35) J. BENECKE and H. P. DÜRR: *Nuovo Cimento* **56** A, 269 (1968).
36) G. WOLF: *Phys. Rev.*, **182**, 1538 (1969).
37) S. C. C. TING, in *Proceedings of the XIVth International Conference on High Energy Physics*, Vienna 1968, p. 43. See also U. BECKER et al.: *Phys. Rev. Lett.*, **21**, 1504 (1968).
38) C. BERGER et al.: Cornell University preprint CLNS-168 (1971), submitted to *Phys. Rev.*
39) G. COSME: *Measurement of the Radiative Decay Modes of the φ Meson with the Orsay Storage Ring*, presented at the *International Conference on Meson Resonances and Related Electromagnetic Phenomena*, Bologna, April 1971. (The partial widths quoted were obtained by multiplying the Orsay branching fractions by $\Gamma_\Phi = 4$ MeV.)
40) AACHEN-BERLIN-BONN-HAMBURG-HEIDELBERG-MUNICH COLLABORATION: *Phys. Lett.*, **27** B, 54 (1968); *Phys. Rev.*, **188**, 2060 (1969).

41) P. G. O. Freund: *Nuovo Cimento*, **48** A, 541 (1967).
42) V. Barger and D. Cline: *Phys. Rev. Lett.*, **24**, 1313 (1970).
43) G. Wolf: *Nucl. Phys.*, B **26**, 317 (1971).
44) This comment does not apply to the SLAC experiment of Bulos *et al.*, discussed in detail by D. W. G. S. Leith in ref. (8).
45) R. Anderson *et al.*: *Phys. Rev.*, D **1**, 27 (1970).
46) S. D. Drell: *Phys. Rev. Lett.*, **5**, 278 (1960); *Rev. Mod. Phys.*, **33**, 458 (1961).
47) P. Söding: *Phys. Lett.*, **19**, 702 (1966).
48) A. Krass: *Phys. Rev.*, **159**, 1496 (1967).
49) T. Bauer: *Phys. Rev. Lett.*, **25**, 485, 704 (E) (1970).
50) J. Pumplin: *Phys. Rev.*, D **2**, 1859 (1970).
51) D. R. Yennie: in *Hadronic Interactions of Electrons and Photons* (Ed. J. Cumming and H. Osborn), 1971, p. 321.
52) G. Kramer: *Recent Theoretical Work in Photoproduction of Vector Mesons*, in *Daresbury Meeting on $\omega\rho$ Mixing*, 1970, DESY T-70/4 (1970); see also DESY 70/23 and 71-40; F. Gutbrod: private communication.
53) H. Satz and K. Schilling: *Nuovo Cimento*, **67** A, 511 (1970); P. Dewey and B. Humpert: *Nucl. Phys.* B **33** 621 (1971).
54) M. Ross and L. Stodolsky: *Phys. Rev.*, **149**, 1172 (1966); G. Kramer and J. L. Uretsky: *Phys. Rev.*, **181**, 1918 (1969); P. D. Mannheim and U. Maor: *Phys. Rev.*, D **2**, 2105 (1970); G. Kramer and H. R. Quinn: *Nucl. Phys.*, B **27**, 77 (1971); G. Kramer: DESY preprint 71/40 (1971).
55) Particle Data Group: *Rev. Mod. Phys.*, **43**, S 1.
56) H. J. Lipkin: *Phys. Rev. Lett.*, **16**, 1015 (1966); H. Joos: in *Hadronic Interactions of Electrons and Photons* (Ed. J. Cumming and H. Osborn), 1971, p. 47; K. Kajantie and J. S. Trefil: *Phys. Lett.*, **24** B, 106 (1967).
57) K. J. Foley *et al*: *Phys. Rev. Lett.*, **11**, 425 (1963); **11**, 503 (1963); **15**, 45 (1965).
58) H. Alvensleben *et al.*: *Phys. Rev. Lett.*, **23**, 1058 (1969); *Nucl. Phys.*, B **18**, 333 (1970).
59) G. McClellan *et al.*: Cornell University preprint CLNS-154 (1971), submitted to *Phys. Rev.*, See also ref. ([38]) and ([75]).
60) F. Bulos *et al.*: discussed by D. W. G. S. Leith in ref. ([8]).
61) Aachen-Hamburg-Heidelberg-Munich Streamer Chamber Collaboration: to be published; E. Rabe: Internal report DESY F1-71/2 (1971).
62) Y. Eisenberg *et al.*: *Phys. Rev. Lett.*, **22**, 669 (1969); J. Ballam *et al.*: *Phys. Lett.*, **30** B, 421 (1969); J. Ballam *et al.*: SLAC-Weizmann-Tel Aviv preprint (1971).
63) Y. Eisenberg *et al.*: *Phys. Lett.*, **34** B, 439 (1971).
64) K. Schilling and F. Storim: *Nucl. Phys.*, B **7**, 559 (1968). The calculation was done using a sharp cutoff at impact parameters $R \leqslant 0.8$ F, and with $\Gamma_{\omega\pi\gamma} = 1.2$ MeV.
65) G. McClellan *et al.*: *Phys. Rev. Lett.*, **26**, 1593 (1971); see also ref. ([38]).
66) M. Davier *et al.*: *Phys. Rev.*, D **1**, 790 (1970).
67) L. Stodolsky: *Phys. Rev. Lett.*, **18**, 135 (1967).
68) J. C. Bizot: *Phys. Lett.*, **32** B, 416 (1970). For $\gamma_\varrho^2/4\pi$ and $\gamma_\omega^2/4\pi$ we take here the new values reported by the Orsay group at the *Amsterdam International Conference on Elementary Particles* (1971).
69) D. O. Caldwell *et al.*: *Phys. Rev. Lett.*, **25**, 609 (1970).
70) R. L. Anderson *et al.*: preprint SLAC-PUB-916 (1971).

71) V. Franco and R. J. Glauber: *Phys. Rev.*, **142**, 1195 (1966); R. J. Glauber: *Lectures in Theoretical Physics*, Boulder (1958), vol. I, p. 315.
72) Aachen- Bonn-Hamburg-Heidelberg-Munich Collaboration: *Nucl. Phys.*, B **23**, 45 (1970); and private communication.
73) Y. Eisenberg *et al.*: Weizmann Institute preprint WIS 71/9 Ph (1971).
74) Aachen-Bonn-Hamburg-Heidelberg-Munich Collaboration: *Nucl. Phys.*, B **21**, 93 (1970); and private communication.
75) G. McClellan *et al.*: *Phys. Rev. Lett.*, **22**, 374 (1969).
76) H. J. Behrend *et al.*: *Phys. Rev. Lett.*, **26**, 151 (1971).
77) H. Meyer *et al.*: *Phys. Lett.*, **33** B, 189 (1970).
78) K. S. Kölbig and B. Margolis: *Nucl. Phys.*, B **6**, 85 (1968); S. D. Drell and J. S. Trefil: *Phys. Rev. Lett.*, **16**, 552, 832 (E) (1966).
79) Excellent and detailed discussions of the experimental and theoretical problems have been presented by D. W. G. S. Leith (ref. ([8])) and D. R. Yennie (ref. ([51])) at the Scottish Universities Summer School in Physics, 1970.
80) G. von Bochmann, B. Margolis and L. C. Tang: *Phys. Lett.*, **30** B, 254 (1969).
81) J. Swartz and R. Talman: *Phys. Rev. Lett.*, **23**, 1078 (1969). See also ref. ([10]).
82) M. Damashek and F. Gilman: *Phys. Rev.*, D **1**, 1319 (1970); H. Meyer *et al.*: Desy report DESY 70/17 (1970).
83) S. A. Jackson and R. E. Mickens: *Lett. Nuovo Cimento*, **3**, 1 (1970); M. Krammer: *Acta Phys. Austria*, **32**, 395 (1970); T. J. Weare: *Lett. Nuovo Cimento*, **4**, 251 (1970); K. Okada: *Progr. Theor. Phys.*, **43**, 1574 (1970).
84) H. Alvensleben *et al.*: *Nucl. Phys.*, B **18**, 333 (1970); *Phys. Rev. Lett.*, **24**, 786 (1970).
85) J. T. Trefil: *Nucl. Phys.*, B **11**, 330 (1969); *Phys. Rev.*, **180**, 1379 (1969); K .S. Kölbig and B. Margolis: *Nucl. Phys.*, B **6**, 85 (1968).
86) G. McClellan *et al.*: *Phys. Rev. Lett.*, **22**, 377 (1969).
87) H. J. Behrend *et al.*: *Phys. Rev. Lett.*, **24**, 336 (1970).
88) F. Bulos *et al.*: *Phys. Rev. Lett.*, **22**, 490 (1969); see also ref. ([8]).
89) H. J. Behrend *et al.*: *Phys. Rev. Lett.*, **24**, 1246 (1970); *Phys. Rev. Lett.*, **27**, 65 (1970).
90) P. L. Braccini *et al.*: *Nucl. Phys.*, B **24**, 173 (1970).
91) R. J. Oakes and J. J. Sakurai: *Phys. Rev. Lett.*, **19**, 1266 (1967).
92) H. Alvensleben *et al.*: *Phys. Rev. Lett.*, **25**, 1377 (1970).
93) P. J. Biggs *et al.*: Daresbury preprint DNPL/P 70 (1971); E. Gabathuler: in *Experimental Meson Spectroscopy* (Ed. C. Baltay and A. H. Rosenfeld), 1970, p. 645.
94) D. R. Earles *et al.*: *Phys. Rev. Lett.*, **25**, 129 (1970).
95) H. Alvensleben *et al.*: *Phys. Rev. Lett.*, **27**, 444 (1971).
96) P. J. Biggs *et al.*: *Phys. Rev. Lett.*, **24**, 1197 (1970).
97) H. Alvensleben *et al.*: *Phys. Rev. Lett.*, **25**, 1373 (1970).
98) H. R. Quinn and T. F. Walsh: *Nucl. Phys.*, B **22**, 637 (1970).
99) This has been reviewed recently by M. Davier: in *Proceedings of the Ve Rencontre de Moriond sur les Interactions Electromagnetiques*, p. II.45 (1970).
100) G. McClellan *et al.*: *Phys. Rev. Lett.*, **23**, 718 (1969).
101) N. Hicks *et al.*: *Phys. Lett.*, **29** B, 602 (1969).
102) F. Bulos *et al.*: *Phys. Rev. Lett.*, **26**, 149 (1971).
103) H. Alvensleben *et al.*: *Phys. Rev. Lett.*, **26**, 273 (1971).

104) S. HAYES et al.: *Phys. Rev. Lett.*, **24**, 1369 (1970).
105) D. EARLES et al.: *Phys. Rev. Lett.*, **25**, 1312, 1738 (E) (1970).
106) S. C. C. TING, private communication.
107) M. DAVIER et al.: SLAC-PUB-666 (1969); and private communication.
108) G. VENEZIANO: *Nuovo Cimento*, **57** A, 190 (1968); J. A. SHAPIRO: *Phys. Rev.*, **179**, 1345 (1969): V. BARGER and D. CLINE: *Phys. Rev.*, **182**, 1849 (1969).
109) P. H. FRAMPTON, K. SCHILLING and C. SCHMID: preprint TH. 1347-CERN (1971).
110) A. BENVENUTI et al.: *Phys. Rev. Lett.*, **27**, 283 (1971).
111) Y. EISENBERG et al.: *Phys. Rev. Lett.*, **23**, 1322 (1969).
112) R. T. DECK: *Phys. Rev. Lett.*, **13**, 169 (1964). For many more references, see the A1, A3, Q, L sections of Review of Particle Physics, *Rev. Mod. Phys.*, **43** S1 (1971).

DISCUSSION

Chairman: Prof. A. H. ROSENFELD
Scientific Secretary: U. KARSHON

DISCUSSIONS

— GOURDIN:

First I have a question concerning the laser experiment on hydrogen which you presented this morning. What is the value of the total ρ width you find, and what value of the γ-ρ coupling constant do you get assuming the quark model relation for the total ρ-proton cross-section? Secondly, I wish to make a comment concerning the relation between the γ-ρ coupling constant you measure in photoproduction experiment and the one deduced from electron-positron annihilation into $\pi^+\pi^-$. The correct factor you have to introduce is $(1/f_\rho)(m_\rho^2/W_\rho(0))$ where in the zero width approximation $W_\rho(0)$ is simply m_ρ^2. The finite width correction factor $m_\rho^2/W_\rho(0)$ is model dependent; and as an example in the Gounaris-Sakurai model we have the relation:

$$\frac{1}{f_\rho}\frac{m_\rho^2}{W_\rho(0)} = \frac{1}{f_{\rho\pi\pi}}, \qquad \left(\text{so}\quad \frac{m_\rho^2}{W_\rho(0)} \simeq 0.93\right)$$

where $f_{\rho\pi\pi}$ is the on-mass shell decay coupling constant. As a remark f_ρ and $f_{\rho\pi\pi}$ can be separately measured experimentally in a high statistics $e^+e^- \to \pi^+\pi^-$ process.

— SAKURAI:

I agree with what Gourdin has said, but this is a relatively small effect. Much more important, the value of $\gamma_\rho^2/4\pi$ based on your experiment appears to be considerably smaller than the values obtained from other (counter) experiments.

— ROSENFELD:

As to Γ_ρ, let me give you the following table:

E_γ	Γ from mass histogram	Γ from Söding model	Average over all estimates
2.8 GeV	160 MeV	150 MeV	
4.7 GeV	145 MeV		~ 155 MeV
9.3 GeV	145 MeV	160 MeV	

As to values of the γ-ρ coupling constant, using only our own data, let me remind you that we made two different calculations:

Calculation 1 uses VMD and the quark model, specifically the assumption that

$$\sigma_T(\rho^0 p) = \sigma_T(\omega^0 p) = \tfrac{1}{2}[\sigma_T(\pi^+ p) + \sigma_T(\pi^- p)].$$

Then our 2.8 and 4.7 GeV data combine to give

$$\gamma_\varrho^2/4\pi = 0.7 \pm 0.1 \;.$$

Calculation 2 uses only the optical theorem

$$\sigma_T(\gamma p) = \sqrt{16\pi} \operatorname{Im} T(\gamma p \to \gamma p)_{0^\circ} \;,$$

and the VDM relation

$$T(\gamma p \to \gamma p) = \frac{e}{2\gamma_\varrho} T(\gamma p \to \varrho^0 p) + \frac{e}{2\gamma_\omega} T(\gamma p \to \omega p) + \ldots$$

Then we find $\gamma_\varrho^2/4\pi$ 0.3 to 0.4. So we get results which are both larger and smaller than other experiments. I remind you that the fit of Anderson *et al.* that I showed as slide 10 gave $\gamma_\varrho^2/4\pi = 0.61$, and that Orsay seems to like $\gamma_\varrho^2/4\pi = 0.5$.

— MORPURGO:

I would like to add that from Compton effect measurements reported at Trieste by Deutsch we have $\gamma_\varrho^2/4\pi = 0.35$. I would also like to raise the question of the double counting when one adds the two diagrams in the Söding model:

Should one not consider just one diagram:

considering the final state interaction (and perhaps in some way also the initial state interaction) of the two pions?

— MANNHEIM:

In reply to Morpurgo's query about double counting: It is not necessarily true that adding diagrams with poles in dual variables is double counting. The double counting prescription refers to sums of poles only. To isolate how much of one diagram is contained in one other cross channel diagram requires more detailed dynamical information. Next, the double counting prescription only refers to adding poles in the same amplitude. In the process $\gamma p \to \pi^+\pi^- p$ there are many helicity degrees of freedom. Further, experimentally the $\langle Y_1 \rangle$ moment has been found not to vanish, showing that there is $l=3$ as well as $l=1$ partial waves in the $\pi\pi$ system. Thus the piece of the Söding diagram which projects on the F-wave may be added to the P-wave ρ meson safely enough, and the major success of the Söding model is then seen to be successful fitting of the $\langle Y_4^0 \rangle$ moment. So much for theoretical comments. Now for two practical distinctions between the double counting problems in the A_1 production and in ρ photo production. The Deck diagram shows a very sharp peak above background, whereas the Söding diagram is smooth through the ρ resonance region (its contribution to the cross-section shows a small peak due to the peaking of the two-body phase space near the ρ mass). Secondly, the sum of Söding and resonance diagrams actually fits the data, whereas a similar sum of A_1 and Deck effect grossly overcounts the data. This suggests that the requirements of double counting are not as severe in the photoproduction process as in the purely hadronic A_1 production.

— CHEW:

If the ρ width determined from the Söding prescription is larger than the « accepted » width, how can you conclude that the prescription is satisfactory?

— ROSENFELD:

The « accepted » width « $\Gamma_\rho = 120 \pm 20$ » in the Particle Data Tables comes from considering values that range all the way from: $\Gamma_\rho = 111 \pm 5$ or 140 ± 14 from $e^+e^- \to \pi^+\pi^-$ to $\Gamma_\rho = 132 \pm 13$ or 147 ± 4 from $\pi N \to \pi\pi N$ (see footnote (c) of the meson table). Hence our average of $\Gamma_\rho \sim 155$ MeV is really not so far out. Moreover, we get the same broad ρ without the Söding model. As just mentioned by Mannheim, the main advantage of the Söding model is that it explains 1) the ρ shape 2) the Y_l^m moments up to F-wave.

— WAMBACH:

Your one-parameter fit for the ω did not look convincing. Do you know where the main deviations come from? Is it VDM or the quark model which does not work well?

— ROSENFELD:

The ω is a less sensitive test of VDM and quark model than is the ρ^0, since 1) the data are worse 2) there are more diagrams to fit (*i.e.* more parameters) *e.g.*:

J^P = Natural exchange

ω — Pomeron — ω / P → P   +   ρ — A_2 — ω / P → P

J^P = Unnatural exchange

ρ — π — ω / P → P

So I am not surprised that the fit is worse.

— MORPURGO:

I would like to note the rather large differences between $\gamma_\omega^2/4\pi$ corresponding to different experiments. We have the following values reported by Söding at Trieste: Bonn-Pisa 5.8±1.3, Rochester 9.5±2.1. At the Amsterdam conference the Orsay (colliding beam) value of 4.5 has not been reported. So before discussing models, one should try to get the experimental values nearer to one another.

— ZICHICHI:

The Bologna-CERN group has an old value near the Rochester value.

— EDWARDS:

What in the ρ production experiment is the strongest piece of evidence which supports the Söding model in preference to the so called « Ross-Stodolsky » factor? I ask because some theorists have come up with a *t*-dependence for this factor, which is equivalent to $n(t)$ decreasing with *t*. In addition, could not the relativistic Breit-Wigner be wrong by say a factor of (m_ρ/m), especially when one fits from 0.4 to 1.8 GeV?

— ROSENFELD:

I think the $1/m^4$ factor did not have a deep argument in it. If some theorists have come up with a theory in which it goes down in *t* that's fine.

— MANNHEIM:

Concerning Rosenfeld's points on the absence of the ρ' and the g-meson and on the nature of the ρ meson mass shift in photoproduction, there is a nice intuitive argument which correlates these phenomena. Strictly speaking, in the vector-dominance model we should photo produce a massless vector-meson, and as such this would be a purely elastic process. In practice we produce a heavy vector-meson in a quasi-elastic diffraction dissociation. The elastic amplitude gets its strength from the inelastic contributions, and as we go to higher masses in the $\pi\pi$ system we go further away from the genuine elastic process, and hence lose intensity. Consequently, we expect the amplitude to behave as some function of $(M_{\pi\pi})^{-2}$. However, without a model we cannot make a more definite statement. Ross and Stodolsky and also myself and Maor have argued for a form $(M_{\pi\pi})^{-4}$, but the arguments are not conclusive. However, once we are given any loss of intensity as we go to higher masses, the ρ meson shape must be skewed to lower masses. Further, the production cross-section for ρ' and g are cut down even more. Accepting for a moment the $(M_{\pi\pi})^{-4}$ factor we would expect

$$\frac{\sigma(\gamma+p \to \rho'+p)}{\sigma(\gamma+p \to \rho+p)} = \left(\frac{m_\rho}{m_{\rho'}}\right)^4 = \frac{1}{q}$$

so that photoproduction is not a suitable place to look for the ρ', and even worse for the g. A parameter of the form $(M_{\pi\pi})^{-n(t)}$ has also been tried and $n(t)$ falls to zero at around $t = -0.5$ (GeV/c)^2. I think this can be correlated with the fact that at this t-value, s-channel helicity conservation also fails, suggesting that already in this region there is a big non-diffractive part. Such a non-diffractive part should not experience any loss of intensity with increasing $M_{\pi\pi}$, so that the overall diffractive and non-diffractive contributions should not cut off the intensity as violently as t increases, so we expect $n(t)$ to fall to zero.

— MASSAM:

How much would the value of γ_ρ^2 change in other experiments when using your interference analysis?

— ROSENFELD:

As I mentioned, the Söding model tends to attribute $\sim 1/5$ of the ρ intensity to the Drell terms. Hence, it gives values of σ or $d\sigma/dt$ for $\gamma p \to \rho p$ smaller by (10-30) % than simpler parametrizations. This will raise or lower our value for $\gamma_\rho^2/4\pi$ depending on which test is made. In what I called calculation 1, we have

$$\sigma(\gamma p \to \rho p) = \left(\frac{e}{2\gamma_\rho}\right)^2 \sigma(\rho p \to \rho p) \text{ via quark model}) + \dots$$

so $\gamma_\rho^2 \sim 1/\sigma(\gamma p \to \rho p)$.

In calculation 2:

$$\sigma_{TOT}(\gamma p) = \sqrt{16\pi}\, \frac{e}{2\gamma_\rho}\, \mathrm{Im}\, T(\gamma p \to \rho p)|_{0^\circ} + \dots$$

so $\gamma_\rho^2 \sim |T(\gamma p \to \rho p)/_{0^\circ}|^2 = d\sigma/dt|_{0^\circ}$.

— TÖRNQVIST:

You mentioned that there is an experiment of γ on deuterium. Can you say something about if there is any charged ρ production ($\gamma n \to \rho^- p$) which would proceed through non-pomeron (π^t) exchange?

— ROSENFELD:

I am not quite familiar with the details of this experiment, but the upper limit is 1.5 μb compared with ~ 10 μb for $\gamma p \to \rho^0 p$.

Quasipotential Approach to the Two-Body Problem in Quantum Field Theory

I. T. Todorov

1. Introduction: three-dimensional *vs.* four-dimensional two-particle equations 953

2. Relativistic Lippmann-Schwinger equation for scalar particles 955
   A. Off-shell kinematics. General form of the equation . 955
   B. On-shell and off-shell requirements. Explicit form of the Green function 956
   C. The homogeneous (Schrödinger) equation 959

3. Scalar Yukawa interaction and relativistic eikonal formula 959
   A. Relativistic reduced mass 959
   B. The eikonal approximation 961
   C. Three-dimensional counterpart of the Wick-Cutkosky model 962

4. Quasipotential equation for electromagnetic interaction . . 962
   A. Determination of an effective four-potential for the interaction of scalar charged particles 962
   B. Relativistic Balmer formula with fine structure splitting 964
   C. Electromagnetic interaction of spin-$\frac{1}{2}$ particles 966

5. Concluding remarks 970

Acknowledgements 970

Appendix I. Breit equation and perturbative calculations for spin-0 and spin-$\frac{1}{2}$ particles 971

Appendix II. Derivation of the quasipotential equation for two Dirac particles 973

References 975

Discussion 978

Quasipotential Approach to the Two-Body Problem in Quantum Field Theory (*)

I. T. TODOROV

International Centre for Theoretical Physics
Miramare (Trieste), Italy

1. Introduction: Three-dimensional *vs.* four-dimensional two-particle equations.

The complexity of the relativistic two-body problem originates in the fact that it is difficult to disentangle a purely two-particle process from all related production processes. There is no generally accepted classical (*i.e.* non-quantum) theory of two relativistic interacting particles [1]. In fact, it was suggested recently [2] that the correct classical equation should be related to the limit $\hbar \to 0$ of an appropriate quantum theory of the relativistic two-body problem.

The work on the two-body problem in the framework of quantum field theory goes in two major lines: *a*) three-dimensional one-time formulation, *b*) four-dimensional formulation in which an individual time variable is ascribed to each particle.

The (more natural) three-dimensional approach originates in the classical papers of Fock and Podolsky [3] in which the Coulomb law is derived from the basic equations of quantum electrodynamics. Quite in the tradition of modern theoretical physics, the idea was first forgotten, then rediscovered (at least twice) and called the Tamm-Dancoff method [4].

The four-dimensional approach also had its origin in the thirties — in the many-time formalism of Dirac, Fock and Podolsky [5]. It assumes its present form in the early fifties [6]. A soluble model of this type — the scalar Coulomb interaction — was considered by Wick and Cutkosky [7].

(*) On leave of absence from the Physical Institute of the Bulgarian Academy of Sciences, Sofia, Bulgaria.

For many years the manifestly covariant four-dimensional approach — the Bethe-Salpeter (B-S) equation — was undoubtedly the most popular one. It appears indeed a natural tool for summing up high-energy contributions of ladder diagrams. However, it does not seem so well appropriate (at least in the commonly used ladder approximation) for the two-particle bound-states problem. The trouble comes from the unphysical variable of relative time (or its conjugate variable, the relative energy) which is involved in the equation. It gives rise to redundant unphysical solutions, as exhibited in the Wick-Cutkosky model ([7]). The physicists ought to have remembered the simple truth that « a proton today and an electron yesterday do not constitute a hydrogen atom » ([8]). The appearance of extra solutions is not the only defect of the B-S equation. In the ladder approximation (which is the one chiefly used in practical calculations) it does not provide the correct limit of a relativistic (Klein-Gordon or Dirac) equation in an external field when the mass of one of the particles tends to infinity. (A partial remedy to this shortcoming is proposed in the case of the Coulomb interaction in ref. ([9])).

It is remarkable that the three-dimensional approach is automatically free of most of these difficulties. However, unlike the four-dimensional approach, it is highly non-unique. The variety of three-dimensional equations is due to the non-uniqueness of the off-shell extrapolation of the scattering amplitude and, even prior to that, to the very choice of variables with respect to which the extrapolation is carried out. We have, for instance, off-mass-shell (symmetric or non-symmetric) and off-energy-shell extrapolations. In addition to this intrinsic ambiguity, different authors start from different premises and pursue different objectives when dealing with two-particle equations.

The quasipotential approach ([10,11]) arose as a compromise between the field-theoretic programme followed in refs. ([3,4,12]) and the work on effective energy-dependent potential that fits a given scattering amplitude ([13]). In contrast to the more ambitious work which starts either with the Heisenberg equations of motion ([3,4]) or with the B-S equation ([12]), or else with the old-fashioned perturbation theory ([14]), and leads to a highly complicated non-local potential, the Logunov and Tavkhelidze approach ([10]) only pretends to fit the on-shell scattering amplitude and to yield the elastic unitarity condition for real potentials. These requirements do not fix the Green function and the potential uniquely and give place to different possibilities corresponding to different criteria of «simplicity» (cf. refs. ([10,11,15-17])). Here I shall review a new local version ([18,19]) of the quasipotential equation. It looks as simple as the non-relativistic Schrödinger equation and, unlike most of the other three-dimensional equations, it yields the proper relativistic equation in an external field when one of the masses tends to infinity. In addition to the material contained in ref. [18] we also treat here the electromagnetic interaction of spinor particles.

2. Relativistic Lippmann-Schwinger equation for scalar particles.

A) Off-shell kinematics. General form of the equation. Consider the elastic scattering of two spinless particles of masses m_1 and m_2 and initial (final) 4-momenta $q_1, q_2 (p_1, p_2)$. We fix the normalization of the invariant amplitude T by its relation to the S-matrix element

$$\langle p_1 p_2 | S | q_1 q_2 \rangle =$$
$$4 p_1^0 p_2^0 \delta(\mathbf{p}_1 - \mathbf{q}_1) \delta(\mathbf{p}_2 - \mathbf{q}_2) + 2\pi i \delta(p_1 + p_2 - q_1 - q_2) T(p_1 p_2; q_1 q_2) \quad (1.1).$$

Usually (in analogy with the non-relativistic case) the Lippmann-Schwinger equation is considered as an off-energy-shell equation. We shall define it instead as an off-mass-shell (on-energy-shell) equation. To do this we consider a minimal way out of the mass shell assuming that the 4-momenta squared always statisfy the relation

$$p_1^2 - p_2^2 = q_1^2 - q_2^2 = m_1^2 - m_2^2 \quad (1.2)$$

(cf. ref. [20]). We shall work from the outset in the s-channel in which the total momentum

$$P = p_1 + p_2 = q_1 + q_2 \quad (1.3)$$

is timelike so that

$$P^2 \equiv w^2 > 0 . \quad (1.4)$$

The centre-of-mass energies E_1 and E_2 of particles 1 and 2 can be defined in an invariant way by

$$E_1 = \frac{1}{w} P p_1 = \frac{1}{w} P q_1 = \frac{w^2 + m_1^2 - m_2^2}{2w}$$

$$E_2 = \frac{1}{w} P p_2 = \frac{1}{w} P q_2 = \frac{w^2 + m_2^2 - m_1^2}{2w}. \tag{1.5}$$

The relative 4-momenta p and q, defined by

$$p = \frac{E_2}{w} p_1 - \frac{E_1}{w} p_2, \qquad q = \frac{E_2}{w} q_1 - \frac{E_1}{w} q_2 \tag{1.6}$$

are orthogonal to P: $Pp = Pq = 0$. In the non-relativistic limit, when $w \to m_1 + m_2$ we have

$$\frac{1}{w} E_i \to \frac{m_i}{m_1 + m_2}, \qquad i = 1, 2$$

so that q and p go into the conventional non-relativistic relative momenta.

After these kinematical preliminaries we postulate the following Lippmann-Schwinger type equation for T:

$$T_P(p, q) + V_P(p, q) + \int V_P(p, k) G_P(k) T_P(k, q) \delta(Pk) \mathrm{d}^4 k = 0. \tag{1.7}$$

It assumes a particularly simple form in the centre-of-mass frame in which

$$P = (w, \mathbf{0}), \quad p = (0, \mathbf{p}), \quad q = (0, \mathbf{q}). \tag{1.8}$$

In this frame eq. (1.7) reads

$$T + V + VGT = T_w(\mathbf{p}, \mathbf{q}) + V_w(\mathbf{p}, \mathbf{q}) + \int V_w(\mathbf{p}, \mathbf{k}) G_w(\mathbf{k}) T_w(\mathbf{k}, \mathbf{q}) \mathrm{d}^3 k = 0 \tag{1.9}$$

where $G_w(\mathbf{k}) = (1/w) G_P(k)$. It is clear that this equation is perfectly relativistic invariant, although it involves only three-dimensional integration.

B) *On-shell and off-shell requirements. Explicit form of the Green function.* In order to give a content to eq. (1.9) we have to define the Green function

G_w and the potential V_w. To do this we shall impose the following general requirements on eq. (1.9) which will provide us with a link between the quasi-potential equation and conventional quantum field theory.

i) Eq. (1.9) is satisfied order by order by the Feynman perturbation expansion of T.

In particular, if G is idependent of the coupling constant (s) and $T = T_1 + T_2 + \ldots$ is the perturbative expansion of T, then $V = V_1 + V_2 + \ldots$ with

$$V_1 = -T_1, \qquad V_2 = -T_2 + T_1 G T_1, \ldots \qquad (1.10)$$

In Sec. 3 we shall use the weaker assumption that eq. (1.10) is fulfilled on the mass shell only.

ii) For a hermitian potential eq. (1.9) should imply the on-shell elastic unitarity condiion

$$T_w(\boldsymbol{p}, \boldsymbol{q}) - T_w^*(\boldsymbol{p}, \boldsymbol{q}) = \frac{\pi i}{w} \int T_w^*(\boldsymbol{p}, \boldsymbol{k}) T_w(\boldsymbol{k}, \boldsymbol{q}) \delta(k^2 - b^2(w)) \, d^3k \qquad (1.11)$$

for $\boldsymbol{p}^2 = b^2(w) = \boldsymbol{q}^2$ and all energies $w \geqslant m_1 + m_2$. Here

$$b^2(w) = \frac{1}{4w^2}[w^4 - 2(m_1^2 + m_2^2)w^2 + (m_1^2 - m_2^2)^2] \qquad (1.12)$$

is the on-shell value of the centre-of-mass momentum squared of each of the two particles.

Writing (formally) the solution of (1.9) as

$$T = \frac{-1}{1+VG}V = -V\frac{1}{1+GV}$$

we obtain (for $V = V^*$)

$$T - T^* = \left(V\frac{1}{1+GV}\right)^* - \frac{1}{1+VG}V =$$

$$\frac{1}{1+VG^*}V(G - G^*)\frac{1}{1+VG}V = T^*(G - G^*)T. \qquad (1.13)$$

Thus, our second requirement fixes the discontinuity of the Green function G.

Assumptions i) and ii) are basic in the sense that they are essentially concerned only with the on-shell properties of the Green function (and potential). They are accepted in nearly all papers on the quasipotential approach. However, they obviously do not fix eq. (1.9) uniquely. In particular, they are satisfied by any of the five different equations considered in refs. ([10-12, 14-16]) Hence, we shall supplement them by the following more specific off-shell-type assumption which will guarantee that the corresponding homogeneous equation will go into the Klein-Gordon equation in an external field when one of the masses goes to infinity (*).

iii) For spinless particles $[G_w(k)]^{-1}$ is a linear function of k^2 (just as in the non-relativistic Lippmann-Schwinger equation).

Requirements ii) and iii) fix the Green function G_w completely. Using (1.11) and (1.13) we obtain

$$G_w(k) = \frac{1}{2w}(k^2 - b^2 - i0)^{-1}. \tag{1.14}$$

The equation thus obtained

$$T_w(p, q) + V_w(p, q) + \frac{1}{2w}\int V_w(p, k)\frac{1}{k^2 - b^2 - i0}T_w(k, q)d^3k = 0 \tag{1.15}$$

differs from the original Logunov-Tavkhelidze equation ([10]) only (**) in that the p^2-dependent factor $(m^2 + p^2)^{-\frac{1}{2}}$ (for the equal-mass case considered in Ref. ([10])) is replaced by $2/w$ in (1.15). This simplification will allow us to write a local exactly soluble equation for the relativistic Coulomb problem.

A shortcoming of eq. (1.15) common to all known quasipotential equations is the fact that it leads to unphysical singularities in w (for $w \leqslant |m_1 - m_2|$) when we restrict ourselves to the Born approximation in the potential. This violation of known analytic properties indicates the domain of applicability of the equation with an approximate potential: it cannot be trusted if the mass defect exceeds say $\sqrt{2m_1, m_2}$. Note that eq. (1.15) reproduces correctly the analytic properties in $t = -(p-q)^2$ (cf. the second paper in ref. ([10])).

(*) The importance of this requirement was stressed to the author by F. J. Dyson.
(**) The additional difference in the sign of V is a matter of convention. Our choice fits the non-relativistic limit of the potential.

C) *The homogeneous (Schrödinger) equation.* In order to obtain a Schrödinger type equation from (1.9) we define the wave function

$$\varphi_q(p) = \delta(p-q) + G_q(p)T_q(p,q) \tag{1.16}$$

where the subscript q in the right-hand side is a short-hand for

$$w_q = \sqrt{m_1^2 + q^2} + \sqrt{m_2^2 + q^2}$$

and G_q is given by (1.14). Multiplying both sides of (1.16) by G_q^{-1} and using (1.9) we get

$$T_q(p,q) = G_q^{-1}(p)\phi_q(p) = -V_q(p,q)$$
$$-\int V_q(p,k)G_q(k)T_q(k,q)d^3k = -\int V_q(p,k)\phi_q(k)d^3k.$$

Extrapolating this equation to arbitrary w we obtain the relativistic Schrödinger equation

$$2w(p^2 - b^2(w))\phi_w(p) + \int V_w(p,k)\phi_w(k)d^3k = 0. \tag{1.17}$$

We note that for a *local potential*, i.e., when $V_w = V_w(p-k)$, eq. (1.17) is equivalent to a local Schrödinger equation in co-ordinate space

$$[2w(b^2 + \Delta) - \mathscr{V}_w(r)]\phi_w(r) = 0 \tag{1.18}$$

where

$$\mathscr{V}_w(r) = \int V_w(k)\exp[ikr]d^3k.$$

3. Scalar Yukawa interaction and relativistic eikonal formula.

A) *Relativistic reduced mass.* In order to get an idea of the content of eq. (1.15) we consider the model of two charged (complex) scalar fields ψ_1 and ψ_2 of masses m_1 and m_2 interacting via a neutral scalar field φ of mass μ with a cubic interaction

$$L_I(x) = [g_1 : \psi_1^*(x)\psi_1(x) : + g_2 : \psi_2^*(x)\psi_2(x) :]\varphi(x). \tag{2.1}$$

(The dots: stand as usual for Wick normal ordering.) Using the prescription (1.10), we obtain for the Born (lowest non-vanishing) approximation for V the Yukawa potential

$$V = V_1 = -\frac{1}{(2\pi)^3} \frac{g_1 g_2}{\mu^2 + (\mathbf{p}-\mathbf{q})^2}. \tag{2.2}$$

The coupling constants g_1 and g_2 in this model have the dimension of mass. We shall introduce a dimensionless quantity α (analogous to the fine structure constants) setting

$$g_1 g_2 = 16\pi m_1 m_2 \alpha. \tag{2.3}$$

Eq. (1.18) with the Yukawa potential (2.2) assumes the form

$$\left(b^2(w) + \Delta + 2\frac{m_1 m_2}{w}\frac{\alpha}{r}\exp[-\mu r]\right)\varphi_w(r) = 0. \tag{2.4}$$

It differs from the corresponding non-relativistic Schrödinger equation

$$\left(E_{NR} + \frac{1}{2m}\Delta + \frac{\alpha}{r}\exp[-\mu r]\right)\Phi(r) = 0. \tag{2.5}$$

only in the kinematical factors. Eq. (2.5) goes into (2.4) if we substitute the non-relativistic reduced mass

$$m = \frac{m_1 m_2}{m_1 + m_2}$$

and the (binding) energy E_{NR} by the following functions of w:

$$m \to m_w = \frac{m_1 m_2}{w}, \quad E_{NR} \to \frac{b^2(w)}{2m_w}. \tag{2.6}$$

The quantity m_w will be called *relativistic reduced mass*. For small momenta and coupling when

$$w \approx m_1 + m_2 + E_{NR} \to m_1 + m_2$$

m_w goes into m.

We shall see that the energy dependence of m_w along with the w-dependence of b^2 (1.12) take proper care of relativistic recoil effects which usually are accounted for in a much more complicated way.

B) *The eikonal approximation.* The simple correspondence between eqs. (2.4) and (2.5) allows us to write down the (exact or approximate) solution of our quasipotential equation whenever such a solution is available for the corresponding non-relativistic problem. In particular, eq. (2.4) yields the relativistic eikonal approximation [21]. Indeed, according to ref. [22], the small-angle eikonal behaviour of the on-shell non-relativistic amplitude is given by

$$T_{NR}(\boldsymbol{p}, \boldsymbol{q}; m) = \frac{-i}{2\pi^3} |\boldsymbol{p}| \int d^2 y \exp[i(\boldsymbol{p}-\boldsymbol{q})\boldsymbol{y}] \left\{ \exp\left[\frac{2im}{|\boldsymbol{p}|} \alpha K_0(\mu|\boldsymbol{y}|)\right] - 1 \right\}. \quad (2.7)$$

The integration in $\boldsymbol{v}$ is performed in the 2-plane orthogonal to $\boldsymbol{p}+\boldsymbol{q}$. The representation (2.7) is certainly valid in the limit

$$\mu \to 0, \quad t = -(\boldsymbol{p}-\boldsymbol{q})^2 \to 0. \quad (2.8)$$

It is also believed to be a meaningful approximation for

$$|\boldsymbol{p}| \to \infty \text{ (or } w \to \infty)\mu, \text{ } t\text{-finite}.$$

Using the substitution (2.6) we obtain from here the eikonal approximation for the relativistic on-shell amplitude

$$T_w(\boldsymbol{p}, \boldsymbol{q}) = w T_{NR}(\boldsymbol{p}, \boldsymbol{q}; m_w).$$

It can be shown by a straightforward study of crossed ladder diagrams that the relativistic eikonal approximation is valid in the limit (2.8).

Let us mention that the ladder approximation in the Bethe-Salpeter equation does not reproduce the correct result. The reason is that the leading asymptotic term in each (ordinary) ladder diagram is exactly cancelled by the leading terms of a set of crossed ladder diagrams (cf. ref. [23]). In fact, one has to take into account an infinite number of irreducible diagrams in the kernel of the B-S equation in order to obtain the eikonal approximation which is reproduced by just taking the Born term in the potential in our three-dimensional equation.

C) *Three-dimensional counterpart of the Wick-Cutkosky model.* For $\mu = 0$ eq. (2.4) is the Schrödinger equation for a particle of mass m_w in a Coulomb potential and therefore is exactly soluble. The substitution (2.6) in the non-relativistic Balmer formula $E_{NR} = -m\alpha^2/2n^2$ gives the following relativistic formula [24]:

$$w_n^2 = m_1^2 + m_2^2 + 2m_1 m_2 \left(1 - \frac{\alpha^2}{n^2}\right)^{1/2}. \quad (2.9)$$

(We have disregarded the negative sign in front of the square root which would have led us out of the domain of applicability of eq. (2.4)—cf. the remark at the end of Sect. 2B). This result demonstrates the remarkable fact that the simple substitutions (2.6) in the non-relativistic Schrödinger equation takes proper care of the relativistic recoil effects. This can be seen by calculating the same energy levels with the accuracy of α^4 from the more conventional (but also more complicated and less satisfactory) Breit equation (cf. ref. [25] and Appendix I below). It should be noted that this result (just as well as the eikonal approximation discussed in the preceding subsection) cannot be obtained from the ladder approximation of the B-S equation. In fact, even leaving aside the difficulty of extra solutions, the B-S equation gives an incorrect contribution of order α^3 to w_n (cf. ref. [7]). The energy levels (2.9) are 0(4)-degenerate since we are dealing with scalar « photons » which do not give rise to a magnetic field interacting with the angular momentum of the system.

4. Quasipotential equation for electromagnetic interaction.

A) *Determination of an effective four-potential for the interaction of scalar charged particles* [19]. When going to the more realistic electromagnetic interaction via a vector photon, it looks attractive to replace the scalar quasipotential V by a 4-vector potential V_μ. This should correspond to the passage from the scalar field φ and the Lagrangian (2.1) to the 4-vector field A_μ and the electromagnetic interaction Lagrangian

$$L_{em}(x) = ie \left(:\psi_1^*(x)\overleftrightarrow{\partial}_\mu \psi_1(x): - :\psi_2^*(x)\overleftrightarrow{\partial}_\mu \psi_2(x):\right)A^\mu(x) +$$
$$+ e^2\left(\psi_1^*(x)\psi_1(x) + \psi_2^*(x)\psi_2(x)\right)A^\mu(x)A_\mu(x) \quad (3.1)$$

where

$$\psi^*(x)\overleftrightarrow{\partial}_\mu\psi(x) = \psi^*(x)[\partial_\mu\psi(x)] - [\partial_\mu\psi^*(x)]\psi(x) \,.$$

Following the analogy with the minimal electromagnetic interaction of a Klein-Gordon particle in an external field, we postulate the following gauge invariant eigenvalue equation for our fictitious particle of mass m_w:

$$[(E-\mathscr{V}_0)^2 - (\boldsymbol{p} - \boldsymbol{\mathscr{V}})^2 - m_w^2]\phi_w = 0 \tag{3.2}$$

where E is the energy of the effective particle

$$E = [m_w^2 + b^2(w)]^{\frac{1}{2}} = \frac{1}{2w}(w^2 - m_1^2 - m_2^2) \,. \tag{3.3}$$

Equation (3.2) can be written in the form (1.17) if we identify the scalar potential in (1.17) with the expression

$$[2EV_0(\boldsymbol{p}, \boldsymbol{q}) - (\boldsymbol{p} + \boldsymbol{q})\,\boldsymbol{V}(\boldsymbol{p}, \boldsymbol{q})] - [V_0^2(\boldsymbol{p}, \boldsymbol{q}) - \boldsymbol{V}^2(\boldsymbol{p}, \boldsymbol{q})] \tag{3.4}$$

where $V_\mu(\boldsymbol{p}, \boldsymbol{q})$ is the kernel of the operator $\mathscr{V}_\mu$. To reconstruct the 4-potential V_μ up to order e^2 we equate (in accordance with (1.10)) the first bracket in (3.4) with (minus) the Born term T_1 of the scattering amplitude:

$$T_1(\boldsymbol{p}, \boldsymbol{q}) = \frac{\alpha}{2\pi^2} \frac{4E_1 E_2 + (\boldsymbol{p} + \boldsymbol{q})^2}{(\boldsymbol{p} - \boldsymbol{q})^2} = 2w[(\boldsymbol{p} + \boldsymbol{q})\,\boldsymbol{V}(\boldsymbol{p}, \boldsymbol{q}) - 2EV_0(\boldsymbol{p}, \boldsymbol{q})] \tag{3.5}$$

where we have set $e^2 = 4\pi\alpha$ and have used the covariant gauge for the photon propagator.

Obviously, eq. (3.5) does not determine the 4-potential uniquely, since we can add to V_μ an arbitrary 4-vector orthogonal to $(2E, \boldsymbol{p} + \boldsymbol{q})$ without changing the right-hand side of (3.5). In order to reduce this arbitrariness (which is related to the freedom in the choice of the gauge for V_μ) we assume that V_0 is given by the Coulomb potential:

$$V_0(\boldsymbol{p}, \boldsymbol{q}) = -\frac{\alpha}{2\pi^2} \frac{1}{(\boldsymbol{p} - \boldsymbol{q})^2} \,. \tag{3.6}$$

Using, further, that

$$Ew = E_1 E_2 + b^2(w) \tag{3.7}$$

and going to the energy shell we find

$$(p+q)\, V(p, q) = -\frac{\alpha}{4\pi^2 w}. \tag{3.8}$$

We can satisfy (3.8) with

$$V(p, q) = -\frac{\alpha}{4\pi^2 w} \frac{p+q}{(p+q)^2}. \tag{3.9}$$

We stress once more that the arbitrariness in the choice of the off-shell 4-potential is higher than in the case of a scalar potential (Sect. 1), since it also depends on the choice of the gauge. Our choice leads to a simple « pseudo-local » expression for $\mathscr{V}_\mu$ in co-ordinate space:

$$\mathscr{V}_0(r) = -\frac{\alpha}{r}, \quad \mathscr{V}(r) = -\frac{i\alpha}{2w} \frac{r}{r^3} I_s \tag{3.10}$$

where I_s is the space reflection operator: $(I f_s)(r) = f(-r)$. Equation (3.10) is easily obtained by taking Fourier transform of (3.6) and (3.9) (the vector potential coming out as an exchange potential). Using the identities $I_s^2 = 1$, $\{r, I_s\} = \{\nabla, I_s\} = 0$, we find that both the anticommutator $\{p, \mathscr{V}\}$ and $\mathscr{V}^2$ are local operators (in co-ordinate space):

$$\{p, \mathscr{V}\} = -\frac{2\pi\alpha}{w} \delta(r), \quad \mathscr{V}^2(r) = \frac{\alpha^2}{4w^2} \frac{1}{r^4} \quad (p = -i\nabla). \tag{3.11}$$

Furthermore, we notice that the four components of the potential (3.10) commute among themselves.

B) *Relativistic Balmer formula with fine structure splitting.* We proceed now to the determination of the energy eigenvalues w_{nl} from eq. (3.2) with 4-potential (3.10). We note that we cannot expect an accuracy better than α^4 since we have not taken radiative corrections (or vacuum polarization) into account. The term V^2 gives a contribution of order α^6 to w_{nl} for

$l < 0$ and is not defined for $l = 0$ (cf ref. ([25])). It will be neglected in what follows.

Separating the angular variables we get the following radial equation:

$$\left[\frac{d^2}{dr^2} + \frac{2}{r}\frac{d}{dr} + b^2(w) + 2E\frac{\alpha}{r} - \frac{l(l+1)}{r^2} + \frac{\alpha^2}{r^2} - \frac{2\pi\alpha}{w}\delta(r)\right]R_{wl} = 0. \quad (3.12)$$

We shall find the energy eigenvalues up to order α^4 treating the last two terms in the brackets as a perturbation (*). The unperturbed equation

$$\left\{\frac{d^2}{dr^2} + \frac{2}{r}\frac{d}{dr} + b^2(w) + 2E\frac{\alpha}{r} - \frac{l(l+1)}{r^2}\right\}R_{wl} = 0$$

differs from the non-relativistic radial Schrödinger equation by the substitutions

$$m = \frac{m_1 m_2}{m_1 + m_2} \to E, \quad 2mE_{NR} \to b^2. \quad (3.13)$$

Inserting (3.13) into the non-relativistic Balmer formula we obtain again a set of SO(4) degenerate eigenvalues

$$w_n^2 = m_1^2 + m_2^2 + 2m_1 m_2 \left(1 + \frac{\alpha^2}{n^2}\right)^{-\frac{1}{2}}. \quad (3.14)$$

(Incidentally, although it was derived in perturbation theory, this formula makes sense also for large α and, in particular, for $\alpha \gg n$ it gives an approximately linearly rising trajectory.)

The last two terms in eq. (3.12) give the following correction to the energy eigenvalues:

$$\Delta w_{nl} = \langle nl | \frac{-\alpha^2}{2Er^2} + \frac{\pi\alpha}{Ew}\delta(r) | nl \rangle = \frac{-m\alpha^4}{n^3(2l+1)} + \frac{m^2}{M}\frac{\alpha^4}{n^3}\delta_{l0}$$

$$+ \text{ higher-order terms} \quad (M = m_1 + m_2). \quad (3.15)$$

(*) One can actually solve exactly the equation in which the term α^2/r^2 is also included (see ref. ([18])). However, the last term $(-2\pi\alpha w^{-1}\delta(r))$ cannot be treated in that case as a regular perturbation.

It is remarkable that we obtain in this way a formula which coincides with the exact answer for the value of w_{nl} up to order α^4, that is usually derived from the more complicated (and less satisfactory) Breit equation ([25]) (see Appendix I).

C) Electromagnetic interaction of spin-$\frac{1}{2}$ particles. Now we proceed to the extension of our method to spinor particles. The clue to this problem is to write down a second-order equation for spin-$\frac{1}{2}$ particles. It is well known that the Dirac equation for an electron of mass m in an external electromagnetic field can be written equivalently as a second-order equation

$$[(E-\mathscr{V}_0)^2-(\mathbf{p}-\mathscr{V})^2-m^2-e\mathscr{F}^{\mu\nu}s_{\mu\nu}]\psi=0 \tag{3.16}$$

where $\mathscr{F}^{\mu\nu}$ is the electromagnetic stress tensor and

$$s_{\mu\nu}=\frac{i}{4}[\gamma_\mu,\gamma_\nu] \tag{3.17}$$

is the spinor part of the angular momentum. (Incidentally, it is most convenient to solve the Coulomb problem for a Dirac electron starting with this form of the equation). Our aim will be to extend eq. (3.16) to the case of electromagnetic interaction of a Dirac particle of mass m_1 with a spin 0 or a spin-$\frac{1}{2}$ particle of mass m_2.

We begin a modification of the normalization condition (1.1) for the scattering amplitude. In the presence of spinor particle we shall require

$$\langle p_1 s_1 p_2 s_2 | S | q_1 s_1 q_2 s_2 \rangle = \mathbf{1}\,\frac{4p_1^0 p_2^0}{(2m_1)^{2s_1}(2m_2)^{2s_2}}\delta(\mathbf{p}_1-\mathbf{q}_1)\delta(\mathbf{p}_2-\mathbf{q}_2)+$$

$$2\pi i\delta(p_1+p_2-q_1-q_2)T(p_1p_2;q_1q_2),\quad s_1,s_2=0 \text{ or } \tfrac{1}{2}. \tag{3.18}$$

Here **1** is the unit matrix with respect to the (four-dimensional) spinor indices.

Consider first the case $s_1=\frac{1}{2}$, $s_2=0$.

The Lippmann-Schwinger equation for T has the form

$$T_w(\mathbf{p},\mathbf{q})+K_w(\mathbf{p},\mathbf{q})+\frac{1}{2w}\int K_w(\mathbf{p},\mathbf{k})\frac{(\gamma k)_1+m_1}{k^2-b^2-i0}T_w(\mathbf{k},\mathbf{q})\mathrm{d}^3k=0 \tag{3.19}$$

where $(\gamma\cdot k)_1=E_1\gamma^0-\mathbf{k}\boldsymbol{\gamma}$. The kernel K_w will be identified with a linear combination of the components of (the kernels of) the 4-potential, V_μ, and of the electromagnetic stress tensor, $F_{\mu\nu}$:

In analogy with (1.16) we set

$$\psi_q(p) = \delta(p-q) + \frac{1}{2w_q} \frac{(\gamma \cdot p)_1 + m_1}{p^2 - q^2 - i0} T(p, q). \tag{3.20}$$

Multiplying by $p^2 - q^2$ and substituting in (3.19) we obtain the following Schrödinger equation for ψ:

$$(p^2 - b^2)\psi_w(p) + \frac{(\gamma \cdot p)_1 + m_1}{2w} \int K_w(p, k)\psi_w(k) \, d^3k = 0. \tag{3.21}$$

Now we would like to identify eq. (3.21) with a gauge-invariant equation of the type (3.16):

$$[(E - \mathscr{V}_0)^2 - (p - \mathscr{V})^2 - m_w^2 + \mathscr{D}_1 i\alpha - \mathscr{B}_1 \sigma]\psi_w = 0. \tag{3.22}$$

Here $\alpha = \gamma_0 \gamma$, $\sigma = \frac{i}{2} \gamma \times \gamma$, and $\mathscr{D}_1$ and $\mathscr{B}_1$ are the electric and magnetic forces acting on particle 1 ($\mathscr{D}_{1j} \leftrightarrow eF_{0j}, \mathscr{B}_{1j} \leftrightarrow \frac{1}{2} e \varepsilon_{jkl} F_{kl}$). Following the procedure by which we derived the expression for $\mathscr{V}_\mu$ in the case of scalar charged particles, we equate the linear term in $\mathscr{V}$, $\mathscr{D}_1$ and $\mathscr{B}_1$ in the lefthand side of eq. (3.22) with the e^2 term in the expansion of the scattering amplitude. More precisely, we set

$$\{(p+q)V(p,q) - 2EV_0(p,q) + D_1(p,q)i\alpha - B_1(p,q)\sigma\} \times$$

$$(E_1 + H_1(q)) = \frac{E_1 + H_1(p)}{2w} \beta T_1(p,q)(E_1 + H_1(q)) \tag{3.23}$$

for $p^2 = q^2 = b^2$ where $H_1(p) = m_1 \beta + \alpha p$ and

$$\beta T_1(p, q) = \frac{1}{2\pi^2(p-q)^2} \{2E_2 + \alpha(p+q)\}. \tag{3.24}$$

(We again made use of the covariant gauge and chose the basis in the spinor space in such a way that $\beta = \gamma_0$.) Equating the coefficients of the unit matrix and of the σ-matrices in both sides of (3.23) we obtain

$$E_1[(p+q)V(p,q)-2EV_0(p,q)] + iq\, D_1(p,q) = \frac{\alpha E}{2\pi^2}\left[\frac{2E}{(p-q)^2} - \frac{1}{2w}\right] + \frac{E_2\alpha}{2\pi^2 w}\frac{(p-q)q}{(p-q)^2}, \quad (3.25)$$

$$-[\mathscr{D}_1(p,q)\times q + E_1 B_1(p,q)]\sigma = \frac{\alpha}{2\pi^2}\frac{ip\times q}{(p-q)^2}\sigma. \quad (3.26)$$

(In deriving (3.25) we used (3.7) and the on-shell condition $p^2 = q^2 = b^2$). We can satisfy (3.25) and (3.26) with the four-potential (3.6) and (3.9) (determined from the electromagnetic interaction of scalar particles) setting

$$iD_1(p,q) = \frac{\alpha}{2\pi^2}\frac{E_2}{w}\frac{p-q}{(p-q)^2}, \quad B_1(p,q) = -\frac{\alpha}{2\pi^2 w}\frac{ip\times q}{(p-q)^2}. \quad (3.27)$$

The corresponding expressions in co-ordinate space are given by (3.10) and

$$\mathscr{D}_1(r) = \frac{\alpha E_2}{w}\frac{r}{r^3}, \quad \mathscr{B}_1(r) = \frac{\alpha}{wr^3}L \quad (3.28)$$

where $L = r\times p = -ir\times\nabla$ is the angular momentum.

Thus, eq. (3.22) assumes the form

$$\left(b^2 + \Delta + 2E\frac{\alpha}{r} + \frac{\alpha^2}{r^2} - \frac{2\pi\alpha}{w}\delta(r) + \frac{\alpha E_2}{wr^3}ir\alpha - \frac{\alpha}{wr^3}L\sigma\right)\psi_w(r) = 0. \quad (3.29)$$

(We have again neglected the $\mathscr{V}^2$ term.)

It is easily verified that this equation goes into (3.16) for $m_2\to\infty (E_2/w\to 1)$ and into eq. (3.2), (3.10) for $m_1\to\infty (m_1/w\to 1)$. In order to solve eq. (3.29) in perturbation theory we choose the basis in the spinor space in such a way that γ_0 be diagonal and we eliminate the small components of ψ_w: This amounts to the substitution

$$\alpha\to\frac{1}{2m_1}(p+ip\times\sigma), ir\alpha\to\frac{1}{2m_1}(r\nabla - L\sigma) \quad (3.30)$$

where σ are already the 2×2 Pauli matrices (see eq. (12.7) of ref. ([25])). In this approximation the energy eigenvalues can be labelled by the total angular momentum $J^2 = j(j+1)$ where

$$J = L + \tfrac{1}{2}\sigma \tag{3.31}$$

is exactly conserved in all orders and by the orbital angular momentum $L^2 = l(l+1)$ which is a good quantum number up to order α^4 in the energy eigenvalues. We have

$$L\sigma = j(j+1) - l(l+1) - 3/4 . \tag{3.32}$$

We note that, for a given value of l, j can take two values: $j = l \pm \tfrac{1}{2}$ (except for $l = 0$ when j takes only the value $j = \tfrac{1}{2}$). A straightforward calculation (see Appendix I) leads to the following expansion in α of the energy eigenvalues:

$$w_{njl} = M - \frac{m\alpha^2}{2n^2} + \frac{m\alpha^4}{8n^4}\left(3 - \frac{m}{M}\right) -$$

$$\frac{m\alpha^4}{Mn^3}\left(\frac{m_1 - m}{2l+1} + \frac{m_2 + m}{2j+1}\right) + o(\alpha^4). \tag{3.33}$$

This result again agrees with the conventional calculation from the Breit equation (Appendix I).

A longer calculation on exactly the same lines (see Appendix II) leads to the following quasipotential equation for the electromagnetic interaction of two spin-$\tfrac{1}{2}$ particles:

$$b^2 + \Delta + 2E\frac{\alpha}{r} + \frac{\alpha^2}{r^2} - \frac{2\pi\alpha}{w}\delta(r) + \frac{i\alpha r}{wr^3}(E_2\alpha_1 - E_1\alpha_2)$$

$$- \frac{\alpha}{wr^3}L(\sigma_1 + \sigma_2) - \frac{2\pi\alpha}{3w}(\sigma_1\sigma_2 + \alpha_1\alpha_2)\delta(r)$$

$$+ \frac{\alpha}{2wr^3}\left[\sigma_1\sigma_2 - \alpha_1\alpha_2 - \frac{3}{r^2}((\sigma_1 r)(\sigma_2 r) - (\alpha_1 r)(\alpha_2 r))\right]\psi_w(r) = 0. \tag{3.34}$$

(Note again that (3.34) goes into (3.16) when any one of the masses tends to infinity.) We leave it as an exercise for the assiduous student to calculate the energy eigenvalues from this equation.

5. Concluding remarks.

We shall single out some properties of the approximate quasipotential equations (2.4), (3.2), (3.29) and (3.34) (corresponding to different quantum-field-theoretic Lagrangians) which distinguish them favourably from the ladder approximation in the Bethe-Salpeter equation in the same cases.

a) For small momenta and for weak coupling one can write

$$w = m_1 + m_2 + E_{NR}$$

where the non-relativistic (binding) energy E_{NR} is small compared to the rest masses. Then any of the above equations goes into the corresponding non-relativistic equation. In particular, the relativistic effective mass m_w goes into the non-relativistic reduced mass m.

b) If one of the masses, say m_2, tends to infinity, then the quasipotential equation goes into the Klein-Gordon or Dirac equation for the particle 1 in an external field. (We note that $w/m_2 \to 1$ for $m_2 \to \infty$.)

c) In terms of Feynman diagrams the quasipotential equation sums up all crossed-ladder graphs in the limit of small exchanged mass μ and small momentum transfer $t = -(p-q)^2$.

The properties *b*) and *c*) are actually related. It is just the lack of the latter property in the ladder approximation of the Bethe-Salpeter equation which does not allow the proper static limit to be obtained from it when the proton mass goes to infinity. It may also be the origin of the unwanted solutions in the Wick-Cutkosky model.

Acknowledgements.

I am grateful to Professors Abdus Salam and P. Budini, the International Atomic Energy Agency and UNESCO for their kind hospitality at the International Centre for Theoretical Physics, Trieste, where the notes were prepared. I would like to thank Professor A. Zichichi for his warm hospitality at the International School of Subnuclear Physics « Ettore Majorana » in Erice, where the lecture was delivered. It is also a pleasure to thank Dr. R. Faustov and Dr. C. Itzykson for helpful discussions at early stages of this work.

Appendix I. Breit equation and perturbative calculations for spin-0 and spin-½ particles.

The Breit equation for the electromagnetic interaction of two spin-0 particles is derived in the following way [19] (compare with the derivation of the Breit equation for two spin-½ particles in ref. [25]). The free Hamiltonians of the two particles are expanded in powers of p^2 up to order p^4:

$$\sqrt{m_i^2 + p^2} \approx m_i + \frac{1}{2m_i} p^2 - \frac{p^4}{8m_i^3}, \qquad i = 1, 2. \tag{I.1}$$

The potential is defined by the Born approximation to the scattering amplitude calculated in the Coulomb gauge [26] times the four particles' wave functions (a factor $(2E_i)^{-\frac{1}{2}}$ for each particle). The resulting Breit equation is

$$\left[M + \frac{1}{2m} p^2 - \frac{1}{8m^3}\left(1 - 3\frac{m}{M}\right) p^4 - w_{nl} \right] \Phi_{nl}(p) =$$

$$\frac{\alpha}{2\pi^2} \int \left\{ \frac{1}{(p-q)^2} - \frac{1}{2Mm} \left[1 - 2\frac{p^2 + q^2}{(p-q)^2} + \left(\frac{p^2 - q^2}{(p-q)^2}\right)^2 \right] \right\} \Phi_{nl}(q) \, d^3q \tag{I.2}$$

or, in co-ordinate space,

$$\left\{ w_{nl} + \frac{1}{2m} \Delta + \frac{1}{(2m)^3}\left(1 - 3\frac{m}{M}\right)\Delta^2 - M + \right.$$

$$\left. \frac{\alpha}{r}\left[1 - \frac{1}{2Mm}\left(\frac{1}{r^2} r(r\nabla)\nabla + \Delta\right)\right] \right\} \Phi_{nl}(r) = 0. \tag{I.3}$$

[We have replaced $(2E_1 E_2)^{-1}$ by $(2m_1 m_2)^{-1} = (2Mm)^{-1}$ in the right-hand side of eq. (I.2) in agreement with the approximations made in the expansion of both the free Hamiltonians and the potential.]

For the perturbative calculation of the energy spectrum we note that

$$\frac{1}{2}\left[\frac{1}{r^2} r(r\nabla)\nabla + \Delta \right] = \Delta - \frac{1}{r^2} r \nabla + \frac{1}{2r^2} L^2 \tag{I.4}$$

and use the known formulae (see, e.g., ref. [25]) for the expectation values of

r^{-n} and Δ^n:

$$\langle nl|r^{-1}|nl\rangle = \frac{m\alpha}{n^2}$$

$$\langle nl|r^{-2}|nl\rangle = \frac{2m^2\alpha^2}{n^3(2l+1)}$$

$$\langle nl|r^{-3}|nl\rangle = \frac{2m^3\alpha^3}{n^3 l(l+1)(2l+1)}$$

$$\langle nl|\Delta^2|nl\rangle = \frac{(m\alpha)^4}{n^3}\left(\frac{8}{2l+1} - \frac{3}{n}\right). \tag{I.5}$$

The three remaining terms in (I.3) and (I.4) can be treated in the following way:

$$\langle nl|\frac{\alpha}{Mmr}\Delta|nl\rangle = \frac{\alpha^2 m}{Mn^2}\langle nl|\frac{\alpha}{r}|nl\rangle - 2\frac{\alpha^2}{M}\langle nl|\frac{1}{r^2}|nl\rangle + 0(\alpha^6) =$$

$$= -\frac{m^2\alpha^4}{Mn^3}\left(\frac{4}{2l+1} - \frac{1}{n}\right) + 0(\alpha^6),$$

$$-\frac{\alpha}{Mm}\langle nl|\frac{1}{r^2}\frac{\partial}{\partial r}|nl\rangle = -\frac{\alpha}{Mm}\int_0^\infty \frac{d}{dr}\left(\frac{1}{2}R_{nl}^2(r)\right)dr = \frac{\alpha}{2Mm}R_{nl}^2(0) = \frac{2m^2\alpha^4}{Mn^3}\delta_{l0},$$

$$\langle nl|\frac{\alpha}{2Mmr^3}L^2|nl\rangle = \frac{m^2\alpha^4}{Mn^3}\frac{1-\delta_{l0}}{2l+1}. \tag{I.6}$$

The appearance of the δ_{l0} term in the right-hand side of the last equation needs some explanation. In fact $L^2|n0\rangle = 0$; however, the expectation value of $1/r^3$ in an s-state diverges (according to (I.5), so that the left-hand side of (I.6) is actually undetermined for $l=0$. This ambiguity is studied carefully in ref. ([25]) (cf. especially the discussion after eq. (13.11)). The result can be summarized as follows: in order to get the correct answer for such expressions one has to perform the angular integration in the expectation values first. This rule leads to eq. (I.6). Summing up our results we obtain

$$w_{nl} = M - \frac{m\alpha^2}{2n^2} + \frac{3}{8}\frac{m\alpha^4}{n^4} - \frac{m\alpha^4}{n^3(2l+1)} - \frac{m^2\alpha^4}{8Mn^4} + \frac{m^2\alpha^4}{M n^3}\delta_{l0} \tag{I.7}$$

in accord with (3.14) and (3.15).

The advantage of our calculation of Sect. 3-B (performed on the basis of the quasipotential equation) as compared to this more conventional calculation, is not only in the fact that it is technically simpler. Unlike the quasipotential equation, the Breit equation only makes sense in perturbation theory:

nobody has ever seriously attempted to treat it as a fourth-order equation. It is also not so readily adapted as the quasipotential equation for taking higher-order corrections into account.

Finally, we remark that eqs. (I.5) and (I.6) can also be used to get the energy eigenvalues (3.33) in the case when particle 1 has spin-$\frac{1}{2}$: To obtain (3.33) we need (in addition to the above formulae) the identity

$$\frac{1}{2}\left[\delta_{l0} + \frac{j(j+1)-l(l+1)-\frac{3}{4}}{l(l+1)(2l+1)}(1-\delta_{l0})\right] = \frac{1}{2l+1} - \frac{1}{2j+1} \quad \text{(I.8)}$$

for $j = \frac{1}{2}, \frac{3}{2}, \ldots, l = j \pm \frac{1}{2}$. (We leave the straightforward verification of this identity to the reader.)

Appendix II. Derivation of the quasipotential equation for two Dirac particles.

The counterpart of eq. (3.23) for two spin-$\frac{1}{2}$ particles (*i.e.* the equation from which the linear in $\alpha = e^2/4\pi$ part of the potential is determined) has the form:

$$\left\{(p+q)V - 2EV_0 + i(D_1\alpha_1 + D_2\alpha_2) - (B_1\sigma_1 + B_2\sigma_2) - \right.$$

$$\left. A\sigma_1\sigma_2 + B\frac{(\sigma_1k)(\sigma_2k)}{k^2} - C\frac{(\alpha_1k)(\alpha_2k)}{k^2} + D\alpha_1\alpha_2\right\}(E_1 + H_1(q))(E_2 + H_2(-q)) =$$

$$(E_1 + H_1(p))(E_2 + H_2(-p))\frac{\beta_1\beta_2}{2w}T_1(p,q)(E_1 + H_1(q))(E_2 + H_2(-q)) \quad \text{(II.1)}$$

for $w = w_p = w_q$ where

$$\beta_1\beta_2 T_1(p,q) = \frac{\alpha}{2\pi^2 k^2}(1 - \alpha_1\alpha_2), \quad k = p - q. \quad \text{(II.2)}$$

The type of matrix structures appearing in the left-hand side of eq. (II.1) is guessed from what we already know from the structure of spin-$\frac{1}{2}$-spin-0 interaction and from the existence of spin-spin interaction (cf. ref. [25]). We could have alternatively written down *a priori* all possible invariant structures in the left-hand side, ending up with the same result (by a longer calculation). In order to determine the unknown coefficients $V_\mu, D_i, B_i, A, \ldots, D$, we use the following relations:

$$(E_1 + H_1(p))(E_1 + H_1(q)) = 2E_1^2 + kq + m_1(2E_1\overset{1}{\gamma_0} - k\overset{1}{\gamma}) +$$

$$E_1\alpha_1(p+q) + ik \times q\sigma$$

$$(E_1 + H_1(p))\alpha_1(E_1 + H_1(q)) = (E_1 + m_1\beta_1)(p + q - ik \times \sigma_1) - (kq)\alpha_1 +$$

$$(p\alpha_1)q + (q\alpha_1)p + \overset{1}{\gamma_5}k \times q \qquad (II.3)$$

and similar formulae for H_2 and α_2. In deriving (II.3) (as well as in the subsequent calculations leading to eq. (3.34)) we make use of the identities

$$(a\alpha)(b\alpha) = ab + ia \times b\sigma$$

$$(a\sigma)(b\alpha) = i\gamma_5(ab) + ia \times b\alpha \qquad (II.4)$$

valid for any two vectors a and b.

Equating the coefficients of the matrices $\mathbf{1}$, σ_i and $\sigma_1 \otimes \sigma_2$ on both sides of eq. (II.1) we obtain

$$\mathbf{1}: \quad E_1E_2[(p+q)V - 2EV_0] + i(E_2D_1 - E_1D_2)q + C\frac{(kq)^2}{k^2} - Dq^2 =$$

$$E_1E_2\frac{\alpha}{2\pi^2}\left(\frac{2E}{k^2} - \frac{1}{2w}\right) + \frac{\alpha}{2\pi^2wk^2}(E_1^2 + E_2^2)kq + \frac{\alpha}{4\pi^2w}\frac{(kq)^2}{k^2}$$

$$\sigma_1: -E_2D_1 \times q - E_1E_2B_1 + iC\frac{kq}{k^2}k \times q = \frac{i\alpha}{2\pi^2}\frac{k \times q}{k^2}\left(E_2 + \frac{kq}{2w}\right)$$

$$\sigma_2: \; E_1D_2 \times q - E_1E_2B_2 + iC\frac{kq}{k^2}k \times q = \frac{i\alpha}{2\pi^2}\frac{k \times q}{k^2}\left(E_1 + \frac{kq}{2w}\right)$$

$$\sigma_1 \otimes \sigma_2: \; E_1E_2\left[B\frac{(\sigma_1 k)(\sigma_2 k)}{k^2} - A\sigma_1\sigma_2\right] - \frac{C}{k^2}(k \times q\sigma_1)(k \times q\sigma_2) =$$

$$\frac{\alpha}{4\pi^2wk^2}[E_1E_2((k\sigma_1)(k\sigma_2) - k^2(\sigma_1\sigma_2)) - (k \times q\sigma_1)(k \times q\sigma_2)]. \qquad (II.5)$$

These equations are satisfied if we again take the definition (3.6) and (3.9) for V_μ and set

$$iD_1 = \frac{\alpha}{2\pi^2} \frac{E_2}{w} \frac{k}{k^2}, \quad iD_2 = -\frac{\alpha}{2\pi^2} \frac{E_1}{w} \frac{k}{k^2}$$

$$B_1 = B_2 = -i\frac{\alpha}{2\pi^2} \frac{k \times q}{wk^2} \tag{II.6}$$

(in accord with (3.28)) and

$$A = B = C = \frac{\alpha}{4\pi^2 w}, \quad D = 0. \tag{II.7}$$

This leads to eq. (3.34).

REFERENCES

1) For a discussion of the classical theory of *n*-relativistic particles see H. VAN DAM and E. P. WIGNER: *Phys. Rev.*, **138** B, 1576 (1965); H. VAN DAM and E. P. WIGNER: *Phys. Rev.*, **142**, 838 (1966); E. P. WIGNER: *Relativistic Interaction of Classical Particles*, in *Coral Gables Conference on Fundamental Interactions at High Energy*, edited by T. GUDEHUS et al. (New York, 1969), pp. 344-355; D. G. CURRIE and T. F. JORDAN: *Interactions in Relativistic Classical Particle Mechanics* in *Lectures in Theoretical Physics*, vol. **10** A, edited by A. O. BARUT and W. E. BRITTIN (New York, 1968), pp. 91-139; D. G. CURRIE and T. F. JORDAN: *Phys. Rev.*, **167**, 1178 (1968).
2) C. FRONSDAL: *Phys. Rev.*, D **3**, 1299 (1971); C. FRONSDAL: *Relativistic and Realistic Classical Mechanics of two Interacting Point Particles*, UCLA preprint (revised version) (1971).
3) V. FOCK and B. PODOLSKY: *Sow. Phys.*, **1**, 798 (1932); V. FOCK and B. PODOLSKY: *Sow. Phys.*, **1**, 801 (1932); B. PODOLSKY and V. FOCK: *Sow. Phys.*, **2**, 275 (1932); V. FOCK: *Sow. Phys.*, **6**, 425 (1934).
4) I. E. TAMM: *Journ. Phys. (USSR)* **9**, 449 (1945); S. M. DANCOFF: *Phys. Rev.*, **78**, 382 (1950); F. J. DYSON: *Phys. Rev.*, **91**, 1543 (1953); W. ZIMMERMANN: *Suppl. Nuovo Cimento*, **11**, 43 (1954). For a review see H. A. BETHE and F. HOFFMANN: *Mesons and Fields* - Vol. II: *Mesons* (New York, 1955), chapt. 40.
5) P. DIRAC, V. FOCK and B. PODOLSKY: *Sow. Phys.*, **2**, 468 (1932). The interpretational difficulties of the many-time formalism were recognized already at that time: see F. BLOCH: *Sow. Phys.*, **5**, 301 (1934).
6) Y. NAMBU: *Prog. Theor. Phys.*, **5**, 614 (1950); E. E. SALPETER and H. A. BETHE: *Phys. Rev.*, **84**, 1232 (1951); J. SCHWINGER: *Proc. Nat. Acad. Sci. US*, **37**, 452 and 455 (1951); M. GELL-MANN and F. LOW: *Phys. Rev.*, **84**, 350 (1951). For a review and an exhaustive list of references see N. NAKANISHI: *Prog. Theor. Phys. Suppl.*, 43, 1 (1969).

7) G. C. WICK: *Phys. Rev.*, **96**, 1124 (1954); R. E. CUTKOSKY: *Phys. Rev.*, **96**, 1135 (1954). For a more recent discussion see Sect. I. C. of I. T. TODOROV: *On the Three-Dimensional Formulation of the Relativistic Two-Body Problem*, in *Lectures in Theoretical Physics XII*, University of Colorado, 1969, W. BRITTIN and K. MAHANTHAPPA editors (New York, 1971).
8) A. EDDINGTON: *Relativity Theory of Protons and Electrons* (University Press, Cambridge, 1936), p. 110. See also the instructive discussion in: A. EDDINGTON: *Proc. Cambridge Phil. Soc.*, **35**, 186 (1939); P. .A. M. DIRAC, R. PEIERLS and M. H. L. PRYCE: *Proc. Cambridge Phil. Soc.*, **39**, 193 (1942); A. EDDINGTON: *Proc. Cambridge Phil. Soc.*, **39**, 201 (1942).
9) R. BARBIERI, M. CIAFOLINI and P. MENOTTI: *Nuovo Cimento*, **55** A, 701 (1955).
10) A. A. LOGUNOV and A. N. TAVKHELIDZE: *Nuovo Cimento*, **29**, 380 (1963); A. A. LOGUNOV, A. N. TAVKHELIDZE, I. T. TODOROV and O. A. KHRUSTALEV: *Nuovo Cimento*, **30**, 134 (1963).
11) The rather extensive literature on the applications and further development of the quasipotential approach can be traced back from the following recent references: H. GROTCH and D. R. YENNIE: *Rev. Mod. Phys.*, **41**, 350 (1969) R. N. FAUSTOV: *Journ. Theor. Math. Phys.* (*Moscow*), **3**, 240 (1970); R. N. FAUSTOV: *Nuovo Cimento*, **69** A, 37 (1970); R. N. FAUSTOV: *Relativistic Wave Function and Form Factors of the Bound System*, JINR, Dubna, preprint P2-5691 (1971) (submitted to *Ann. of Phys.*); A. N. TAVKHELIDZE, Rapporteur's talk at the *XV International Conference on High-Energy Physics* (Kiev, 1970); V. A. MATVEEV: *Quasipotential Approach in Quantum Field Theory and Models of High-Energy Hadron Interactions*, in *International JINR-CERN School on High-Energy Physics*, Varna, Bulgaria, June 1971. JINR preprint E2-5813 (Dubna 1971), pp. 37-72.
12) W. KROLIKOWSKI and J. RZEWUSKI: *Nuovo Cimento*, **2**, 203 (1955); **3**, 260 (1956); **4**, 975 (1956); G. M. DESIMIROV and M. D. MATEEV: *Nuovo Cimento*, **52** A, 1366 (1967); A. A. LOGUNOV, V. SAVRIN, M. TURIN and O. A. KHRUSTALEV: *Journ. Theor. Math. Phys.* (*Moscow*), **6**, 157 (1971). (It may be noted that none of the above authors seem to be aware of their predecessors.)
13) See, *e.g.*, A. KLEIN: *Progr. Theor. Phys.*, **20**, 257 (1958); J. M. CHARAP and S. P. FUBINI: *Nuovo Cimento*, **14**, 540 (1959): **15**, 73 (1960); A. MARTIN and Gy. TARGONSKI: *Nuovo Cimento*, **20**, 1182 (1961) and references cited there.
14) V. G. KADYSHEVSKY: *Sov. Phys. JETP*, **19**, 443 and 597 (1964); V. G. KADYSHEVSKY: *Nucl. Phys.*, **136**, 125 (1968); V. G. KADYSHEVSKY and M. D. MATEEV: *Nuovo Cimento*, **55** A, 233 (1968).
15) V. G. KADYSHEVSKY, R. M. MIR-KASIMOV and N. B. SKACHKOV: *Nuovo Cimento*, **55** A, 233 (1968); I. T. TODOROV: *Derivation and Solution of an Infinite-Component Wave Equation for the Relativistic Coulomb Problem*, in: *Group Representations in Mathematics and Physics*, Battelle-Seattle, 1969, Rencontres, V. BARGMANN editor (Berlin, 1970), pp. 254-278.
16) C. ITZYKSON, V. G. KADYSHEVSKY and I. T. TODOROV: *Phys. Rev.*, D **1**, 2823 (1970).
17) F. GROSS: *Phys. Rev.*, **186**, 1448 (1969); C. FRONSDAL and L. E. LUNDBERG: *Phys. Rev.*, D **1**, 3247 (1970); C. FRONSDAL and R. W. HUFF: *Phys. Rev.*, D **3**, 933 (1971). (Note that the equations considered in these references are not symmetric with respect to the two particles.)

18) I. T. Todorov: *Phys. Rev.*, D **3**, 2351 (1971); I. T. Todorov: *Schrödinger Equation for the Relativistic Two-Body Problem*, Lectures at the Dubna-CERN School, Varna, Bulgaria, JINR preprint E2-5813 (Dubna, 1971), pp. 7-35; I. T. Todorov: *A Three-Dimensional Approach to the Relativistic Two-Body Problem*, talk given at the *Munich Symposium on Basis Questions in Elementary Particle Physics*, June 1971. The present notes supersede all previous expositions and can be read independently.
19) V. Krapchev, V. Rizov and I. T. Todorov: *Quasipotential Approach to the Electromagnetic Interaction of Scalar Charged Particles* (in preparation).
20) P. N. Bogoliubov: *Journ. Theor. Math. Phys. (Moscow)*, **5**, 244 (1970).
21) H. D. I. Abarbanel and C. Itzykson: *Phys. Rev. Lett.*, **23**, 53 (1969); M. Lévy and J. Sucher: *Phys. Rev.*, **186**, 1656 (1969); B. M. Barbashov *et al.*: *Journ. Theor. Math. Phys. (Moscow)*, **5**, 330 (1970); R. Blankenbecler and R. Sugar: *Phys. Rev.*, D **2**, 3024 (1970).
22) E. Brezin, C. Itzykson and J. Zinn-Justin: *Phys. Rev.*, D **1**, 2349 (1970). The nonrelativistic eikonal approximation was first considered in G. Molière: *Zeits. Naturforsch.*, **2a**, 133 (1947).
23) G. Tiktopoulos and S. B. Treiman: *Phys. Rev.*, D **2**, 805 (1970); G. Tiktopoulos and S. B. Treiman: *Phys. Rev.*, D **3**, 1037 (1971).
24) This formula is a known consequence of the eikonal approximation (C. Itzykson: private communication; cf. also H. Crater: *Phys. Rev.*, D **2**, 1060 (1970)). The same energy eigenvalues were also obtained from certain infinite-component wave equations (see C. Fronsdal and L. E. Lundberg: ref. ([17]), and A. O. Barut and A. Baiquni: *Phys. Rev.*, **184**, 1343 (1969)).
25) H. Bethe and E. Salpeter: *Quantum Mechanics of One-and Two-Electron Atoms*, (Berlin, 1957).
26) It is advantageous to use the Coulomb gauge in this type of calculation since it automatically takes care of the retardation effects (cf. *e.g.*, V. B. Berestetskii, E. M. Lifshitz and L. P. Pitaevskii: *Relativistic Quantum Theory*, part I, (« Nauka », Moscow 1968), Sect. 83).

DISCUSSION

Chairman: Prof. I. T. TODOROV

— MENDES:

Could you comment on the possibility of using your formalism to clarify the correspondence between field theoretical structures and the non-local potentials used by nuclear physicists to fit their data?

— TODOROV:

I think that there is still a long way between quantum field theory and the phenomenological potentials currently used in nuclear physics or in the quark model. This is particularly true for the non-local factorizable potentials you are referring to. I should remind you that in my case the potential is always local or exchanged local.

— BERLAD:

1) When one tries to fit an elastic experiment with a potential linear in energy like the one you have, one needs something like a Gaussian or a sum of Gaussians rather than a Coulomb or Yukawa potential like the one you get. Can you comment on it?

2) What happens to the form factors of the nucleon in a Q.E.D. where more than one photon exchange is important? (Since several photon exchange contributions violate the Rosenbluth formula.)

— TODOROV:

1) One can of course use the quasipotential equation which I was writing with a phenomenological potential, say a Gaussian instead of the one which comes from perturbation theory. Such work has been done in particular in Dubna and is reviewed in Tavkhelidze's Rapporteur's talk at the 1970 Kiev conference. However, unless you justify somehow the use of a Gaussian potential by summing up relevant t-dependent contributions of Feynman diagrams the choice of the phenomenological potential is rather arbitrary, and the results derived out of it are little more than a parameter fit of say the high-energy amplitude by an expression consistent with the elastic unitarity. I prefer at the moment to deal with results which can be derived from quantum field theory with less arbitrariness. We have been fairly successful in dealing with electromagnetic interactions which actually could be foreseen. We also have some hope to be able to say something about the resonance structure of the scattering amplitude starting from the Lagrangian of the broken $SU_2 \times SU_2$ σ-model without baryons, but this work is still in progress, so that I would not like to commit myself to any specific result in this direction. 2) The contribution of the nucleon form factor to the hyperfine structure of the hydrogen spectrum is most conveniently taken into account precisely by the quasipotential method (see, *e.g.* R. N. FAUSTOV: *Nucl. Phys.*, **75**, 669 (1966) and the review article H. GROTCH and D. R. YENNIE: *Rev. Mod. Phys.*, **41**, 350 (1969)). The nuclear formfactor is taken from an independent experiment in these papers; it is not calculated theoretically.

— NEFF:

Let me elaborate on the question about non-local potentials. In field theoretical models scalar exchange builds an effectively local potential—the potential in general is the lowest order connected t-channel exchange and for the scalar case there is just the Born-term (the boson propagator is local). Correlations due to dominant higher-order field theoretic structure being exchanged (*e.g.* ladders or towers) at finite energies produce what may be thought of as non-local potentials. In some recent work Carlson and I have investigated the other possibility of non-local structure resulting from correlation due to the form of coupling. In a pseudo-scalar-spin-one-half theory there are pairwise correlations which result at high energy in a non-local generalization of Wentzel pair theory—totally unlike the scalar case or even electrodynamics, which has its own simple local classical limit. The pseudoscalar theory alone manifests truly non-local structure in its effective coupling.

— TODOROV:

Let me note the difference in the terminology we are using. You seem to call a potential something which is exponentiated in an eikonal type formula for the scattering amplitude. It coincides with my definition of potential only in special cases, such as scalar Yukawa-coupling or minimal vector coupling. As I already said, my potential is always a sum of a local and an exchanged local term (I achieve this by using the freedom in the off-shell extrapolation). I can interpret your remark in my terminology by first claiming that there is no simple eikonal type formula in terms of my local potential in the case of pseudo-scalar pion-nucleon coupling. That seems indeed to be true. I find your paper with Carlson very interesting from the point of view of generalizing the eikonal picture to the NN scattering amplitude in the pseudo-scalar theory. I think that it would be interesting to relate your results to the quasipotential method.

THE GLORIOUS DAYS OF PHYSICS

« My Life as a Physicist »

V. F. Weisskopf

My life as a physicist 983

«My Life as a Physicist»

VICTOR F. WEISSKOPF
Massachusetts Institute of Technology
Cambridge, Mass., USA

I was born in 1908 in Vienna, Austria. I spent my childhood under the Austrian-Hungarian monarchy and lived through the first World War as a child. I witnessed as a child the collapse of the monarchy and went through my secondary education in a time of great changes. I owe much to the cultural traditions of Vienna from Mozart and Beethoven to Freud and Bolzmann. I entered Vienna University and started to study Physics in the fall of 1926. It was just a few years too late for having been an active participant in the creation of early quantum mechanics. Many of my good friends were a little older, like Hans Bethe, Felix Bloch, Rudolf Peierls or Walter Heitler. Three years would have made a big difference at that time. I came to the University in 1926 after quantum mechanics was invented, and, of course, I needed a few years to learn physics. That meant I could not start active work in physics before 1929-1930, and all the fundamental developments in quantum mechanics were made between 1925 and 1930. I made the interesting observation that three or four years mean a lot when one is very young, they mean nothing during your mature life, and they mean again a lot when you are getting old. Today, I am not unhappy about being three years younger.

I was conscious of the existence of modern physics before I went to the University. I read popular books on physics when I was in the gymnasium. It was rather interesting because at that time a lot of popular literature was written about the Bohr-atom and the Quantum theory. The German students here may tell me whether the periodical « Kosmos » still exists. It was a very good journal for high school kids; four times a year they published small booklets about scientific subjects. There were quite a few about the new Bohr-atom, and what made a terrific impression on me at that time was a semi-popular description of the explanation of the periodic table by Niels Bohr by means of the AUDBAUPEINZIP. It was a fantastic revelation of how simply one can explain all these regularities. But it was still on a semi-popular level, and my first real contact with quantum mechanics came later when I actually started my studies. Of course, at that time they would not teach quantum mechanics to freshmen—maybe they shouldn't do it now either, but they do—but at that time certainly they did not, and I got in touch with quantum mechanics in 1928 when I went to the University of Göttingen. The first two years, which correspond roughly to undergraduate studies, were spent in Vienna, and there I learned physics from Thirring, not the Thirring you know, but his father, Hans Thirring, who was a good physicist and an excellent pedagogue. He gave a series of lectures on theoretical physics, classical physics, which to my mind belong to the best one can get in physics education, mechanics, optics, electrodynamic thermodynamics... great! After two years, when I asked him « What shall I study now? », he said, « One thing I must advise you: If you want to learn more physics, go away from Vienna ». I took his advice and went to Göttingen. At that time one had two choices of outstanding schools in Physics in Germany: He could either go to Göttingen—where there was at that time Max Born, James Frank, P. Jordan, W. Heitler and many others. The other Center, at least in German speaking Universities, was München, where Sommerfeld was and his great school. I think I made a mistake and went to Göttingen. If I had gone to Munich I would have received a much better training in mathematical Physics, a training I needed badly, and I missed all through my scientific life.

Anyway, I went to Göttingen and there I met the great physicists who were the creators of quantum mechanics. The important thing, however, was not to meet the great ones, but the many young people who were on my level or a little more advanced, all eager to learn, to discuss and to argue. But there was one older physicist who made a greater impression on me than any of the others and shaped my attitudes towards Physics: He was P. Ehrenfest. He was in Göttingen only one semester in 1929, I think, in order to replace M. Born who was sick. Ehrenfest took a personal interest in me.—We both were born in Vienna—and he taught me for the first time to distrust complicated mathematics and formalisms—these items were very popular in Göttingen.—He loved to ask and encouraged others to ask «stupid» questions, refused to admit that something is understood if one understands only the mathematical derivation. He showed me how to get at the real physics, how to distinguish between physics and formalism, how to get at the depth of things: « Physics is simple, but subtle », he used to say. The older I get, the more aware I am of his influence.

Let me return to the young people there. There were young instructors like Heitler, Herzberg, Nordheim and Wigner, or graduate students, people of my age or a little older, such as Delbrueck and Teller and Maria Meyer. We learned quantum mechanics together. It was a great experience and sensation; we discussed it with each other. I will never forget G. Herzberg—he also remains in my memory as one of the outstanding teachers—he at that time taught for the first time the course which is now immortalized in his book which you all know, « Introduction to Atomic Physics ». At that time it was an outstanding course and still is, a fantastic achievement after forty years! All these insights, the consequences of symmetry, the term spectra, the systematics of spectroscopy, the transition probabilities, all this was great because it was brand new, only a few years old.

It was a great thing to be a graduate student at that time and very disagreeable too. It was disagreeable because too many new ideas came around. You had barely digested the Schroedinger equation and Heisenberg's quantum mechanics and you already heard your colleagues talking about the Dirac equation and quantum electrodynamics. It went a little too fast. It was interesting, but a little discouraging. Let me come back to my statement that I came three years too late. Those fellows like Bethe, Peierls, Bloch, Heitler were lucky. Every Ph. D. thesis at that time opened up a new field. Peierls worked on heat conduction and opened one part of solid state physics. Bethe wrote his Ph. D. paper on electron diffraction of crystals and opened up another part of solid state physics. Heitler and London opened up quantum chemistry, Wentzel the theory of the Photo-effect.

When I came to my doctor's thesis I was thinking about quantum electrodynamics—Dirac had published his first paper on quantum electrodynamics, on the interaction of light with particles, and I was specially interested in the question of radiation damping, the natural width of spectral lines. I dabbled around for myself and tried to find exponential solutions of electrodynamics—I did not get very far because I was a little boy who did not know much. I asked the great Wigner for help; he was a few years older than I, but he already was very famous at that time. He helped me, of course, right away; we wrote together a paper on the natural width of spectral lines, a paper which contained for the first time a divergent integral. I tried to convince Wigner that the integral can be made to vanish. Wigner said, « no, no, it is infinite ». I didn't believe him, but he was right, of course. This paper, part of which then became my thesis, was the first paper in which divergent integrals appeared. Until now they have not been resolved. They are still there after 40 years; one ought to be ashamed of it. Another remark to this paper: Imagine here a young man completely unknown, whose name starts with the letter W and he has the luck to publish his first paper with Wigner, so that the paper is Weisskopf-Wigner and not Wigner-Weisskopf? At that time I made a vow and said «The gods were favorable to me by letting me work with Wigner, so I shall from now on, whatever paper I write, with whatever man I shall write it, I shall always stick to the alphabetical order». And I have done it all my life. I had to fight for it when I wrote a book with someone you may know, namely, Blatt and Weisskopf. The publisher insisted that it should be Weisskopf and Blatt, because I was supposed to be the senior author. I said, «I cannot do this, I have made a vow and I cannot break a vow». They said, «We don't care about vows, we want you first, you are the senior author, sir», and I finally convinced the publisher only by pointing out that if it is «Weisskopf and Blatt», the emphasis is on Blatt, but if it is «Blatt and Weisskopf» the emphasis is on me», and they accepted it. So much about this.

Another more interesting story from this period: It was a very exciting time, because of the invention of the Dirac equation; everybody was completely flabbergasted that Dirac, out of sheer intuition, could write down an equation that completely explains the properties of the relativistic electron. In fact, the equation had in it much more than even Dirac thought. It contained the positron also. But that came on later. I was in Göttingen 1928-1931; the Dirac equation was published in 1927, and everybody discussed the Dirac equation and the fact that the gyro-magnetic factor of the electron comes out to be two; How wonderful! A good example of the arrogance of theorists, which has not changed in forty years, is the following story:

There was a seminar held by the theoretical group in Göttingen, and we had a visit of Otto Stern, who was in Hamburg, not very far. Otto Stern came down to Göttingen and gave a talk on measurements he was about to finish of the magnetic moment of the proton. He explained his apparatus, but he did not tell us the result. He took a piece of paper and went to each of us saying, «What is your prediction of the magnetic moment of the proton?» and everyone of them, from Max Born to Victor Weisskopf all said, «Well, of course, the great thing about the Dirac equation is that it predicts a magnetic moment of one Bohr magneton for a particle of spin one-half». Then he asked us to write the predictions down; everybody wrote down «one magneton». Then, two months later, he came to give again a talk about the finished experiment, which showed that the value was 2.8. He projected the paper with our signatures on the screen. It was rather disagreeable.

Let me now say a few words which have some bearing on the situation in the 1970s. I am not sure whether you all know the history of the economic development of the Western world to remember that 1931 was a very bad time, even worse than 1971, especially for young physicists who were looking for jobs. It was both economically and politically a very terrible time. Hitler was already quite powerful, in fact, everybody predicted that Hitler would take over, and there was an economic disaster, both in America and in Europe. So, what should one do? Of course, positions were not available, the situation was much worse than now, today since the really good students still get jobs, whereas, at that time, even people like Bethe and Bloch had a hard time getting jobs. It was very difficult to get jobs, even for the best ones. There was a difference: We did not have any expectations. The students of today were brought up under the illusion that if they studied physics, they would find jobs. In our time, we never had such expectations. In fact, my father told me that I was crazy to study physics, and that I should study something that was more realistic, like engineering, or a « pratical » profession. So, we did not grow up with this expectation, and that made it easier to live with temporary half-jobs. Anyhow, I did not have a job. First, I went to Heisenberg as a post-doc, but unpaid, please, unpaid, since paid post-docs did not exist at that time. So I asked my parents for a little money and had a very good time with Heisenberg and his collaborators. That year, 1932, was a fantastic year; Fermi published his theory of weak interactions, the neutron was discovered by Chadwick, and Anderson and Neddermeyer discovered the positron. The base was laid of weak interactions, of strong interactions and of the concept of the antiworld. For us, the appearance of another paper by Fermi, his simple formulation of quantum electrodynamics, was a revelation; after having ploughed through longish papers by Jordan and Wigner, and Pauli and Heisenberg, Fermi's formulation was simple and crystal clear and one that even a non-mathematically inclined physicist can understand. We had an interesting time in Leipzig. I would like to relate a little story there.

I remember we were discussing how it is that the electron and the neutrino come out of the nucleus. Nowadays of course, every student knows that the pair is created, but at that time the idea of particle creation was quite new; the positron theory was not yet conceived. I remember we were sitting in a coffee house in Leipzig that faced the entrance to a swimming pool, and Heisenberg looked at the door. We were discussing how it is possible that an electron comes from the nucleus without having been there before. He said, « You are all making the wrong conclusions; look at this door », he said, «You see everybody entering fully dressed and coming out fully dressed; would you conclude from this that the swimmers inside are fully dressed?».

A few words about my job problems: I was lucky enough to get a job for half a year in Berlin as an assistant to Schrödinger, because F. London, who was the permanent assistant to Schrödinger was asked to go to America for half a year, and I took his place. Then, after this was over and the money from home became scarce, I decided I had to go somewhere where I could live. I would not get any job in Germany, or England, or France, and I went to Russia—where it was possible to get a job with subsistence at that time— and I went for almost a year to Kharkov in 1933. To work there was very interesting because in Kharkov at that time were L. Landau, Lifschitz, and Pomeranchuk, and a lot of other young Russian physicists. Life in Russia was by no means a great pleasure at that time. It was the time when there was a serious famine because of the breakdown of the collectivitation. But life was interesting and instructive. After this, I had a stroke of luck—I think it was Schrödinger who did this for me—one day I got a letter from America telling me that I had received a Rockefeller fellowship—today they are no longer given to physicists. That meant one year's support for wherever one wanted to do physics; all you had to do was report what you had done. I do not know whether you can imagine what this meant at that time, when one was sort of giving up hope and said, « Well, I shall have to teach in high school for my life »—which, by the way, I also did for a certain time and enjoyed it. The amount you got was impressive to—at that time prices were very different in America and Europe, and the $ 1,800 a year was unexpected wealth. I decided to go to Copenhagen to the great Bohr, and afterwards, for the second part of the year, I wanted to go to Cambridge, to the great Dirac.

When I arrived in Copenhagen, I was met by my friend, Max Delbrueck, who is now a biologist, but at that time was a physicist. He told me that Copenhagen was a wonderful place, mainly because of its beautiful girls. I said, « That is very interesting information, but it has no value for me because I would like to do some physics. Delbrueck said, « Well, yes, but at least you could have a look ». So then, he took me out the next evening to some dancing place with some of his friends and indeed, the information turned out to be correct: one of them is now my wife. A wife is of some importance in the life of a physicist; she makes life bearable to him, if he makes it bearable to her. So, this happened to me in Copenhagen, but nevertheless, there were other attractions in Copenhagen, such as Niels Bohr and his institute; there was an interesting group there at that time: Felix Bloch, G. Placzek, M. Delbrueck, Chandrasekhar, and Williams, the famous Williams of « Weizsacker and Williams, and Weizsacker also. I was still interested in quantum electrodynamics. At that time there were two problems to be faced: one was the problem of the positron, whether it really is contained within the Dirac equation, the problem of the charge conjugation symmetry, as we say today, and the problem of the nuclear force, the beginning of nuclear physics. Here we faced something completely new, it was like a bomb shell; there is a nuclear force there, what shall we do with this force? Can we apply quantum mechanics again? All discussions turned around the nuclear structure on the one hand and the quantum electrodynamics on the other. I stayed there for more than half a year because of all these and other attractions; however, I thought I should go to Dirac, after all, and I moved for a few months to Cambridge, England.

In Cambridge I was a little disappointed; Dirac is a very great man, but he is absolutely unusable for any student: you can't talk to him, or, if you talk to him, he just listens and says, « Yes ». So that was, from that point of view, a lost experience. I met Peierls there who also had a Rockefeller fellowship. I learned an enormous amount from him. He introduced me to all these complicated calculations of electrodynamics, the so-called « alpha-gymnastics »-traces and all that kind of thing I learned from Peierls. Then again I had a stroke of luck. I got a letter from Wolfgang Pauli, telling me that I should come to him as an assistant. This was Pauli, the great Pauli. I did not know him at that time, I had only heard about him. I saw him at some of the conferences, of course, and I was tremendously impressed: first, that I got a job—the job situation was still very bad—and second, a job with Pauli. I went to Peierls and said « I just got a job from Pauli! » Now, Peierls was older than I and was assistant to Pauli a few years before, and he told me « Oh, well, you think that is a desirable job? Then, you are wrong, it is a terrible thing to be assistant to Pauli ». I asked why? « Well, you will see! » He gave me a few words of advice; I shall talk about this later. A few weeks later, Pauli asked me to come to Zürich. I came to the big door of this office, I knocked at the door, and no answer. I knocked again, and no answer. After about five minutes he said, rather roughly, «Who is it? Come in!» I opened the door, and there was Pauli—it was a very big office—Pauli was at the other side of the room, at his desk, writing and writing. He said, « Who is this? First I must finish calculating. Erst, muss ich ixen » he said. He let me again wait for about five minutes and then: « Who is that? » « I am Weisskopf » « Uhh, Weisskopf, ya, you are my new assistant » and then he looked at me and said, « Now, you see I wanted to take Bethe, but Bethe works now on the solid state, and the solid state I don't like—Den Festen Korper Mag ich nicht. Solid state I don't like, although I started it. This is why I took you ». Then I said,

« Well, what can I do for you, sir? » and he said, « I shall give you right away a problem ». He gave me a problem, I don't know what it was, some calculation, and then « Gehen sie, go and work ». So I went, and after ten days or so, he came and said, « Well, show me what you have done ». And I showed him. He looked at it and exclaimed: « I should have taken Bethe! » Well, he was probably right. Anyhow, I enjoyed the work no end. Peierls gave me good advice, he couldn't have predicted the above story, but he predicted many other things. For example: you know, Pauli was very disagreeable when you gave a colloquium, it was dramatic, I mean. At the colloquium Pauli was sitting in the first row and when Pauli didn't like a statement he would get up and say: « This is wrong! Falsch! » and he would say « Go home, you are not prepared, such nonsense, how can you tell such nonsense! » and he would tell that to anybody, were they big shots or small shots. Now Peierls gave me the following advice: « If you ever give a colloquium, the following procedure should be followed: If the colloquium is to be given in the afternoon, the morning you go to Pauli and say « Professor Pauli, I want to tell you what I am going to say this afternoon » and then you tell him. He will start scolding you, saying « Nonsense, Dummheit and go—go home », so you take it all, you don't need even to listen to it, and then, in the afternoon, you give your colloquium exactly the same way you have prepared it. Nothing would happen, because Pauli would sit in the first row and he would sort of listen and mutter to himself « Well, I have told him already! ». And it worked every time.

I loved it with Pauli. First of all, my admiration had no limits, we really need Pauli today to—the loss of Pauli was the greatest loss theoretical physics has had, because of his wonderful criticism, his positive attitude, and his no nonsense attitude against anything that is not really good. I learned a lot of physics from him and I enjoyed it tremendously. One of the things which we did together was a paper which turned out to be the beginning of meson theory, the quantization of the scalar wave equation. It started out that I had some vague ideas about the Klein-Gordon equation, in particular, I was struck by the fact that the total number of particles, interpreted as the absolute square of the wave function, is not conserved. I thought that maybe there is something like pair-creation there, but it didn't work well, because I was very inept in applying second quantization. So I tried to go to Pauli and tell him the problem.

He was in bad humor. I tried to tell him, «Listen, Pauli, there is something which I think is interesting » and then he said, « Dummheit, nonsense, go away ». Again and again I tried, « Look, tell me, I want to ask a question ».

«Dumm, dumm». Then I got mad about it and told him a quotation «Ach, meister, warum so viel eifer warum so wenig ruh, mich duenkt euer urteil waere reifer, hoertet ihr besser Zu». This means, in English, « Oh, meister, why so much excitement and so little calm, I think that your judgement would be more mature if you listened more carefully ». He then looked at me and said, « What is that? » and I said, « This is from Richard Wagner, "Die Meistersinger" ». And then he said, « Wagner? Mag ich ueberhaupt nicht! », « Wagner? I don't like him at all ». And then, of course, it was over, I had to go. Two days later, I again came to him, saying, «Look, there is an interesting problem here», and he said « Uh, why didn't you tell me this right away? » But then began a very nice collaboration and we had tremendous fun in working out something which, at that time, was quite unexpected, that one can get pair-creation and pair-annihilation without a Dirac equation.

I was also interested at that time in the study of the electromagnetic properties of the vacuum, the polarization of the vacuum by electric fields, and pair-creation. I collaborated on these topics with Euler and Kockel, two students of Heisenberg. Euler, an excellent physicist, the grandson of the famous mathematician, was later killed by the Nazis. We were interested in the infinities occuring in electrodynamics; if we had only been more clever, we could have had the whole renormalization theory at that time—it was 1934. We had it, the main ideas were formulated in a paper that I wrote in 1934. We could show then that the divergent expressions are essentially unobservable—in other words, that they can be incorporated into renormalized mass and charge. So, the whole idea of renormalization was there, but we did not sit down and work it out. We did it in a very primitive way.

At that time I derived—on a suggestion by Pauli—the electromagnetic self-energy of the electron, and I could show how positron theory decreases the degree of divergence to a logarithmic one. I must admit that I made a bad mistake in my first publication. W. Furry pointed it out to me— what a shame for me—and the correct result emerged only afterwards in a second publication based on Furry's remark.

Later on, nuclear physics became the center of interest, first because an increasing amount of experimental results became available, and second because electrodynamics sort of got stuck. At that time, 1935, I went fully into nuclear physics, especially after Bohr invented the compound nucleus picture. I worked on the concept of nuclear temperature, and applied thermodynamics to small units; it was interesting and I learned a great deal about nuclei and about thermodynamics. At that time I had to leave Zürich and got an auxiliary position with Niels Bohr. It was paid from funds designated to support scientists who were out of jobs because of the Hitler persecution—such jobs were, of course, only temporary—but, anyhow, to be in Copenhagen again was a wonderful thing. Bohr went to America for one of his regular visits. At these visits to America he tried to get jobs for his refugee physicists, who accumulated in Copenhagen. One day he came back and said he had a position ready for me at Rochester, New York. It was an instructor position for $ 2,400 a year. I was glad to part from a Europe which did not look very promising at that time.

Rochester was a very pleasant little University—and still is. I mean, both pleasant and little. It had very good physics at that time (it still has), a good deal of nuclear physics, they had a cyclotron and did quite advanced work, nuclear excitations and penetrations of potential barriers. My experience in nuclear physics turned out to be very useful. We had an extremely pleasant life there and met a lot of physicists, both Americans and European—recent immigrants—for example, Bethe, who were very nearby in Ithaca, only a few miles from Rochester. In the summers we went to the West Coast, visiting Berkeley and Stanford where Oppenheimer and Bloch had assembled a large and active group of physicists.

In thinking back on those first years in the United States, I cannot help being deeply impressed by the way we were received in the American community of scientists. We were warmly welcomed, treated as equals and sometimes even as superior, we felt immediately at home and part of the community, as if we had been with them from the beginning. In no other country—and we lived in many—did we feel so quickly and immediately accepted and appreciated.

The war broke out in 1939, two years after we arrived in America. First America stayed out of it, but science and the scientists were deeply affected long before America entered the war openly (1941). Most of the physicists went either to work on radar or on the atomic bomb. The atomic bomb is a later development, so most of my friends, Americans and Europeans, were working on radar. Schwinger was the great radar expert and he developed the theory of wave guides at that time. Some of the Europeans who came relatively recently to the United States, like myself, were still considered as «enemies», coming from Germany or Austria, they were not admitted to war-work; they had to take over the teaching. At that time I taught theoretical physics at Rochester, at Ithaca and at other places, just to replace those people who had gone to the war laboratories—A rather interesting experience.

I have to return to the discovery of fission and the development of its use for a bomb and for power production. Fermi succeeded in 1942 in setting up a nuclear chain reaction and the technical applications of the fission process became realistic possibilities. At that time many physicists were asked to join in the effort of development, whether they were « enemy aliens » or not. The brain power was needed. At the beginning of 1943 I was asked by Oppenheimer to join a group of physicists at Los Alamos to develop the atomic bomb.

It is very difficult to describe—let alone to judge—ones feelings and one's decisions after thirty years have passed. There are many people now who say that a physicist should devote his time to the search of truth, he should not devote his abilities to produce weapons of destruction. It is easy to say this and may even be right. There were *very* few who actually stuck to it. Pauli also had to leave Europe at that time and was in Princeton—Pauli had never even thought of joining any of these war projects. But for a man in my position, and for so many others, it would have been a very difficult path to follow. I cannot tell you *why* I went to Los Alamos. The fear that Hitler would make the bomb had much to do with it. If somebody suggests I went just because everybody else did it, he may be right. The significance of physics is a very difficult thing to describe; physics is not only the search of truth. Physics is also something else—it is potential power over nature and you cannot separate these two aspects. You may say that you are a physicist and search for truth only, and that you leave the power over nature to somebody else; but then you are actually skirting the subject and not looking at reality. It is just the great point about our science—and of most of the sciences—that they are not only philosophy, they are also deeply involved in action, in life, in death, in tragedy, in abuses, in the human predicament. Whether this is good or bad, nobody can tell. One can argue on both sides. Some terrible things have happened since man made use of fission. But the first bomb may have ended the war—at least, that is what we thought, and we thought we had saved a million lives—it may even be true. The second bomb was much harder to defend. We did participate in all this and I don't want to condemn or justify it.

I cannot deny that those four years in Los Alamos were a great experience, from the human and from the scientific point of view, in spite of the fact that they were devoted to the development of the most murderous device ever created by man. Such are the contradictions which one encounters in life. From the human point of view, to live together, day and night, intellectually and otherwise, with the best people in physics from the whole world (we had Niels Bohr, Enrico Fermi, Chadwick, Peierls, Segre, and many more there) was quite an experience. The discussions we had on philosophy, art, politics, physics and on the future world under the shadow of a super-weapon will remain unforgettable. But also from the purely professional level, we had to face tasks that you never had to face before. We had to deal with matter under unusual conditions, the compressibility of matter under extreme conditions, very high temperatures; in other words, predicting the behaviour of matter and making experiments about it, under conditions that are by factors of thousands outside of the ordinary. To hold in your hand a piece of metal that man made all anew, to see events and processes develop actually before your eyes, which never have been seen before, that was something quite remarkable.

Then came the great test; the first nuclear explosion. I was at that time in charge of the theory at the test in a desert in New Mexico which had the interesting name « Jornado del Muerte », which means something like, « Journey of Death ». I had to go from one station to the other in a jeep and to tell them what intensities of this or that they had to expect. Of course, we had calculated what would be a safe distance for a man to be. They wanted—or so they said—to put me in an iron cage at exactly that distance where the theorists said « It's safe ». In fact we were wrong by a factor five. I would have been dead at the «theoretically safe place». The gamma ray intensity was much higher than we thought, we misjudged the energies, and the absorption.

At the end of the war we all were glad to go back to physics because of many reasons. One was that so many new tools were now available to experimental physics from the war-time developments of radar and of nuclear techniques. New possibilities in particle detection and in particle acceleration were created. The other reason was the immense desire again to apply one's intelligence to basic physics research. We went back to our old interests. Let me tell you an experience I had at that time which may be of « educational value ». There were vague rumors since 1936—the so-called Pasternak effect—that the observed hydrogen levels did not exactly coincide with the predictions of the Dirac equation. There were some speculations as to how to calculate this effect with our divergent quantum electrodynamics. After the war, I thought I should take this problem up with a very very good graduate student by the name of Bruce French—he is now well known in nuclear structure physics. We thought of calculating this effect, which is commonly known as the Lamb-shift, and we calculated by trying to isolate the infinite self-energy of the electron. It was a difficult calculation because the renormalization techniques were not invented yet, and we had to calculate the difference of the energy of the free electron, and of the bound electron, both being infinite; taking differences of divergent magnitudes is risky, so we had to be very careful. But we worked our way through the difficulties at a slow pace since there were no really good experimental results yet available. Then, one day, Lamb and Rutherford made a good experiment and we worked a little harder, but a lot of other people did so too—we did get a result, which fitted the experiments quite well.

I told our result to Julian Schwinger and Dick Feynman with whom we were in very close touch. Schwinger was across the street and Feynman was in Ithaca at that time, and they repeated our calculations, but they did not get our number, they got a different number and it turned out that the number that Schwinger got was the same as the number of Feynman, but different from ours. I said to Bruce French: « Schwinger and Feynman got the same number, their number is different from ours, well, the probability is high that they are right and that we are wrong ». We postponed our publication in order to find the mistake. We searched for half a year, and in the meantime Lamb and Kroll published their calculations of the same effect which were more or less identical with ours. Then I got a telephone call from Ithaca from Feynman, « You are right, I am wrong! » Now, had we had the guts to publish our own results, our papers would have appeared before the experimental paper of Lamb and Rutherford. So, what was the lesson of this story? You've got to believe in what you are doing; you get Nobel prizes not for what you do, but for the fact that you really stick to it.—We did not— that was our fault and our weakness. Of course, later on, the methods were refined and improved, and today every student can do it in a few hours, but that is the progress of—I wouldn't say of science—but of the mathematical formalism. The two are not the same.

My main interest turned to nuclear physics for quite some time. My collaborators—mainly Herman Feshbach—and I developed some new ways of looking and explaining resonances and scattering effects. One of our models described the nucleus as a transparent and partially absorbing sphere. It is often referred to as « the clouded crystal ball »-model, but it did rather well reproduce many properties of the nucleus. I wrote a fat book on « Theoretical Nuclear Physics » with John Blatt and both of us learned a great deal of physics in doing so. Among the problems my collaborators and I were most interested in at the time was the surprising validity of the shell model of the nucleus. In this model the nuclear constituents are seemingly moving as almost free particles within the nucleus, in spite of the strong interaction between the nucleons. I tried to explain this in a qualitative way as an effect of the Pauli-principle, which prevents a nucleon from being scattered by its neighbours, when all states into which it could be scattered are occupied by others. In a collaboration with F. Friedman we tried to show how effects of strong interaction—such as a complete amalgamation of an incident nucleon with the target nucleus—and effects of quasifree particle motion—such as the so-called direct reactions— can simultaneously occur without logical contradictions.

After many years of work in nuclear structure, the field became a little to « complicated » for me. I don't like complicated things, and therefore, I thought, « High energy physics may be the right thing to go to ». In some ways I always was involved in high energy physics. I mean, the difference between nuclear structure and high energy physics is only fifteen or twenty years old, Nuclear physics was high energy physics before. The real reason for me to change fields was that after having written a big book I become an « expert ». There is a remark of Pauli, who said: «Don't became an expert, because of two reasons: first, you become a virtuoso of formalism and forget about real nature, and second, if you become an expert, you risk that you are not working for anything really interesting anymore ».

During the years after the Second World War I become more and more involved in helping to establish contact and collaboration between scientists of different countries. I was convinced that there is such a thing as an international scientific community. Scientists have a way to understand each other quickly; their common interest and common aim of obtaining deeper insights into nature establishes firm bonds that easily bridge over geographical frontiers, political and social differences. The scientific frontiers, the scientific problems, are truly international—one should say « a-national »— and to a large extent independent of the political and economic systems. This is why science is able to establish bridges and contact between the different parts of our divided planet. The years after the war were difficult in this respect; contacts were broken and there were many ideological and bureaucratic obstacles to a free exchange of ideas and to free collaboration. I have spent much effort—not always successful—to bring scientists from different countries together, and to overcome the travel restrictions between East an West.

The ravages of World War II left their mark upon European Science. The community was dispersed and many of its facilities were out of date or damaged. Something had to be done in order to reestablish opportunities for the tremendous European intellectual power to participate in the development of modern science as it did so successfully before. Good physics must be created on both sides of the ocean. I tried to do what was in my power to help. I often came to Europe and taught and discussed Physics with my friends. In 1950 I was the first « professeur étranger » at the Sorbonne. In 1960, after the tragic death of J. Backer, the Director of CERN, I was asked to replace him and here was my opporunity to do something important. I accepted and remained for five years as the Director-General of CERN. They were among the most wonderful years of my life. When I look back, these five years play the role of twenty years, because there was so much to do, because there was so much to learn, and because there was so much excitement and exhilaration in the challenge of creating an atmosphere of intense collaboration and discussion, in dealing with problems of human relations of different nations, different physicists, different professions, engineers, mechanics, workmen and even politicians. And it was a great adventure to be involved in the planning of future European developments such as the Proton Storage Rings and the 300 GeV accelerator. You will ask me why did I quit after five years. I don't know why I did it and whether I regret it or not. It also was interesting to come back to America with all those new experiences which I had at CERN.

I must stop here with this account of my life as a physicist. But I would like to be sure that I did not give you the impression that physics was more interesting and exciting in the past. True enough, the early years of Quantum mechanics were unique in the sense that so much was understood and explained. But the rate of exciting new discoveries in particle physics has not slowed down. Just look back over the last 15 years of particle physics alone: The antiproton in 1955, the violation of parity in 1956, the discovery of baryon and meson resonances around 1960, the hadron symmetries and the prediction of the omega particle in the early sixties, the second neutrino in 1962, the violation of CP-conservation in 1964, the discovery of some pointlike structure within the nucleon in 1968. This is a rate as exciting and challenging as ever. Sure enough, our theoretical insight into these phenomena has lagged behind, but we expect too much. We are apt to forget how much experimental material had to be accumulated before Quantum mechanics was discovered. When we learn about these things today, we never hear about the tedious and torturous ways in which those insights were reached, but we only learn the most logical and direct approach. Physics has not become less exciting, and I hope that your lives as physicists will be as interesting and exhilarating as mine was and still is.

CLOSING REMARKS

Platitudes on the State of Our Art
G. F. Chew

Platitudes on the state of our art 1001

Platitudes on the State of Our Art.

G. F. CHEW

Lawrence Berkeley Laboratory
Berkeley, Cal., USA

What follows is a collection of observations that, despite their self-evidence, tend to be ignored in our pursuit of particle physics. It is my belief that the discipline of our subject has fallen to an inappropriately low level; we have become careless in habits of thought, diminishing not only the esthetic satisfaction from our work but also the rate of progress. A major cause of the deterioration of standards may be presumed to be the growth in our numbers. There are now so many of us that it is impossible to chastise each individual case of careless reasoning. But even if explicit chastisement is no longer practicable (as it was as recently as 20 years ago), some of you young people are capable in your own thinking, writing and speaking of maintaining higher standards of precision and clarity than is currently the « norm » in particle physics. I appeal to you to strive for these higher standards even if your competitors, colleagues and elders seem to be ignoring them.

I propose here to give examples of what is bothering me by considering the notion of « model » and its relation to « general principles ». A model represents some departure from general principles and should be characterized in the physicist's mind by the nature and degree of its consequent inadequacy. Physics has always progressed through models and perhaps always will, but it is important that we be aware of the limitation of each model. Almost every question discussed in this seminar has related to one model or another, not to general principles, but in listening I rarely have been aware of an effort to keep in mind the individual model limitations. One has the feeling that, in the minds of many, one model is as good as another, there being no useful general principles in which to have confidence.

So let me begin by reminding you that in fact the collective efforts of particle physicists have by now established a lengthy list of principles with a good chance of generality. That is to say, it may be a long time before experiments become sufficiently accurate to detect flaws in these principles.

Consider the following list, which I present in the language of the S-matrix:

Poincaré invariance.
Unitarity.
Analyticity (including Hermitian analyticity and the $i \in$ prescription).
Crossing (including TCP invariance).
Connection between spin and statistics.
Conservation of baryon number and electric charge for strong interactions.
Parity conservation and time reversal invariance.
Isospin symmetry and hypercharge conservation.
Connection between baryon number and spin.
Landau-Cutkosky rules for location and nature of singularities (including pole-particle correspondence with factorizability of pole residues)
Regge asymptotic behaviour.

Next allow me to list some of the strong-interaction models currently under study:

Quark (or parton) model.
Potential (or optical) model.
Statistical model.
Multiperipheral model.
Dual resonance (Veneziano) model.

What general principles do each of these models violate? Quark models are among the worst offenders, often being so nonrelativistic in character, like the potential model of classical nuclear physics, as not even to satisfy Poincaré invariance. Frequently they violate the spin-statistics rule. Quark models make no effort to satisfy crossing and pay less attention to unitarity than do potential models. Statistical models typically violate every principle that cannot be expressed by a conservation law.

The most satisfactory performer from an all-round point of view is the dual resonance model, which in its most advanced forms fails only to satisfy unitarity. Optical models pay serious attention to unitarity in « direct » reactions but ignore this principle in «crossed» reactions, and so evidently do not satisfy crossing. Optical models, furthermore, do not have Regge behaviour. Multiperipheral models pay some attention to unitarity in both direct and crossed reactions and have Regge behaviour in one asymptotic direction but not in all directions.

No model gives a completely accurate description of any phenomena, but each model, if it is of physical interest, succeeds in at least roughly correlating some collection of observations. We may think of a « region » of the S-matrix within which a particular model has some relevance. The potential model of classical nuclear physics, for example, is relevant to the energy region close to the lowest channel thresholds, for baryon number 2 and greater. The quark model, in contrast, is relevant only to baryon number 0 and 1 and describes neither threshold phenomena nor multiple production. The multiperipheral model is restricted to small momentum transfers at high energy. The dual resonance model works only for narrow resonances.

There is often some overlap between these « domains of relevance », so that different models with differing inadequacies may have significance for common regions of the S-matrix:

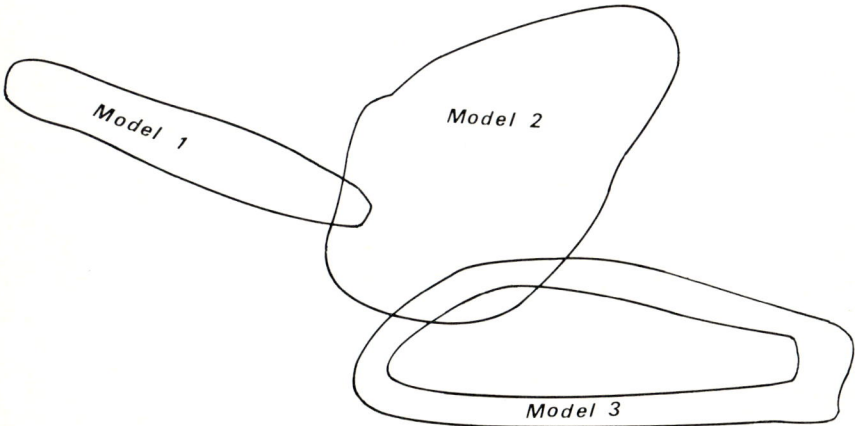

This circumstance of « overlap » has profound import for the bootstrap concept, but it is not the point of my remarks here.

I content myself here with two observations:

1) It is the responsibility of the physicist not only to « discover » useful models but to understand why a particular model can have relevance to nature while violating general principles. A satisfactory understanding has been achieved for the *potential model*, where it has been shown that the smallness of the pion mass, compared to other characteristic hadronic energies, allows a variety of general principles to be violated without causing a large error in the domain of classical nuclear physics. It appears, on the other hand, that the *dual resonance model* can afford to mistreat unitarity because

certain resonance widths are small in comparison to other quantities with the dimension of energy. Understanding in such fashion the reason for a model's validity allows appreciation of the limitations on the domain of relevance. There is no hope, for example, for relevance of the potential model when a low-mass pole is absent from crossed reactions, nor can the model be used, even for systems containing such a singularity, if one moves far away from the pole. The dual resonance model, on the other hand, may be expected to become useless in regions where the pion singularity is prominent if, in comparison to the pion mass, resonance widths can no longer be considered as « small ».

It seems obvious that to derive maximal benefit from a model we must understand its limitations, but it has recently become acceptable in the practice of our art to use models blindly. Failure to inquire into the reasonableness of a particular model-application is no longer considered sinful. It would seem that the existence of general principles, which transcend our models, is being forgotten.

2) My second observation relates to semantics. Certain terms in the vocabulary of particle physics are defined through general principles, while certain have meaning only in the context of a specific model, but many of us ignore this distinction when we write and speak. Such casual practice is so widespread that some of the most frequently-used terms, ones that are capable of precise meaning through general principles, have become blurred in significance.

Consider the terms « resonance » and « particle ». Were these terms consistently associated with isolated poles of the S-matrix (carrying factorizable residues), important benefits would accrue to our collective analytical capacities. Such a definition is entirely model-independent, but in current practice, « resonance » carries a variety of imprecise meanings associated with different models.

What about the related term, « background »? Here there has never appeared the possibility of a precise meaning; the significance is *inevitably* model-associated. I am not suggesting that terms like « background », which derive meaning only through models, are not useful, but we have an obligation when we employ such terms to inform our listener or reader (as well as ourselves) what model we have in mind.

Here are a few additional examples of terms that are incapable of meaning apart from specific models, but which nonetheless are widely employed–without qualification–in particle physics:

« Force », « potential », « exchange degeneracy », « C.D.D. poles », « single-particle exchange contribution », « threshold enhancement », « peripheral interaction », « absorptive correction ». Ask yourselves: When you use such a term, do you have clearly in mind the related model?

Let me list, also, some terms in addition to « resonance » that *are* capable of precise meaning through general principles but which more often are employed in a model-dependent sense: « Diffraction », « duality », « resonance width », « resonance energy ». To illustrate my point, the latter two terms are most often associated with parameters in Breit-Wigner formulas–which are non-unique. Resonance « width » and « energy » may alternatively, however, be respectively associated with the residue and position of a (complex) pole of the S-matrix–uniquely determinable by extrapolation.

I am persuaded that many of you younger people are capable of improving the level of discipline in the practice of particle physics and might begin to take appropriate action if you felt that some of us older people cared. Sooner or later, of course, the intrinsic value of discipline in science will inevitably lead to renaissance of this virtue in particle physics. But I should personally prefer this renaissance to occur sooner rather than later.

Closing Ceremony

The Closing Ceremony took place on Saturday, 24th July 1971 in the, San Martino Church. A concert was given in honour of all participants by the Bologna String Quintet.

The Director of the School presented the prizes and scholarships to the winners as specified below.

Prizes and Scholarships

● The following prizes and scholarships were open for competition among the participants. They have been attributed as follows:
— Prize for **Best Student** - attributed to Dr. G. BERLAD - Israel Institute of Technology, Haifa, Israel.
— Prize for **Best Scientific Secretary** - attributed to Dr. G. ECKER - Institute für Theoretische Physik, Wien, Austria.
— **Giorgio Ghigo** Scholarship - attributed to Dr. P. KERNER - Université de Paris, France.
— **Ettore Majorana** Scholarship - attributed to Dr. T. L. NEFF - Stanford University SLAC, Stanford, Calif., U.S.A.
— **Enrico Persico** Scholarship - attributed to Dr. U. M. WAMBACH - Institut für Theoretische Physik, Bochum/Querenburg, Federal Republic of Germany.
— **Gianni Quareni** Scholarship - attributed to Dr. N. TORNQVIST - University of Helsinki, Finland.
— **Antonio Stanghellini** Scholarship - attributed to Dr. D. M. TOW - University of California, Berkeley, Calif., U.S.A.
— **Alberto Tomasini** Scholarship - attributed to Dr. V. G. SNELL - University of Toronto, Ontario, Canada.

● The following students received honorary mentions for their contributions to the activity of the school:
— **S. Chadha** - Oxford University, United Kingdom.
— **B. de Wit** - Institut voor Theoretische Fysika, Ultrecht, The Netherlands.
— **P. Gensini** - University of Lecce, Italy.
— **J. F. Grivaz** - Laboratoire de l'Accelérateur Lineaire, Orsay, France.
— **B. W. Keck** - University of Southampton, United Kingdom.
— **D. Mettel** - Institut de Physique Nucléaire, Paris, France.
— **D. P. Roy** - Rutherford High Energy Laboratory, United Kingdom.

● The following scholarships were open for competition among the applicants. They have been attributed as follows:
— **Amos De-Shalit** Scholarship - attributed to Dr. A. PATRASCIOIU - Massachusetts Institute of Technology, Cambridge, Mass., U.S.A.
— **Gunnar Källen** Scholarship - attributed to Dr. P. MANNHEIM - Université Libre de Bruxelles, Belgium.
— **Giulio Racah** Scholarship - attributed to Dr. J. KATZ - Purdue University, Lafayette, Indiana, U.S.A.

Participants

ADAMS, J. B.	C.E.R.N., 1211 Geneva 23, Switzerland.
ALTHOFF, K. H.	Physikalisches Institut der Universität Bonn, Nusallee 12, 53 Bonn, Federal Republic of Germany.
ANTONIOU, N.	Nuclear Research Center « Democritos » Aghia Paraskevi Atticus, Athens, Greece.
BAGGETT, N.	Institut für Hochenergiephysik der Universität Heidelberg Albert-Uberle-Strasse 2, 69 Heidelberg, Federal Republic of Germany.
BARBARO-GALTIERI, A.	University of California, Lawrence Berkeley Laboratory, Physics Department, Berkeley, Calif. 94720, U.S.A.
BARNHAM, K. W. J.	University of California, Lawrence Berkeley Laboratory, Physics Department, Berkeley, Calif. 94720, U.S.A.
BASILE, M.	Istituto di Fisica dell'Università, 40126 Bologna, Italy.
BENARY O.	Department of Physics and Astronomy, Tel-Aviv University, Ramat-Aviv, Israel.
BERLAD, G.	Technion, Israel Institute of Technology, Department of Physics, Haifa, Israel.
BIRKHOLZ, C.	Institut für Theoretische Physik der Freien Universität, Arnimallee 3, D-1000 Berlin 33, Federal Republic of Germany.
BOLDRIGHINI, C.	Istituto di Fisica « G. Marconi », Piazzale delle Scienze 5, 00185 Roma, Italy.
BONORA, L.	Istituto di Fisica « G. Galilei », Via F. Marzolo 8, 35100 Padova, Italy.
BORDES, G.	Collège de France, Laboratoire de Physique Atomique et Moléculaire, Place Marcelin Berthelot 11, Paris V^e, France.
BORENSTEIN, J. M.	Harvard University, Department of Physics, Lyman Laboratory of Physics, Cambridge, Mass. 02138, U.S.A.

BORZATTA, P.   Istituto Nazionale di Fisica Nucleare,
Via Celoria 16, 20133 Milano, Italy.

BOSE, S. K.   The Schuster Laboratory,
Department of Theoretical Physics,
The University,
Manchester M13, 9PL, U.K.

BOSIO, C.   Istituto Superiore di Sanità,
Viale Regina Elena 299, 00161 Roma, Italy.

BUCCELLA, F.   Istituto di Fisica «G. Marconi»
Piazzale delle Scienze 5, 00185 Roma, Italy.

BUDGEN, D.   University of Durham,
Department of Physics,
South Road, Durham City, U.K.

BURKHARDT, E.   Institut für Hochenergiephysik der Universität Heidelberg,
Albert-Uberle-Strasse 2,
69 Heidelberg, Federal Republic of Germany.

CABIBBO, N.   Istituto di Fisica « G. Marconi»
Piazzale delle Scienze 5, 00185 Roma, Italy.

CALVA-TELLEZ E.   Collège de France,
Laboratoire de Physique Atomique et Moléculaire,
Place Marcelin Berthelot 11, Paris V^e, France.

CAMPANI, E.   Scuola Normale Superiore,
Piazza dei Cavalieri, 56100 Pisa, Italy.

CARRERAS, B.   Daresbury Nuclear Physics Lab.,
Daresbury Near Warrington,
Lancashire U.K.

CARROTTE, J. B.   University of Durham, Department of Mathematics,
Science Laboratories,
South Road, Durham City, U.K.

CECCHET, G.   Istituto Nazionale di Fisica Nucleare,
Via Celoria 16, 20133 Milano, Italy.

CELEGHINI, E.   Istituto di Fisica Teorica,
Largo Enrico Fermi 2, 50125 Firenze, Italy.

CHADHA, S.   Oxford University, Department of Theoretical Physics,
12 Parks Road, Oxford OX1 3PQ, U.K.

CHEW, G. F.   University of California,
Lawrence Berkeley Laboratory, Physics Department,
Berkeley, Calif. 94720, U.S.A.

List of participants

COLEMAN, S. Harvard University, Department of Physics,
Cambridge, Mass. 02138, U.S.A.

COMBE, P. H. Centre de Physique Théorique,
31 Chemin J. Aiguier,
13 Marseille 9e, France.

CONSTANTINESCU, D. H. Scuola Normale Superiore,
Piazza dei Cavalieri, 56100 Pisa, Italy.

CONTI, A. Istituto di Fisica,
Via Arnesano, 73100 Lecce, Italy.

D'ADDA, A. Istituto di Fisica Teorica,
Via P. Giuria 1, 10125 Torino, Italy.

DALITZ, R. H. University of Oxford,
Department of Theoretical Physics,
12 Parks Road, Oxford OX1 3PQ, U.K.

DAVIES, P. T. Queen Mary College, Department of Physics,
Mile End Road, London E. 1, U.K.

DE ALFARO, V. Istituto di Fisica dell'Università,
Via P. Giuria 1, 10125 Torino, Italy.

DEREM, A. Départment de Physique des Particules Elémentaires,
CEN-Saclay, B.P. n. 2,
91 Gif-Sur-Yvette, France.

DE WIT, B. Instituut voor Theoretische Fysica,
Maliesingel 23, Utrecht, Holland.

DIETL, H. Max-Plank Institut für Physik und Astrophysik,
Föhringer Ring 6,
8000 Munich 23, Federal Republic of Germany.

DONNELLY, M. University of Toronto, Department of Physics,
Toronto 5, Ontario, Canada.

ECKER, G. Institut für Theoretische Physik,
Boltzmanngasse 5, A-1090 Wien, Austria.

EDWARDS, R. T. D.E.S.Y.,
Notkestieg 1,
2 Hamburg 52, Federal Republic of Germany.

FERRARA, S. Laboratori Nazionali di Frascati,
C.P. 70, 00044 Frascati, (Roma), Italy.

FINJORD, J. University of Trondheim, Department of Physics,
7000 Trondheim, Norway.

List of participants

GASIOROWICZ, S. — University of Minnesota,
School of Physics and Astronomy,
Twin Cities, 148 Physics Buildings,
Minneapolis, Minn. 55455, U.S.A.

GENSINI, P. — Istituto di Fisica,
Via Arnesano, 73100 Lecce, Italy.

GIESECKE, J. — Institut Hochenergiephysik der Universität Heidelberg,
Albert-Uberle Strasse 2,
69 Heidelberg, Federal Republic of Germany.

GILDENER, E. — Harvard University, Department of Physics,
Lyman Laboratory of Physics,
Cambridge, Mass., 02138, U.S.A.

GLASHOW, S. L. — Harvard University, Department of Physics,
Cambridge, Mass., 02138, U.S.A.

GOLDHABER, G. — University of California,
Lawrence Berkeley Laboratory, Physics Department,
Berkeley, Calif. 94720, U.S.A.

GORDON, W. A. — Massachusetts Institute of Technology, Department of Physics,
Cambridge, Mass. 02139, U.S.A.

GOTTFRIED, C. H. — Institut für Hochenergiephysik
der Österreichischen Universität der Wissenschaften,
Nikolsdorfergasse 18, 1050 Wien, Austria.

GOURDIN, M. — C.E.R.N.,
1211 Geneva 23, Switzerland.

GRILLO, A. F. — Laboratori Nazionali di Frascati,
C.P. 70,
00044 Frascati, (Roma), Italy.

GRIVAZ, J. F. — Laboratoire de l'Accélérateur Linéaire,
Bâtiment 200, 91 Orsay, France.

GROSSMAN, P. — University of Liverpool, Oliver Lodge Laboratory,
Oxford Strees, P. O. Box 147,
Liverpool L69 3BX, U.K.

GROVES, E. S. — Rutherford High Energy Laboratory,
Chilton, Didcot, Berkshire, U.K.

HALL, G. S. — The University, Department of Natural Philosophy,
Glasgow W. 2, U.K.

HEMINGWAY, R. J. — C.E.R.N., TC Division,
1211 Geneva 23, Switzerland.

HEUSCH, C. A.	University of California, Division of Natural Sciences, Santa Cruz, Calif. 95060, U.S.A.
HOJVAT, C.	Queen Mary College, University of London, Mile End Road, London E. 1, U.K.
JACOB, M.	C.E.R.N., TH Division 1211 Geneva 23, Switzerland
JENTSCHKE, W.	C.E.R.N., Director General, 1211 Geneva 23, Switzerland.
JOHANSSON, E.	University of Stockholm, Physics Department, Vanadisvägen 9, 46 Stockholm, Sweden.
JOHNSTAD, H.	Niels Bohr Institute, Blegdamsvej 17, DK-2100 Cøpenhagen Ø, Denmark.
JONES, K.	Niels Bohr Institute, Blegdamsvej 17, DK-2100 Cøpenhagen Ø, Denmark.
KARSHON, U.	Weizmann Institute of Science, Department of Nuclear Physics, Rehovoth, Israel.
KATZ, J.	Purdue University, Department of Physics, Lafayette, Indiana 47907, U.S.A.
KECK, B. W.	University of Southampton, Department of Physics, Southampton S09 5NH, U.K.
KERNER, R.	Université de Paris, Départment de Mécanique, 11 Quai Saint Bernard, Paris V^e, France.
KESSLER, P.	Collège de France, Laboratoire de Physique Atomique et Moléculaire, 11 Place Marcelin Berthelot, Paris V^e, France.
KLEINERT, H.	Institut für Theoretische Physik der Freien Universität, Arnimallee 3, D-1000 Berlin 33, Federal Republic of Germany.
KNUDSEN, C. P.	Nordisk Institut für Teoretisk Atomfysik, Blegdamsvej 17, DK-2100 Cøpenhagen Ø, Denmark.
KONETSCHNY, W.	Institut für Teoretische Physik der Technischen Hochschule in Wien, Karlsplatz 13, A-1040 Wien, Austria.
KORKEA-AHO M.	University of Helsinki, Department of Physics, Siltavourenpenger 20, Helsinki, Finland.

List of participants

LEMOIGNE, Y. — Département de Physique des Particules Elémentaires,
CEN-Saclay, B.P. n. 2,
91 Gif-Sur-Yvette, France.

LIOTTA, L. — Istituto di Fisica,
Via Celoria 16, 20133 Milano, Italy.

LJUNG, S. B. — University of Helsinki, Department of Physics,
Siltavourenpenger 20, Helsinki, Finland.

LOPEZ, C. — Universidad de Madrid, Dept. de Fisica Teorica,
Madrid 3, Spain.

MANDELKERN, M. — Départment de Physique des Particules Elémentaires,
CEN-Saclay, B.P. n. 2,
91 Gif-sur-Yvette, France.

MANNHEIM, P. D. — Université Libre de Bruxelles, Pool de Physique,
50, Avenue F. D. Roosevelt, 1050 Bruxelles, Belgium.

MARTIN, A. — C.E.R.N., TH Division,
1211 Geneva 23, Switzerland.

MASSAM, T. — Istituto Nazionale di Fisica Nucleare,
Via Irnerio 46, 40126 Bologna, Italy.

MATTIOLI, G. — Istituto di Fisica « G. Marconi »
Piazzale delle Scienze 5, 00185 Roma, Italy.

MENDES, R. V. — Junta de Energia Nuclear,
Lab. de Fisica e Engenharia Nucleares,
Estrada Nacional n. 10, Sacavem, Portugal.

METTEL, D. — Institut de Physique Nucléaire,
9 Quai Saint Bernard, 75 Paris V^e, France.

MILLER, C. E. — University College London, Department of Physics,
Gower Street, London W.C. 1, U.K.

MORPURGO, G. — Istituto di Fisica dell'Università,
Viale Benedetto XV 5, 16132 Genova, Italy.

NAVACH, F. — C.E.R.N., TC Division,
1211 Geneva 23, Switzerland.

NAVARRIA, F. L. — Istituto di Fisica,
Via Irnerio 46, 40126 Bologna, Italy.

NEFF, T. L. — Stanford University,
SLAC, P.O. Box 4349,
Stanford, Calif. 94305, U.S.A.

NEUHOFER, G.	Institut für Hochenergiephysik, Oesterreich Akad. Wissenshaften, Nikolsdorfergasse 18, Wien 1050, Austria.
NICOLINI, C.	Istituto di Fisica, Via Amendola 173, 70126 Bari, Italy.
NULMAN R.	Istituto di Fisica, Via P. Giuria 1, 10125 Torino, Italy.
OLIVER, L.	Laboratoire de Physique Théorique et des Hautes Energies, Bâtiment 211, 91 Orsay, France.
PARROUR, G.	Laboratoire de l'Accélérateur Linéaire, Ecole Normale Supérieure, Bâtiment 200, 91 Orsay, France.
PATRASCIOIU, A.	Massachusetts Institute of Technology, Department of Physics, Cambridge, Mass. 02139, U.S.A.
PEVSNER, A.	Johns Hopkins University, Department of Physics, Homewood Campus Baltimore, Maryland 21218, U.S.A.
PIGUET, O.	Institut de Physique Théorique, Place du Tunnel 21, 1005 Lausanne, Switzerland.
PITTNER, L.	Institut für Theoretische Physik der Universität Graz, Universitättsplatz 5/1, A-8010 Graz/Stmk, Austria.
POLITZER, H. D.	Harvard University, Department of Physics, Cambridge, Mass. 02138, U.S.A.
PREPARATA, G.	Istituto di Fisica « G. Marconi », Piazzale delle Scienze 5, 00185 Roma, Italy.
RIELLA, G.	Istituto di Fisica Teorica, Via P. Giuria 1, 10125 Torino, Italy.
RODRIGUES, W.	Istituto di Fisica, Via Archirafi 36, 90123 Palermo, Italy.
ROSENFELD, A. H.	University of California, Lawrence Berkeley Laboratory, Physics Department, Berkeley, Calif. 94720, U.S.A.
ROSS, D.	University of Oxford, Department of Theoretical Physics, 12 Parks Road, Oxford OX1 3PQ, U.K.
ROSS, G. G.	Rutherford High Energy Laboratory, Chilton, Didcot, Berkshire, U.K.

ROTHE, K. D. — Institut für Theoretische Physik der Universität Heidelberg,
Philosophenweg 16,
69 Heidelberg, Federal Republic of Germany.

ROY D. P. — Rutherford High Energy Laboratory,
Chilton, Didcot, Berkshire, U.K.

SAKURAI, J. J. — University of California, Department of Physics,
405 Hilgard Avenue, Los Angeles, Calif. 90024, U.S.A.

SAWADA, T. — Istituto di Fisica, Universidade de Sao Paulo,
20516 Sao Paulo, Brazil.

SCHLEIN, P. E. — University of California, Department of Physics,
Los Angeles, Calif. 90024, U.S.A.

SCHWEDA, M. — Institut für Theoretische Physik
der Technischen Hochschule in Wien,
Karlsplatz 13, A-1040 Wien, Austria.

SEKERA, Z. — C.E.R.N., TC Division,
1211 Geneva 23, Switzerland.

SINHA, B. C. — University of London
King's College, Department of Physics,
Strand, London WC2R 2LS, U.K.

SNELL, V. G. — University of Toronto, Department of Physics,
Toronto 5, Ontario, Canada.

TAIT, W. — University of Cambridge,
Department of Applied Mathematics and Theoretical Physics,
Silver Street, Cambridge CB3 9EW, U.K.

TEODORO, D. — Istituto di Fisica,
Viale Benedetto XV, 5
16132 Genova, Italy.

TODOROV, I. — Bulgarian Academy of Sciences, Institute of Physics,
72 Bld. Lenin, Sofia 13, Bulgaria.

TORNQVIST, N. — University of Helsinki, Department of Nuclear Physics,
Siltavourenpenger 20, Helsinki, Finland.

TOTH, K. — Hungarian Academy of Sciences,
Central Research Institute for Physics,
P.O. Box 49, Budapest 114, Hungary.

TOW, D. M. — University of California, Lawrence Berkeley Laboratory,
Berkeley, Calif. 94720, U.S.A.

TREIMAN, S. B.	Princeton University, Department of Physics, Joseph Henry Laboratories, P.O. Box 708, Princeton, N. J. 08540, U.S.A.
UCHIYAMA-CAMPBELL, F.	University of California, San Diego, Post Office Box 109, La Jolla, Calif. 92037, U.S.A.
VANNUCCI, F.	Laboratoire de l'Accélérateur Linéaire, Bâtiment 200, 91 Orsay, France.
VENDRAMIN, I.	Istituto di Fisica « G. Galilei », Via F. Marzolo 8, 35100 Padova, Italy.
WAHL, H.	Institut für Hochenergiephysik, Oesterreich Akademie Wissenschaften, Nikolsdorfergasse 18, Wien 1050, Austria.
WALTZ, R. E.	University of Chicago, The Enrico Fermi Institute, 5630 Ellis Avenue, Chicago, Ill. 60637, U.S.A.
WAMBACH, U. M.	Institut für Theoretische Physik 11, Ruhr-Universität Bochum, Bochum-Querenburg, NB 6, Federal Republic of Germany.
WEILHAMMER, P.	Max-Plank Institut für Physik und Astrophysik, Föhringer Ring 6, 8000 München 23, Federal Republic of Germany.
WEISSKOPF, V. F.	Massachusetts Institute of Technology, Department of Physics, Cambridge, Mass. 02139, U.S.A.
WEISZ, P.	University of Cambridge, Department of Physics, Silver Street, Cambridge CB3 9EW, U.K.
WEITSCH, A.	Sektion Physik der Universität, Lehrstuhl Prof. Meyer Berkhout, Amalienstrasse 54, 8 München 13, Federal Republic of Germany.
WETHERELL, A. M.	C.E.R.N., NP Division, 1211 Geneva 23, Switzerland.
YAO, A. C.	Centre de Physique Théorique, 31 Chemin J. Aguier, 13 Marseille 9e, France.

ZALLO, A.   Laboratori Nazionali di Frascati,
C.P.70,
00044 Frascati (Roma), Italy.

ZEPEDA, A.   The Rockefeller University, Physics Department,
New York, N.Y. 10021, U.S.A.

ZIEGLER, A.   Institut für Theoretische Physik der Universität Frankfurt/M.
Robert-Mayer-Strasse 8-10,
6 Frankfurt/Main 1, Federal Republic of Germany.

Tipografia Compositori - Bologna - Italy